Saunders and Saro Aircraft

since 1917

The outstanding Saunders-Roe SR.A/1 jet flying-boat. (*Saro*)

Saunders and Saro Aircraft

since 1917

Peter London

PUTNAM

ISBN 0 85177 814 3
© Peter M London 1988
Typeset by Witwell Ltd, Southport
Printed in Great Britain for
Putnam, an imprint of
Conway Maritime Press Ltd,
24 Bride Lane, Fleet Street
London EC4Y 8DR
at the University Printing House, Oxford
First published 1988

CONTENTS

Preface

Saunders/Saro designed and built mostly flying-boats and amphibious aircraft, a natural evolution from an earlier involvement with boat-building. The aircraft varied greatly in terms of success. A number have gone largely unrecorded, especially some of the early prototypes. A small number of landplane designs were also conceived. The term 'Saunders/Saro' is used to describe a Limited Company which existed between 1908 and 1959. For twenty years, S.E. Saunders Ltd was engaged in boat-building, sub-contracted aircraft construction, and the development of a few aircraft to the company's own designs. In late 1928 the firm was reorganised and a new name was adopted—Saunders-Roe Ltd, usually abbreviated to Saro. The latter concern laid greater emphasis on aircraft design, and other interests were over a period made virtually autonomous.

Despite fluctuations in the success of its aircraft, the company continued with its work and by the early 1950s was the last stronghold of flying-boat development in Great Britain. Saunders/Saro was always a small enterprise compared with the major aircraft manufacturers and so a frequently one-sided battle was waged in terms of obtaining orders and developing new types. It has been suggested that the company might have done well to concentrate solely on boat-building. Certainly a significant proportion of its aircraft remained unsold or were unpopular with those who flew them. Others, however, were more successful and a few were outstanding. This is the story of all these aircraft and the company which produced them.

Acknowledgements

The author wishes to acknowledge with gratitude the help of the organisations and individuals listed below. Without their co-operation, freely and generously given, this work would not have been completed.

Army Air Corps; Aeroplane and Armament Experimental Establishment; Air Historical Branch (RAF); Aeronautical Quality Assurance Directorate (especially Ken Meekcoms); D.B. Allison; G. Allison; V.F. Arnold; L.S. Ash; Mrs D. Austin; Lord Balfour of Inchrye PC MC; British Aerospace; BBC Radio Solent; BBC Television South; British Hovercraft Corporation; British Powerboat Co; I.E. Bliss; G. Boothroyde; Chaz Bowyer; Civil Aviation Authority Library; Helen Cookson; Mrs W.E. Cozens; B. Dibbens; J. Hamon; H. Hanna; Mrs J Harpley; M Hermiston; Capt B. Hygate; Inspectorate of Recruiting RAF; Isle of Wight County Press; Imperial War Museum; Mrs M. Keen; Mrs D. Knowler; A.P. Kitcher; S.J. Lake; P.K. Langdon; D.E.C. Lockyer; A.G. London; Luftwaffen-Museum; Miss L. Manning; R.J. Mitchell Hall; I.R. Murray (HM Consul Porto); W.F. Murray; Mrs M. New; Parkhurst Photographic; Public Records Office; Liz Radcliffe; Bruce Robertson; S.J. Rose; Royal Aircraft Establishment Farnborough (especially Dennis Goode and Brian Kervell); Royal Aeronautical Society; Royal Air Force Association; Royal Air Force Museum; W.J. Saunders; Science Museum; L.G. Seager; Shell UK; C.A. Sims; Southern Evening Echo; B.J. Saxton; L. Smith; Mrs R. Stevenson; R. Stratton; John Stroud; Rev P. Tongeman; I.T. Ward; Westland Helicopters; Bob Wealthy; Mrs M. Woodhouse-Jones.

Special thanks to Eric Morgan for his encouragement as well as practical support.

This book is dedicated to my mother and father.

History of the Companies

Beginnings

The origins of S.E. Saunders Ltd can be traced to the 1830s, when a small family business was established by Moses Saunders, an engineer by trade, in the village of Streatley, Berkshire. This enterprise was concerned with the construction of locks and weirs, as part of the process designed to make the Thames navigable as far as Oxford. Involvement with one kind of marine work encouraged Saunders to look at a more specific aspect; the science of boat-building. As the concern prospered it expanded, boat-building became its primary work, and the products, a series of high-speed steam launches, established a fine reputation. A variety of skiffs and punts were also constructed. Saunders even guaranteed their punt poles, offering to pay £20 to anyone who broke one under normal use—as far as is known, the firm never had to pay.

Moses Saunders died in August 1859 but the business was continued by members of his family. As the demand for boats increased, premises were obtained at Goring, on the Oxford side of the Thames, in 1870. During the late 1880s, the firm opened a new and much larger site at the Spring field Works in South Stoke, and was gradually centralised there until 1901. In the late 1870s, meanwhile, while still situated at the Streatley and Goring sites, the concern was taken over by Moses Saunders' grandson, Sam.

Sam Saunders was born in 1856, when the family still lived at Streatley. He grew up to be an untypical Late Victorian businessman; he lacked the complacency that ruined many of his peers. A single-minded and dynamic personality, Saunders was also shrewd, and looked enthusiastically for new ideas to improve his boats. As a boy, he had single-handedly constructed a small dinghy, which had received much acclaim from the villagers of Streatley. Marine work was in Sam's blood, and the company provided a solid basis on which to build. When reliable internal combustion engines became available, Saunders was one of the first to experiment with the idea of using such a powerplant in marine craft. His results were successful, and offered a good chance to capture a share in the then emerging market for high-speed motor-boats. Saunders did not stop at merely introducing new engines into old-fashioned hulls. He considered the possibility of improving hull strength to take full advantage of the increase in speed and power offered by the new engines, while at the same time remaining mindful of the necessity to minimise any weight penalty introduced by the strengthening process.

Sam Saunders' method of hull construction was the result of logic and imagination combined. Laminated plywood skinning applied to hull structure had been attempted before Saunders' development but the bonding agents then available, casein and blood albumen, were prone to weaken after prolonged immersion in water. Neither was sufficiently fungus-proof. Saunders eventually found inspiration in the Canadian

1

Indian birch-bark canoes, the skins of which were stitched together with animal sinew. From this, he experimented with the idea of sewing laminated plywood constructed from Honduras mahogany (later mahogany with cedar), using as his 'thread' either annealed copper or occasionally brass wire. He soon found that here was an answer to the problem of a strong but light structure. Saunders' sewing method consisted of stitching the wire round the edges of the plywood sheets and at intervals across them, to prevent separation of the layers. This technique was later improved by sewing the wires in overlapping, staggered patterns, and, for added watertightness, by applying calico soaked in boiled linseed oil between the sheets.

Hand-sewing the sheets was of course laborious and tiring, so Sam, aided by his daughter, converted a series of large (conventional) sewing machines to do the job more profitably. The sewn method of construction was given the name Consuta, and a 51 ft launch, completed in 1898, was named after it; a free advertisement. Consuta was still in use some 53 years later, by a BBC Television camera crew filming the Oxford and Cambridge Boat Race, and is currently under restoration by Graham Lindsay at Kew. The term 'Consuta' means in Latin 'stitched together', and interestingly it is also the name of a group of small plankton-like animals, which float rather than roam submerged. The Consuta principle was patented (No. 222) on 31 December, 1898.

Convinced that here he had a technique with an important future, Sam formed the Saunders Patent Launch Building Syndicate in early 1899, his principal associates being Sidney Porter, a highly creative draughtsman, and Fred Goatley, a master boat-builder. Soon, boats with sewn hulls began leaving the Springfield Works regularly. Gradually, Springfield began to supersede Goring and Streatley in importance, the latter sites being let and used for storage of boats and spares.

Consuta construction clearly had applications beyond small motor-boats. When in the late 1890s Sam surveyed the boat-building industry as a whole, he saw that Cowes, on the Isle of Wight, was becoming the centre of British yachting, as well as for the very new sport of motor-boat racing, which was then gaining popularity. In 1901, he opened a branch works there, on the former site of a Wesleyan chapel at West Cowes. The Syndicate, their families and much of the labour force moved from Berkshire with him. Again, the firm expanded; new customers included Trinity House, the Admiralty, and the Eastern Telegraph Company. Soon after the new branch was established, Saunders was astute enough to acquire sole British rights to the Fauber Principle, which had been devised originally by the Rev C.M. Ramus and later resurrected by a Mr Fauber, an American resident in France. This involved a method of creating a stepped hydroplane hull, refined by Fauber through the concept of introducing air via tubes to a point beneath the hull just aft of the step. The effect created was to break the water suction behind the step, a measure designed to allow the hull to ride on the forward area only, thus reducing friction. Study of the idea gave Saunders an added insight into the development of fast waterborne craft.

By the early 1900s Saunders was gaining an enviable reputation for competitive high-speed boats. A number of hulls for craft entering the British International Races at that time were built by the company, nearly

2

all of Consuta construction. New premises were opened near the Folly Inn at Whippingham on the Isle of Wight, for the manufacture of Consuta on a large scale.

Also, in 1906, Sam Saunders began to look into a new form of craft, his experiments being based at Springfield. Early that year the experimental craft was tested in model form. She was broad-beamed and flat-bottomed for most of her length. A full-size version appears to have been built at Springfield, but there is no surviving record of its performance. The craft was 33 ft long with a beam of 8 ft and a bottom which sloped up at the forward end. Two sidewalls were adopted as well as a centre wall, with fourteen fences between them, all running the full length of the hull. Through the hull bottom between the fences were cut a number of holes slanted aft, through which air was passed under pressure. The boat was propelled by the air thrust from the holes against the water and the air was contained between the sidewalls. The boat was thus planned to ride on an air cushion.

This craft was designed by F.W. Schroeder; Saunders merely constructed it. What happened to the prototype is unknown, but it is fascinating to note that nearly 60 years later Sam Saunders' old site at Cowes would be used for the production of another type of vehicle riding on a cushion of air, the Hovercraft.

1906 was a formative year for Saunders. His agreement with the Launch Building Syndicate expired but he did not renew it. He felt that his inventive powers and freedom of action were being hampered by the commitment required for such a partnership. Though he did not sell the Springfield Works until January 1912, most of his assets were transferred to the Isle of Wight, where he acquired a bigger site. As it was derelict, he bought it cheap. After repairs had been made, the new yard, on the east bank of the Medina, was named Columbine. Finally, in 1908 Saunders converted his business into a private limited company. With capital of £5,000, aided financially by the Wolseley Tool and Motor Car Company, with himself as Chairman, the firm of S.E. Saunders Ltd was established.

1908 saw a continuing interest in the air cushion; Saunders filed a patent titled 'Hulls, Lubricating'. This patent suggested that air be injected to the hull underside of a boat, using sidewalls to prevent dispersal, to try to minimise the violent rising and falling of the forebody of powerful boats in rough waters. The intention was to achieve reduced drag and a smoother passage.

On the practical side, as the interest in motor-boat racing grew, so did Saunders' success. Cowes-built craft soon made their presence felt in various racing competitions. Typical was the 49 ft *Ursula* built in 1909, which won the Coupe des Nations four years in succession. Another example was E. Mackay Edgar's *Maple Leaf IV*, a multi-step hydroplane, which was awarded the British International Trophy in 1912 and retained it the following year. *Columbine*, a 1910 hydroplane, took 14 first places and two second places from 18 starts at British motor-boat meetings. Another hydroplane, the 22 ft *Rip III*, achieved 31 mph using a 60 hp Vauxhall, while *Angela*, a similar type of 21 ft craft, made a planing maximum of 27 mph—this from a Wolseley engine of just 44 hp.

Sam Saunders was determined to investigate as many outlets as possible to build up the firm. In November 1909, he announced his entry into the

3

The Ravaud craft on the Medina, early 1911. The new Saunders shed, in the background, was at that time under construction. (*BHC*)

then infant field of aeronautics. He placed a lot of confidence in the application of the Consuta principle in designs for 'aero navigation' because of its lightness and strength. Over the next 20 years or so, Consuta construction was used in a large number of aircraft designs.

In January 1911, a particularly strange craft was launched onto the Medina from the Saunders sheds, then in the process of being expanded and rebuilt. Designed by a Frenchman, M. Roger Ravaud, this machine employed two transverse floats and an aerodynamic, rather than water, rudder for directional control. The craft was powered by a 50 hp Gnome aero-engine driving an airscrew rather than a water propeller. Indications are that it was fairly successful, though rather on the slow side; Ravaud intended installing a 100 hp Gnome, which he perhaps optimistically hoped would yield speeds of up to 60 mph. It is difficult to classify Ravaud's craft because it employed such a peculiar variety of features. Intended for Monaco, it never arrived; indications are that it operated in the Shoreham area instead.

Participation in the construction of the Ravaud machine indicates Saunders' wish to explore new fields, perhaps the most attractive being in the aeronautical world. A number of aviation pioneers sought Saunders' aid because his method of Consuta construction followed their required criteria—lightweight but strong, an asset at a time of low-powered, unreliable aero-engines and dubious aerodynamic properties. Pertinent in shaping the future of the company was the interest shown by some of the pioneers in water-based aircraft. Once they had (after a fashion) mastered landplanes, they wanted to try something new, and Saunders' skill in producing resilient but light structures became sought after. During the years leading up to the First World War, the company supplied a number of floats and hulls for various experimental water-based aircraft, only some of which were succssful.

4

The Sopwith Bat Boat had a Saunders-designed hull and is seen here in its original, single fin and rudder, configuration. Initially, it was powered by an Austro-Daimler engine. (*Hawker Siddeley*)

During early 1911 the concern built two engine gondolas for the rather unimaginatively-named Naval Airship Number 1 *Mayfly*, to house the 200 hp Wolseley motors, construction of the other components of the *Mayfly* being undertaken by Vickers. *Mayfly* was a rigid-type airship of 660,000 cu ft. Sadly, it broke its back, being hit by a gust as it was being taken from its shed, and never flew.

In the autumn of 1912, Saunders was approached by T.O.M. Sopwith, who asked the company to build a hull for a small two-seat flying-boat he was designing. Saunders produced a beautifully streamlined 21 ft, 180 lb single-step hydroplane hull with side-by-side seating and a skin of Consuta, aided by Sydney Porter, who by that time was responsible for drafting most of Saunders' boats. External scoops were incorporated on the hull sides to inject air under the step. The hull itself was bolted to a conventional biplane superstructure carrying the tail assembly and the 90 hp Austro-Daimler engine. Named Bat Boat, Sopwith's aircraft was exhibited at the February 1913 Olympia Aero Show and later purchased by the Admiralty for various tests, being consigned to the experimental station at Calshot. After research into bomb-dropping, at first using potatoes and later practice bombs, the Bat Boat was finally destroyed in a gale on 21 November, 1914, while at its war station at Scapa Flow, but was not officially struck off charge until the following March.

5

In the summer of 1913, the Bat Boat took part in the Mortimer Singer Competition for British amphibian aircraft. Singer, the American sewing-machine magnate, had offered a prize of £500 for the first all-British amphibian to complete, within five hours, six out-and-back flights from land to a point on the water some five miles distant.

The Bat Boat required certain alterations to become eligible for the competition. A retractable undercarriage was fitted, the Austro-Daimler engine replaced by a 100 hp Green, and the single rudder altered to twin configuration. The Bat Boat fullfilled the requirements of the competition on 8 July, 1913, the pilot being Harry Hawker and the official observer Lieut Spenser Grey RN, the Flight Commander at Calshot. Curiously, the competition sponsored by Singer had been won by an aircraft employing a sewn hull in its construction.

The Bat Boat became the world's first successful amphibian and Sam Saunders could reflect that his company had played a significant part in its achievements. Saunders also became involved with other aircraft projects, though not always with such gratifying results. The third aircraft in the Bristol-Burney X series—the X.3—employed a Consuta-covered hull. This aircraft was an experimental type built to assess the possibility of a hydrofoil type undercarriage. Though initial towing tests made in August 1913 were fairly satisfactory, the sole X.3 was wrecked on a sandbank before a flight was made and the project was abandoned.

The Bat Boat in modified form, with twin fins and rudders, 100 hp Green, undercarriage and revised wing floats. (*Hawker Siddeley*)

The sole Bristol-Burney X.3 experimental hydrofoil aircraft.

Saunders also became involved, during 1912, with the ideas of Henri Coanda. A Rumanian, Coanda was a romantic whose aircraft were unorthodox at best. After causing mayhem at the British and Colonial Aeroplane Co, Coanda produced a bastardised GE 3 floatplane which was erected at Cowes. The first float absorbed too much water and was replaced by a Consuta example. The aircraft eventually stalled and sank on 15 April, 1912, while being flown by Harry Busteed.

Autumn 1913 saw Saunders engaged in building another hull, this time for the Perry-Beadle biplane flying-boat designed by F.P. Hyde Beadle (who later designed the Saunders Kittiwake) and Copland Perry at Twickenham. The hull was again Consuta-covered, with the 60 hp ENV engine, enclosed in the bows, driving two airscrews via chain transmission. Streamlined to a fish-like profile reminiscent of some of Sir George Cayley's 'solids of least resistance', the hull was divided into two parts. The forward area was of deep section with a perpendicular bow, the underside forming a planing bottom. The rear portion was of monocoque construction with an integral fin and tailplane. A step was formed where these two structures joined. The lower wing and entire tail unit were also Consuta-covered; the upper wing was fabric-covered. In lieu of floats or sponsons, lateral stability was maintained by the watertight lower wing itself.

The Perry-Beadle flying-boat was not a success. After its exhibition at the 1914 Olympia Aero Show, trials delayed by the start of war eventually took place in late July 1915 on Lake Windermere. Tests revealed that the aircraft floated with its lower wing trailing edge and lower rudder submerged, the drag preventing the aircraft from attaining flying speed. After the engine had been removed, the airframe was abandoned and subsequently broken up.

7

The Perry-Beadle flying-boat and a partially completed B.E.2 in the Saunders shed, autumn 1913.

Two other prototypes, of lesser importance, were completed at Cowes before the First World War, the Wigram and the Bass-Paterson. Little is known of these aircraft. The Wigram was never completed because its promoter, the Australian Arthur Wigram, had insufficient funds. His aircraft incorporated a deep flying-boat hull with pronounced upward sweep at the stern to keep the tail clear of the water. The Bass-Paterson was completed but, immediately before flotation tests, it caught fire when the engine, a Green, was run up in the Saunders shed adjacent to Columbine. The fire could not be brought under control and, to save the shed, the blazing aircraft was dragged outside and left to consume itself.

Consuta hulls were also commissioned by the White and Thompson Company and its successor, the Norman Thompson Flight Company Ltd. The first aircraft to be fitted with one of these hulls was the White and Thompson No. 3 Boat. Built for the 1914 *Daily Mail* Round Britain Race, this type was similar to the early Curtiss flying-boat design, though in fact it was a wholly original conception. A two-seat single-engined biplane flying-boat, the No. 3 Boat went into military service on the outbreak of war, when all aerial sporting events were cancelled. Six examples were ordered after successful flight testing of the original in August 1914, and eventually at least eight were delivered to the RNAS for coastal patrol. All these 'boats employed Consuta hulls, though construction of flight surfaces and erection was done by the parent company.

By the time war started in August 1914, S.E. Saunders was very well established. The company had secured a first-class reputation for its marine craft. In addition to building yachts and motor-boats, Saunders

8

had won a large contract for the supply of lifeboats from the RNLI, the first Admiralty order for a motor-boat and a Royal Warrant as Launch-Builder to His Majesty King Edward VII. The company had also been involved with a number of prototype aircraft from which some design and much constructional experience had been gained. A small contract for the production of several B.E.2 biplanes was also awarded to Saunders. With such considerable knowledge of boat-building, however, the company might reasonably have been expected to produce naval craft as its major contribution to the war effort. In fact the Admiralty decided that Saunders, because of its experience with high-speed hull forms together with its knowledge of aircraft construction, should concentrate on the production of marine (and perhaps other) aircraft for the duration. Thus a fundamental change took place at Cowes during the early war years; transition from boat-building to aircraft production was completed before the end of 1915, the sole maritime contract to survive being the continued output of lifeboats.

The First World War

The Admiralty instruction meant that maritime contracts held by Saunders were with few exceptions brought to an end. The imposed commitment to the production of aircraft was swiftly implemented at Cowes.

The first wartime order from the Admiralty came within a few days of the declaration of war, as a sub-contract for Short seaplane floats. Having examined the float's design, the Cowes firm was unimpressed and submitted an amended design which was accepted. Applying its knowledge of hydrodynamics to aircraft design, Saunders was exactly the company needed by the Admiralty at a particularly critical time, and this pushed Saunders firmly into the world of aviation. As the war progressed, the aircraft manufacturing interest came of age.

During late 1914, the company received an order for fuselages for the White and Thompson 'Bognor Bloater'. Designed by F. P. Hyde Beadle, the 'Bognor Bloater' was a land-based two-seat tractor biplane powered by a 70 hp Renault and employing a monocoque Consuta-covered fuselage. The type's sole claim to fame is that it was probably the first aircraft incorporating a monocoque fuselage to enjoy a production run.

The fuselage was a boat-built structure and the Consuta stitching was made flush with the surface; earlier Consuta had been criticised as having raised stitching. The whole fuselage was varnished when structurally complete and represented a very impressive piece of craftmanship. Manufacture of the fuselages took place at Cowes.

The 'Bognor Bloater' was, however, a mediocre performer. The first example was tested by E.C. Gordon England during March 1915, and twelve, serialled 1171–1182, were eventually ordered. At least ten were built, and the type was used for training.

In view of Saunders' predominantly maritime concern at the time, it is perhaps surprising that the first contract for production of complete aircraft was an order for fifty Avro 504A trainers, in the summer of 1915. A little later, a contract for thirty Short 184 seaplanes was awarded, at a total cost of £81,000. By early 1916, Saunders was producing for the

Norman Thompson Flight Company the first of fifty Consuta-covered hulls for the NT.4 and NT.4A twin-engined biplane patrol and training flying-boats. Later in the same year, the company undertook construction of twenty-four complete Norman Thompson NT.2B single-engined biplane flying-boat trainers. A large new erection shop had to be built. Completed by the time the first Short 184s were ready for assembly, the new shop was subsequently used for the production of all the smaller sub-contracted types. Extended demand led to a total production of two hundred and one Avro 504s, of both A and J variants, and eighty Short 184s, as well as the work from Norman Thompson.

The company also undertook a certain amount of experimental work. Saunders assisted Commander John Porte in his development of the early series of F boats, large twin-engined biplane patrol flying-boats derived from the Curtiss H-4. Several prototype hulls were constructed, including that for Saunders/Curtiss H-4 1231. As a result of this initial experience, the Air Board proposed in early 1917 that the company should build complete Porte/Felixstowe F.2A flying-boats at Cowes. This proved a considerable undertaking, as the F.2A was a large aircraft for its time, with a wing span of 95 ft $7\frac{1}{2}$ in and an all-up weight of 10,978 lb. Saunders' plant was duly expanded and the area around Cowes on both banks of the Medina became populated with small workshops. In addition, a larger site was established near the Consuta-manufacturing plant at Whippingham.

By the time the Armistice was signed, one hundred F.2As had been completed and another contract secured for fifty of the later F.5s, with Consuta hulls. The war effort at Cowes had been immense. It had yielded,

Felixstowe F.2As under construction in the East Cowes shed, summer 1918.

in addition to complete airframes and hulls, a large number of spare hulls, as well as floats, naval pontoons, and eight airship gondolas. Furthermore, Sam Saunders had been astute in seizing the opportunity to build a prototype aircraft of his own; the Saunders T.1.

With the emphasis having swung toward aircraft manufacture during the course of the war, it was perhaps natural that the company should consider the possibility of designing its own aeroplane. Bearing in mind the loss, temporary or otherwise, of his boat-building contracts, it seemed advisable to Sam Saunders to move toward aircraft design as soon as the chance arose. As early as 1917 the T.1 had emerged, the product of a tiny design team formed in the same year under the leadership of H.H. Thomas. The team consisted of five men, two boys and a single tracer, all working in a small shed known disrespectfully as 'the sardine tin'. The resulting aircraft was prosaic in appearance, being a simple two-seat biplane. Only one example was built and, though it suffered no major vices, the design was abandoned shortly after H.H. Thomas died in the 1918–19 influenza epidemic. Though the T.1 was not a commercial success, it was not in itself a notable failure. There seemed reasonable hope for the future.

The Armistice, however, caused a slump in the aircraft industry as wartime contracts were trimmed and discarded military aircraft were sold on the civil market. S.E. Saunders had expanded greatly in the war years.

Felixstowe F.5 N178 with Saunders 'hollow-bottom' ventilated hull. (*BHC*)

As well as the additions to plant, an aerodrome at Somerton, Cowes, had been laid out and from here the Avros had been delivered. Practically all company profits had been ploughed back into land and plant in an effort to increase aircraft output. In addition, wartime demand for Consuta had led to the construction of a large £53,000 factory known as the Osborne Plywood Works in which to manufacture the ply in quantity.

Initially, it appeared that there would have to be an equally rapid contraction of plant after the war ended. In fact the process was slowed by the continuing orders from the Air Ministry for F 'boats. Saunders' contract for F.2As was allowed to run on for several months after the Armistice, and production of F.5s also continued. A number of Cowes-built F.5s were later taken out of store, where they had lain after completion, and put into service as the standard RAF patrol flying-boat.

Saunders also received frequent orders for the reconditioning and servicing of F 'boats, and a small contract for the reconditioning of de Havilland D.H. 9A day-bombers helped when so many other firms were finding work difficult to obtain. The main impact of the war on Saunders had been to create a first class organisation and plant for the manufacture of aircraft, and for waterborne aircraft especially, and it was inconceivable that aircraft manufacture should be wholly abandoned after the war. The Saunders T.1 had been an attempt, under adverse conditions, to produce an original aircraft. The company was also allotted more experimental work, building a 'hollow-bottom' ventilated hull for Porte/Felixstowe F. 5 N178 in an attempt to improve water performance. There seemed to be reason for cautious optimism at Cowes.

Mixed Fortunes

S.E. Saunders was understandably reluctant to abandon boat-building, and decided to concentrate on high-speed motor-boats initially, in the hope of winning back some of the lost contracts; racing winners would put Saunders firmly back in the public eye. Saunders-built boats again began to win honours in postwar sporting events.

Maple Leaf V, a 40 ft boat powered by four 400 hp Sunbeam engines, established a water speed record of 66·2 mph over one mile in 1920. *Ardenrun I*, a 20 ft boat with a single 70 hp Wolseley, was the fastest 3 litre class racer of the 1923 season. The slightly smaller *Ardenrun II* won the 100 km race at Cannes in the following year. Betty Carstairs won the Duke of York's Trophy using the hydroplane *Newg*, which was powered by a 1·5 litre engine, and indeed ordered a whole fleet from Saunders—*Leumas*, the *Estelle*s and *Jack Stripe*s. The fifth, sixth and seventh *Maple Leaf* hydroplanes were some of the fastest of their class, but failed to stop Gar Wood, in *Miss America I*, winning the Harmsworth Trophy and keeping it for the next decade.

In addition to the racing boats, a large variety of craft were marketed. Typical was the 30 ft standard launch for eleven people, powered by a 32 hp Wolseley giving 17 kt, and its smaller brother of 25 ft, with an 18 hp Wolseley. Cabin cruisers were also produced, as well as 75 ft and 120 ft motor yachts. A new launch for the Royal Yacht *Britannia* was supplied, and the Whitehead Torpedo Company commissioned a 40 ft torpedo recovery launch, *Lulworth*.

Kittiwake undergoing final erection in the Saunders sheds, summer 1920. (*A.J. Jackson collection via R.T. Jackson*)

An unusual product was the Saunders Revolving Summerhouse, which was exhibited at the 1923 Empire Exhibition at Wembley.

Contracts for the manufacture of lifeboats continued throughout the First World War and afterwards.

Immediately after the War, government expenditure on civil aviation generally was minimal, but the Air Ministry instigated a competition for commercial aircraft, which was held at Martlesham Heath and Felixstowe during the autumn of 1920. Offering substantial prizes for the best amphibians and landplanes, the competition attracted many entries of both original and modified design; however, one amphibian at least failed to arrive at Martlesham in time for the competition for which it was specifically designed—the Saunders Kittiwake twin-engined biplane.

S.E. Saunders had viewed the competition as a firm starting point for the manufacture of its own aircraft in the post-war world. The amphibian category allowed the company to produce the type of aircraft it knew most about; the waterborne variety. Very soon after the competition was announced, an entrant from Cowes was designed and constructed. The man who designed the Kittiwake for Saunders was F.P. Hyde Beadle. The Kittiwake was hideously ugly and has been unkindly described as an 'Isle of Wight ferry-boat with wings'.

Intricacy of construction delayed its completion in time for the competition, but a first flight was finally made during September 1920. The flight test was disastrous, no purchaser was found and the Kittiwake passed into obscurity.

Though the failure of the Kittiwake was a reversal for Saunders, the company still had an interest in the outcome of the competition. The Vickers Viking III, with a Consuta hull, won the £10,000 first prize in the amphibian class. Other marks of Viking also incorporated Consuta hulls, as did the Saunders/Vickers A.5 Valentia twin-engined military flying-boat intended as a replacement for the F.5 but never used as such. The A.5 was nominally a Vickers design, with Saunders' senior hull designer,

13

Saunders/Vickers A.5 N124 at the mouth of the Medina. (*BHC*)

Sydney Porter, responsible for the hull. The Valentia hulls were built at Cowes but as it was not a successful design, the work that could be gleaned from the A.5 was limited. Altogether three examples (N124–N126) were built between 1918 and 1922.

In fact the Saunders-Vickers link was a strong one. In 1918, Vickers had obtained a 50 per cent financial interest in Saunders, which was one of the reasons why the Cowes company found survival comparatively straightforward. Three Vickers representatives joined Saunders' board, and one, Sir Arthur Trevor Dawson, served for a short time as chairman. In this way, Vickers brought sub-contract work to Cowes at a vital time, but nevertheless failed to solve the postwar financial problems which grew within the company until a solution was reached in late 1928.

The Vickers link broke in early 1921. Saunders needed additional capital to continue aircraft design studies of its own. By using sums built up from wartime profits Sam Saunders bought out Vickers and, at the same time, the Wolseley interest. He thereby placed the company in a fully independent financial position.

In 1923 a more professional aviation design bureau was established after F.P. Hyde Beadle had left the company in disappointment over the Kittiwake. The new design team consisted of Bertie Thompson, from the Air Ministry via Hawker, as chief designer; Capt D. Nicholson; and Henry Knowler. Knowler had been with Vickers since 1914 but had later moved to the English Electric Co, and during his long stay with Saunders/Saro he

The sole A.3 Valkyrie, N186, Henry Knowler's first design for S.E. Saunders.
(Author's collection)

became one of the greatest authorities on flying-boat design in Great Britain. Work was begun on two new aircraft; Bertie Thompson on the A.4 Medina and Knowler the A.3 Valkyrie.

Knowler's design was in response to Specification 22/24, for a large maritime patrol 'boat. In October 1924 Knowler's design was tendered and eventually awarded a contract for a single prototype. The Valkyrie first flew in mid-1926. It was large for its day, and represented a bold attempt to enter the previously uncharted area of the indigenous long-distance military patrol 'boat, but its flying qualities failed to meet the minimum requirements of the specification and it was not developed further.

The other Saunders prototype, the Medina, was built for the Air Council, work beginning in the spring of 1925 and the first flight taking place in the following year. It was a twin-engined civil biplane flying-boat of all-wood construction. Only one example, G-EBMG, was built, but such were the hydrodynamic difficulties encountered that the design was abandoned. Thompson left Cowes but Knowler stayed, being appointed chief designer shortly afterwards.

With no new injection of capital and a series of unwanted prototypes, Saunders began to look at the possibilities of financial restructuring. Even more disconcerting than the failure of the aircraft was the knowledge that, with the advent of the metal hull, a major application of Consuta to aircraft construction would very soon be outmoded. All four Saunders prototypes had incorporated Consuta construction to some extent. A switch to metal hull construction would require a large amount of capital and it was difficult to see how this could be managed if the business continued on a family basis.

The Saunders A.14, a Supermarine Southampton incorporating a Saunders-designed prototype metal hull had flown by 1928 but there were insufficient funds available to develop this new process or implement it on a profitable scale. Two new prototypes, the A.10 landplane fighter and the A.7 patrol flying-boat, were started under Saunders but their development was slowed by lack of money. Small aviation sub-contracts, such as the construction of floats for the Parnall Peto, did not keep the aircraft plant in regular work. Sam Saunders had gambled; he had bought out the financial interests in his company and had chosen to go his own way, hoping that his aircraft would be successful and that he could compete for aircraft orders. By 1927, it was apparent that this gamble was not a safe bet.

Even earlier, in 1925, talks had been held concerning a financial reorganisation involving Swan, Hunter and Wigham Richardson Ltd and William Beardmore Ltd. Although these eventually came to nothing, it became increasingly clear that such a move could not long be postponed.

Growing difficulties during 1926–28, with the A.3 and A.4 both failing to find buyers, accelerated matters. During 1928 there seemed some hope that the link with Vickers might be reforged; Vickers was at the time planning to make its aircraft activities a separate subsidiary and it was suggested that Saunders might join what would then be a powerful part of the aircraft industry. However, Sam Saunders found the terms unacceptable. His company might have benefitted; although the boat-building side was generally financially stable, not enough cash came in to pay for any expansion of the aircraft works, nor indeed did current demand warrant it. By 1928 the aviation side was making a substantial loss and the workforce was frequently on short time, or allotted other tasks. As Saunders was without funds for the necessary investment, perhaps he made an error of judgement in rejecting the Vickers offer. Certainly he was determined to run a business controlled by himself but by 1928 the financial reality was that this was impossible. At the same time, he refused to close the aircraft plant, which was adequate apart from its inability to handle large-scale manufacture of metal hulls.

Reconstitution

By mid-1928, significant changes in ownership of the aircraft manufacturing industry were starting to take place. Armstrong Siddeley began to show great interest in the holdings of Crossley Motors in A.V. Roe and Company. Armstrong Siddeley already controlled Sir W. G. Armstrong Whitworth Aircraft Ltd. By mid-1928, John Siddeley (later Lord Kenilworth) had acquired a major part of A.V. Roe. It was announced at Hamble, where the Avro Design and Experimental Departments were situated, that the design team would be transferred to the Manchester headquarters at the beginning of September.

Sir Alliott Verdon Roe relinquished his share in Avro, as did his business associate of many years, John Lord. Roe had for some time been fascinated by the concept of waterborne aircraft and had a great desire to become involved in the development of the very large flying-boat. An unfulfilled hope that Avro would increase income by the maufacture of car bodies encouraged Roe and Lord to sell out. They took the opportunity to inject capital into S.E. Saunders. Both Roe and Lord believed that Saunders could be made into a profitable concern over the long term, if the necessary money was available. Between them, they had acquired a controlling interest in Saunders by late 1928 and a new Board was assembled.

With Sam Saunders as honorary president, the reorganised Board consisted in the first place of Roe and Lord, as joint managing directors. The position of general manager was filled by H.E. Broadsmith, who had left Avro shortly after Roe and Lord. Other directors were Sam's son Hubert S. Saunders and Capt Nicholson, from the old Saunders Board. R.V. Perfect also joined the new company, from Avro, eventually rising to become sales director. Henry Knowler remained chief designer.

By the time of the Board changes, Sam Saunders was in his early seventies. In effect he retired from the company after it was taken over by Roe and Lord. He still took an interest in the Isle of Wight pottery industry, with which he had developed connections over the years, and in the Afton Brickworks, which he had bought. Spare time was spent on his estate, Padmore, at Whippingham, where he put much effort into landscaping the grounds. He had always been a dynamic man and it seems that, sadly, the comparatively slow pace of retirement did not suit him. His health became impaired and on 17 December, 1933, he died, aged 77. His son Hubert resigned from the new Board and went to Groves and Guttridge, taking the lifeboat contracts with him, and the last vestige of a family business disappeared.

Sam Saunders' place as president was taken by A.V. Roe. As joint managing director, Roe had been concerned with the design and technical side of the aircraft interest; John Lord's work was of a commercial nature. Roe never superseded Henry Knowler in a design capacity though, and when he became president, the time he could devote to such work naturally became much reduced. However, it was Roe's interest as well as Knowler's knowledge that led to a decision to continue and expand production of new waterborne aircraft.

It is interesting to note something of the abilities of the men who took control of S.E. Saunders. Alliott Verdon-Roe was one of Britain's outstanding aviation pioneers. Roe was an inventive genius of a retiring nature, whose modesty and preoccupation with design work needed to be balanced by someone with the ability to manage the finances of the new enterprise. John Lord was a successful and astute, as well as popular, businessman. These two, Roe and Lord, had found Avro in 1910 and had worked together ever since, and their decision to become involved with Saunders was in fact a joint one. Harry Broadsmith had joined Avro in 1912 and by 1916 had risen to become works manager. After a few years in Australia, he returned to Avro. When in 1928 John Siddeley took control of Avro it was perhaps natural that the three acquaintances of such long standing should stay together. John Lord remained at Cowes until his death in January 1936, when Sqn Ldr C. J. W. Darwin was appointed managing director. Roe stayed until 1958, when he too died.

Unexpectedly, the name of the company remained S.E. Saunders for some time after the takeover, and when a brand new flying-boat prototype, the A.17 Cutty Sark, was exhibited at Olympia in July 1929, the stand on which it was presented was labelled S.E. Saunders. However, by October 1929, a new name for the firm had been substituted—Saunders-Roe Limited, usually abbreviated to Saro.

The financial position of the new company was certainly an improvement on that of S.E. Saunders but, in spite of new designs, by October 1930 part of the workforce was again on short time. Initially,

£42,000 had been subscribed by Roe and Lord but more investment became desirable in order to modernise the works fully, at least on the aircraft side.

Part of this aid was forthcoming from the Aircraft Investment Corporation (AIC). The AIC was formed in July 1929 with the object of financing British commercial aviation, and swiftly acquired interests in Saro and the Blackburn Aeroplane and Motor Company Ltd. Sir Henry Segrave was on the Board of the AIC and when he designed the Meteor low-wing twin-engined cabin monoplane, Saro was entrusted with the building of the first prototype. To the money injected by the AIC, A.V. Roe and his associates added further large sums.

The most significant investment in Saro after the 1928 reshuffle came from Whitehall Securities Corporation Ltd, a banking house founded by Lord Cowdray as part of the Pearson Group of companies. Lord Cowdray, a prominent businessman, had a number of interests, including mining and Mexican oil. Managed by the Hon Clive Pearson, Cowdray's second son, Whitehall Securities acquired a great many interests in various aviation concerns. Opportunity for investment in aircraft manufacture arose through the flagging fortunes of Simmonds Aircraft Ltd, of Weston, Southampton. Simmonds produced in the late 1920s light aeroplanes that sought economy through interchangeability of some of the main airframe components. Whitehall Securities gained a controlling interest in Simmonds during the spring of 1930, the reconstituted company being re-named Spartan Aircraft Ltd.

Later in 1930, Whitehall Securities learned that Saro was considering seeking further investment, began to examine the new company and found a number of designs at prototype stage. Whitehall Securities invested in the Cowes firm, financing both loan and share capital. Three Whitehall representatives joined the Saro Board, among them Capt H.H. Balfour (later the Right Hon Lord Balfour of Inchrye PC, MC), who was later made Under Secretary of State for Air, from 1938 to 1944.

In February 1931, under instructions from Whitehall Securities, Spartan Aircraft moved from Weston to a new site at East Cowes, starting operations in a hangar formerly belonging to John Samuel White. In an attempt to integrate Spartan and Saro, more boardroom changes took place. The Spartan Board, consisting primarily of Oliver (later Sir Oliver) Simmonds and Lt-Col L.A. Strange, as well as Whitehall Securities' men, was swelled by the arrival of Roe, Lord and Broadsmith. Under the new arrangement, Saro undertook considerable design and some construction work for Spartan. The two companies complemented each other; while Saro continued to build mostly waterborne types, Spartan concentrated on the development of landplanes. Whitehall Securities eventually acquired a controlling interest in both companies and it proved impractical to keep them as separate units. In January 1933, the Spartan design team was absorbed into Saro. Though aircraft bearing the Spartan name were produced after this date, an effective merger was completed by the spring of 1933. By late 1935, even the name Spartan had disappeared.

Shake-down

During the 1930s, the new company began to concentrate more on aircraft design and construction and the boat-building side of the firm diminished. However, the boats that continued to emerge from Cowes were still to dominate high-speed racing.

In 1929, Sir Henry Segrave had planned an attack on the water speed record. Lord Wakefield sponsored the attempt and Saro was entrusted with the construction of *Miss England II*, Segrave's new boat. This craft was powered by two 1,750 hp Rolls-Royce engines and was launched on Lake Windermere on 5 June, 1930, only six months after the start of construction. Following a very rapid fitting-out process, on 13 June Sir Henry made two fast test runs on Windermere, then a full throttle run, during which he was estimated to have reached a speed in excess of 110 mph. Tragically, toward the end of this run the craft struck a floating obstacle; both Sir Henry and his mechanic were killed in the ensuing crash. The average speed of 98·2 mph established during the initial runs was a new world water speed record. *Miss England II* was recovered and later repaired. Subsequently raced by Kaye Don, she raised the record first to 103·4 mph at Buenos Aires and then to 110·2 mph on Lake Garda in Italy during 1931.

As a postscript, in 1936 Saro constructed the high-speed motor-boat *Bluebird* for Sir Malcolm Campbell. With this craft, Campbell raised the record to 130·9 mph in 1938. Both *Miss England II* and *Bluebird* were designed by Fred Cooper.

The Saunders/Saro A.10, Cowes, July 1929. (*BHC*)

19

Nevertheless, it was aircraft work which gradually assumed a dominant role at Cowes, at least in financial terms. Although the boat-building side remained unaffected for many years by problems with materials, by 1930 Consuta was rendered obsolete in the construction of aircraft hulls. Of course, by 1928 an attempt had already been made to produce a prototype metal flying-boat hull at Cowes. The new hull was designed by Henry Knowler and the aircraft, using a Supermarine Southampton superstructure, was designated the Saunders A.14. Thinking behind the hull's design lay firmly in economy and ease of construction, the former to prevent excessive cost of development under the company's ailing finances, and the latter to aid the workforce in their transfer from wood- to metalworking.

Water and flying trials with the A.14 were made during late 1928 and Saro went on to produce a series of flying-boats and amphibians through the 1930s which incorporated the new 'corrugated' hull construction method of integral skin stiffening. Double curvature was dispensed with wherever possible to minimise effort in panel-beating. Easy construction allowed the workforce to become accustomed to largescale metalworking, without wholesale import of appropriately skilled labour. In fact the 'corrugated' method was not without its problems, though these were not immediately exposed.

At the time of the company's reconstitution, it had two other prototypes taking shape. The first was an aircraft in sharp contrast to the usual waterborne products. Because of the dearth of orders for Saunders flying-boats, it had been decided to create, on a private venture basis, a type entirely new to the company; a land-based fighter, designated the A.10. Nicknamed the 'Multi-gun', because it carried four machine-guns at a time when most fighters had only two, the A.10 first flew in late January 1929. After interminable and unfavourable type trials the programme faltered; yet another Saunders aircraft had failed to secure a production order.

Begun during 1927 but not flown or tested until 1930 was another prototype, this time more in company tradition. Employing the new Saunders method of 'corrugated' hull construction, the A.7 Severn was a three-engined military patrol flying-boat, built to Air Ministry Specification R.4/27. Somewhat smaller than the A.3 Valkyrie, the Severn was tested rigorously by the Marine Aircraft Experimental Establishment (MAEE) during the summer and autumn of 1930. It later embarked on a proving cruise to the Near East. Despite the aircraft's performance, which was in some ways outstanding, MAEE concluded that a major fault lay in the A.7's extreme frailty and again only one example was built.

The A.7 and A.10 were the last S.E. Saunders designs. Both prototypes were finished after the company had been reconstituted, but both were given rather low priority compared with the all-new designs swiftly begun by the reborn Saunders-Roe. In fact, the A.7 did serve operationally for a short period, with No. 209 Squadron, but only because 209 was under-equipped at the time. The facilities required to produce such large types as the A.3 and A.7 had been considerable and the failure of the prototypes explain in part Saunders' precarious financial position by 1928.

The designs begun under the new management were to keep the company generally quite well occupied during the 1930s.

The new generation of aircraft were simpler and less experimental than

A.17 Cutty Sark G-ACDP, off Hamble, 1936. (*Saro*)

some of the old Saunders offerings and were generally calculated to appeal to an expanding civil market as well as military. A 'family' series of three small related flying-boats and amphibians stabilised the reconstituted concern and allowed it to develop in a more orderly and profitable way.

The first design by Saunders-Roe was begun during March 1929 and was a small twin-engined cantilever monoplane flying-boat. It was named Cutty Sark, had Saro type number A.17, and was broadly similar to another design begun during the summer of 1929, the A.19 Cloud. Both types, as a general rule, had twin engines mounted on pylons above the wing. With a variety of powerplants, twelve Cutty Sarks were completed during the early 1930s, providing the first commercial success for the new company.

The similar but larger A.19 Cloud first flew in 1930. Four civil examples were built, again with a variety of engines, and the Air Ministry purchased another for trials as a navigational trainer. Following this, a further sixteen Clouds were built as military variants and performed sterling if undramatic service on training duties for a number of years. The military version of the Cloud was allotted the type number A.29.

The third member of the 'family' to be produced was the three-engined A.21 Windhover, intermediate in size between the Cutty Sark and the Cloud. It is possible that the added complexity of the third engine deterred potential buyers, for only two examples were built, both for the civil market.

A.19 Cloud G-ABHG *Flying Amo*, at Southampton Airport.

Although most of the 'family' appeared as amphibians, occasional examples flew as flying-boats, with the undercarriage removed. The success of these three types, and especially the Air Ministry contract for the Cloud, sustained Saro through the early 1930s. The company also continued sub-contract work, the most important of which was the manufacture of the Blackburn Bluebird IV all-metal light civil biplane. Production at Cowes ran from early 1930 to May 1931, by which time fifty-five had been completed. They were manufactured at West Cowes because of lack of space across the water, but wing construction was undertaken by Boulton Paul.

At the same time, Saro undertook detail design and construction of an advanced light touring aircraft conceived by Sir Henry Segrave, and the prototype first flew in the spring of 1930. Designated the Saro/Segrave A.22 Meteor, it was a beautifully streamlined twin-engined low-wing monoplane. After construction of the first prototype, G-AAXP, production was switched to Blackburn, where the wooden fuselage was replaced by an all-metal type. Two more examples were eventually completed. After Sir Henry was killed, and as Blackburn became increasingly involved with military orders, further Meteor production was abandoned.

During the early 1930s, Saro began to co-operate with the newly transferred Spartan Aircraft, who were by then also situated at East Cowes. The aeroplane on which collaboration was initiated did not

22

Third member of the 'family'; A.21 Windhover ZK-ABW, Cowes, late 1930. (*BHC*)

Blackburn Bluebird IV G-AACC, of the type produced under sub-contract by Saro.
G-AACC won the 1931 King's Cup and was powered by a Hermes I.

23

originate from Cowes at all, but was the design of Edgar Percival. ,
a three-engined single-seat low-wing cantilever monoplane with a ply
fuselage and wooden wing. Intended for long-range mail-carrying ᵢ
named the Saro/Percival A.24 Mailplane, the prototype was built aᵢ
Cowes during 1931 as a joint project between Percival and Saro, and
gained its Certificate of Airworthiness early in the following year. Soon
afterwards, Percival sold his interest in the design, which was then renamed
the Saro A.24 Mailplane. However, when the close association between
Saro and Spartan led to a decision to allot development to Spartan, the
name was again changed, this time to Spartan A.24 Mailplane.

Though the pure mail-carrying variant had no real commercial future
and only one example was built, the concept was not abandoned. Instead
the aircraft was developed by Spartan and Saro into a passenger-carrying
type, the Spartan Cruiser series. The Cruiser I, as indicated by the type
number A.24M, was given a metal fuselage, as well as other modifications,
and first flew in the spring of 1932. By February 1933, the Cruiser II
production version had flown. Several were eventually sold abroad, as well
as on the home market, and were economical and successful.

Also, on 2 February, 1933, Whitehall Securities and Spartan formed a
small airline, naming it Spartan Air Lines. It began a scheduled summer
service between Heston and Cowes on 12 April, using the sole Cruiser I
G-ABTY. From 12 May, the frequency was increased to twice daily, with
the arrival of Cruiser II G-ACDW. On 2 October, the service was
suspended for the winter. Spartan Air Lines resumed operations on 1 May,
1934, offering a thrice daily service. These services were operated in
conjunction with the Southern Railway, the London terminus becoming
Croydon. This route also included request-stops at Bembridge and Ryde.
From 1 October the route became Bembridge—Cowes—Southampton—
Croydon. On 31 October, Railway Air Services, represented by the
Southern Railway, withdrew from the operation and only a skeleton
service was operated during the winter.

The 1935 season opened on 14 April, the London terminus reverting to
Heston. From 1 June, an additional summer service was provided to
Sandown, again in conjunction with Railway Air Services, and using
Cruiser IIs and the developed Cruiser IIIs. However, on 1 October Spartan
Air Lines was taken over, becoming part of the new British Airways, and
its aircraft were dispersed. Three Cruisers remained in use until 1940,
adequate evidence of the robust nature of the design.

In the same year as Spartan Aircraft transferred from the mainland to
Cowes, the Air Ministry issued Specification R.24/31 for a twin-engined
military patrol flying-boat, and Saunders-Roe put in a tender. The new
Saro design was similar in some respects to the frail Saunders A.7 Severn
and again used the patented method of corrugated hull construction,
though this time in strengthened form. Henry Knowler was again
responsible for this new type, designated A.27 and named London.
Though previous attempts at military aircraft designs had failed, this time
there was no disappointment. The prototype London, K3560, flew in 1934
and after successful trials at MAEE the design was accepted by the Air
Ministry. In March 1935, an order for seven Mk I aircraft was secured.
Following successful modification of the original prototype to
Specification R.3/35, a production run of Mk IIs resulted, the essential

Saro London I K5258, at MAEE Felixstowe for type trials, early 1937.
(RAE, Crown Copyright)

difference being the change from Bristol Pegasus III to Pegasus X engines. The London II was adopted as the major RAF version and, altogether, one prototype, seven Mk Is and twenty-three Mk IIs were built.

Expansion

The first Saro London contract marked the onset of an increasing amount of Air Ministry work. Production of the London demanded large assembly areas and major alterations to the Cowes works became necessary. In mid-1935, work began on the erection of a new shop on the Medina at East Cowes, named Columbine after Sam Saunders' original boatyard. Completed by Boulton and Paul Ltd in 1936, this large building contained not only erecting and sub-assembly shops but also the works offices, the Aeronautical Inspection Bureau, lecture and schoolrooms, parachute packing room and pilots' offices and kit rooms. Columbine had a clear floor capacity of over 30,000 sq ft and an unobstructed height of 40 ft in the manufacturing area. An extended apron and a new and larger slipway were also constructed, in front of the new shop, designed to take aircraft of up to 50 tons. After the Second World War, the apron was reinforced and Columbine, with its curved roof and huge SAUNDERS-ROE hoarding, by the early 1950s was to become a familiar photographic backdrop for its most famous inhabitant, the SR.45 Princess. At the same time, offices for the works staff and planning department were erected on the west bank of the Medina.

East Cowes in 1936. Columbine had recently been erected and the apron and slipway were extended at the same time. The Medina hangar had not yet been built.

Saro A.33 K4773, on the Columbine apron after its accident, late 1938.

By 1933, having finalised the design of the London, the company began to consider the requirements of a subsequent Air Ministry Specification, R.2/33. This was for a large, four-engined monoplane patrol flying-boat intended to replace the biplane types then in service. The new Saro design to R. 2/33 departed from the usual company practice in a number of ways. The patented hull form incorporating longitudinal 'corrugations' was set aside. That type of construction had never proved entirely durable, even in the case of small aircraft and, though simple to manufacture, was no longer held by the company to be viable. Wingform of the new design was of monospar parasol arrangement and sponsons were adopted to provide lateral stability.

Late in 1936 work began at Cowes on the construction of the prototype R.2/33, by then designated A.33 but not named. Component testing slowed progress considerably; the aircraft was not completed until the autumn of 1938, first flying on 14 October that year. The A.33 remained intact for only a very short time, porpoising to destruction just before its fifth take-off. The starboard side of the wing suffered a structural failure and the hull was holed, fortunately above the waterline. Amazingly, none of the crew was seriously injured. The A.33 was towed back to the Columbine slipway and later beached. The entire programme was reluctantly abandoned soon after the accident and only one A.33 was built,

Saro Lerwick L7248, with rudder modification, off Cowes during the summer of 1939. (*BHC*)

27

this decision was made in the knowledge that an Air Ministry order had been received for another Saro design, this time completely off the drawing-board.

Disappointment over the A.33 was eased by the challenge of another new type, the S.36 Lerwick, a twin-engined monoplane flying-boat. Since 1936, when a contract for production of the S.36 had been placed, work on construction of the first few Lerwicks had continued in Columbine near where the A.33 was built. Proposed in response to Specification R.1/36, the Lerwick was initially a private venture intended to replace the medium-range biplane patrol flying-boats in service during the mid-1930s. The design was rapidly developed because of the threat of war and was accepted by the Air Ministry as part of the re-equipment programme of the late 1930s. The first three production Lerwicks were also intended to serve as prototypes. No firm rival to the Saro offering had emerged and consequently the Air Ministry had little choice but to order the Lerwick.

The need for rapid production had caused the decision to order from the drawing-board, and the Lerwick was so hastily designed and constructed that it suffered from a number of defects. Protracted testing and modification programmes failed to cure its poor hydrodynamic and flying performance, and the S.36 was withdrawn from service in 1942, as soon as the first United States Consolidated PBY Catalinas became available.

To accelerate production of the Lerwick the Medina shop was erected at Cowes, adjacent to Columbine, during 1939 and early 1940. In 1937, a workshop at Luton, managed for Saro by the Adamant Engineering Company Ltd, had been used for the manufacture of early Lerwick components, and the obvious geographical disadvantage of this arrangement prompted a move to Southampton Airport (Eastleigh) later in 1937, where a small building was leased and this work resumed. With no follow-on orders for the Lerwick after completion of the first and only batch, the Southampton factory was used during the war for sub-contract work and after the war became part of another Saro presence at Eastleigh, the Helicopter Division.

Also during 1937, an addition to personnel was made when Capt E.D. Clarke took the post of commercial director. He became joint managing director in 1939 and managing director in 1945, until he resigned in 1960.

Shortly before the Second World War, Saro began to rationalise. The various interests of the company were made semi-autonomous. Saunders Shipyard Ltd was formed in 1938 as an associate company, and began to run the boat-building activities based at Cornubia Yard, half a mile up the Medina from the main aircraft works.

Also in 1938, Saro Laminated Wood Products Ltd (SLWP) was formed, situated at the Folly Works at Whippingham. Production of Consuta had been replaced by large-scale manufacture of a great variety of articles, including all types of doors, trolley-bus roofs, and cubicles for swimming-baths. In addition, new processes such as pre-forming and resin-impregnation had been developed during the 1930s. By 1939, SLWP was producing nearly 40 per cent of all aircraft plywood manufactured in Great Britain.

Rationalisation left the parent company free to concentrate on aircraft production, and this aspect was thus strengthened and raised to a more important level than ever before. With orders for the London and Lerwick

28

Saro A.37 G-AFZS under test over the Solent, late 1939. (*BHC*)

fulfilled, however, there was a lull in production even though the Project Office remained highly active. By the time the Lerwick was beginning to reveal its problems, in 1939, the most advanced project underway at Cowes was in answer to Specification R.5/39; this was the S.38 study (*see* Appendix Five). A small flying scale model of S.38 was built during 1939 to assess the qualities of the full-size project, with the Saro number A.37. Colloquially known as the 'Shrimp', the A.37 was a four-engined monoplane flying-boat produced purely as a research vehicle, as a prelude to the very much larger S.38 project, and was built as a private venture. After the difficulties encountered with the A.33 and S.36, it is perhaps not surprising that Saro resorted to the construction of an experimental model with which to test their next full-size design. In the event, the S.38 was never built, but the A.37 was used to test some of the Short/Saro S.35 Shetland components in model form.

Only the London and the Lerwick represented Saunders-Roe during the Second World War. Though the Project Office was busy, no new aircraft types were built between 1939 and 1945, although the company did other essential and outstanding work. The newly-expanded aircraft manufacturing plant was fully employed during the course of the war and sub-contract construction of various aircraft became a major task.

The Second World War

When hostilities with Germany began in September 1939, Saro had little to

29

offer in the way of aircraft for the war effort, except for the elderly London and the troublesome Lerwick.

One consequence of the war was the increased need for amphibian Air/Sea Rescue aircraft. Vickers-Supermarine was by the late 1930s the traditional source of such aircraft, having produced the Walrus biplane amphibian and by 1938 its eventual replacement the Sea Otter, in prototype form. A severe production problem arose when it became clear that Vickers-Supermarine would have to concentrate on building Spitfires. In order to avoid any drop in production of the Walrus, the Ministry of Aircraft Production (MAP) decided in 1939 to delegate Walrus construction to Saro.

Saro worked closely with Vickers-Supermarine throughout most of the war, building under licence the Walrus I and II, some examples being built with wooden hulls. Then followed production of the later but similar Sea Otter, while the parent company concentrated on the Spitfire and its derivatives.

The first problem faced by the company when war started was one of dispersal. Cowes was exceptionally vulnerable to enemy air attack and, during the first half of 1940, continuous air-raid warnings seriously interfered with work. Towards the end of 1940, new bases were in various stages of preparation and operation.

X1045, the prototype wooden-hulled Walrus II, East Cowes, summer 1940.

A certain amount of work continued at Cowes, with assembly and flight testing of the Walrus and later the Sea Otter. These aircraft, once erected, were launched from Columbine slipway and, having made a short flight, landed at Somerton. This operation served as a proving routine for the production aircraft, which were afterwards flown from Somerton to the mainland for dispersal. A subsidiary site at West Cowes was, through the early part of the war, concerned with overhaul and repair of the Walrus. After the destruction of this base by enemy action, the operation moved to Forest Side on the Newport-Yarmouth road. Another large hangar was subsequently erected at Place Road, Cowes, for the task of additional repair work.

The Eastleigh factory acquired in 1937 became occupied with the manufacture of components for the amphibians once work on the Lerwick was completed, as did several smaller sites which swiftly grew up on the Island itself. The head office and company directorate were evacuated during 1940 to Melchett Court at Romsey, Hampshire, and administration was then centralised there. Cornubia Yard, under the control of Saunders Shipyard Ltd, also became involved in aircraft repair work, while the Folly Works continued the manufacture of aircraft plywood. However, after an air raid during May 1942, when these two bases were severely damaged, this work was transferred to Parkhurst Forest.

Another site developed as a wartime expedient was situated on the Weybridge trading estate at Addlestone in Surrey. There were also two much smaller works at Hersham and Byfleet. Weybridge produced the Walrus II with wooden hulls supplied by Elliotts of Newbury, in addition to the more usual metal ones, because of wartime shortages of metal. By 1941, a small airfield near the main factory had been made available for

JN185, a production Sea Otter I, Saro-built. (*MoD, Crown Copyright*)

the amphibians to fly from, though it was surrounded by high-tension cables on tall pylons and was thus far from ideal; at least one Walrus was destroyed while attempting to leave.

Weybridge also sub-contracted minor component manufacture for the Fairey Barracuda, during 1943. By January 1944, orders for the Walrus were completed. Hulls for Sea Otters were begun by mid-1944, these being taken to Cowes where assembly of the aircraft took place. The rest of the Weybridge area resources became involved with the manufacture of Fairey Firefly components and later the maintenance of the Barracuda.

Immediately after the war, Saro interest in Weybridge ended. The staff were withdrawn and by mid-1946 the trading estate had almost fully reverted to civil use. Production of the Sea Otter continued at Cowes, orders being fulfilled by July 1946.

Production of Saro-built Walrus aircraft amounted altogether to 461 examples. A contract and an initial order were placed with the company in October 1939, specifying a purchase price of £10,500 per unit, including £500 profit. Subsequent orders were placed in July and August 1940 and, despite some haggling over profit margins, these and yet more orders were completed by January 1944, after which production stopped. Preparations for the building of Sea Otters were begun in mid-1943 and the first example entered service in late 1944. Production ended after completion of 291 examples, nearly all Sea Otters being completed by Saunders-Roe rather than the parent company.

Another site to be established after the outbreak of war was that at Beaumaris, on the Isle of Anglesey. Arrangements for this move were made during the summer of 1940 and the area was prepared for the reception of staff by October of that year. The design department was then evacuated to the new Beaumaris offices, situated in a large house named *Fryars*, about a mile from the Menai Straits.

Catalina II AM266, the first Catalina handled at Beaumaris. (*Saro*)

Consolidated Catalina IVA JX215 at Beaumaris, showing ASV and Leigh light installations.
(Saro)

Also during the summer of 1940, the company was instructed by the Ministry of Aircraft Production (MAP) and the Directorate of Production, Canadian and American (DPCA) to undertake the task of converting the American-built Consolidated PBY Catalina long-range patrol amphibian to RAF requirements. The Catalinas were to be flown from the United States to Greenock, on the Clyde, where conversion followed by dispersal would take place.

Arrangements were made by MAP for the reception of the first Catalinas on behalf of Saro by Scottish Aviation Ltd of Prestwick, in the half-derelict Cairds Yard at Greenock; these began to arrive during January and February 1941. Work started on conversion in late February, some of the Saro design team travelling to Greenock in order to develop a series of Alteration and Modification kits. Primitive conditions, inclement weather and finally a severe air raid in early May, combined with the small size of the yard, all impeded progress. As a result, the majority of aircraft arriving for work by Saro were directed to a hastily prepared but much larger reception site at Beaumaris. This had become a permanent arrangement by late 1941.

Through the course of the war, Saro became the Central Firm for British Catalina conversion, working on the Mks I, IB, II, IIA, III, IV, IVA and IVB. Modifications were numerous; fitting of Air to Surface Vessel (ASV) radar, the Leigh searchlight, British gyro-compass and flight instruments; strengthening of the step; adding cooking facilities and removing overload tanks needed for the long delivery flights. Most of this work was done at Beaumaris, with a small amount going to Greenock. It was a huge undertaking handled with astonishing speed. By the end of the war, Beaumaris had handled over 310 Catalinas. Also, Saro was made responsible for similar modifications to the Consolidated PB2Y Coronado, the Martin PBM Mariner, the Sikorsky 0S2U Kingfisher and the Curtiss SO3 Seamew, all of which arrived at Beaumaris, though in much smaller numbers.

33

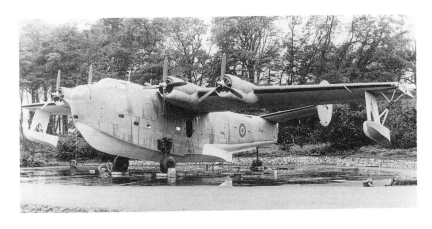

Consolidated Coronado I JX496, Beaumaris, 1944. (*Saro*)

Together with the design and project facilities, the wind-tunnel and structural test equipment were also moved to Beaumaris for the duration, and were soon in operation. The project study of S.38, the long-range patrol flying-boat for which the A.37 had been built as a research vehicle, was continued. This work on large flying-boats was encouraged by the emergence of Specification R.14/40 during 1940. This called for a very long-range military patrol flying-boat to eventually supersede existing types. It was to be four-engined, with a normal range of about 4,000 miles, heavy defensive turret armament, and a crew of eleven. The proposed engine was the Bristol Centaurus. Maximum weight was to be 120,000 lb.

Saro made a rapid design study to R.14/40, producing the project S.39(R). Short Brothers also submitted designs to R.14/40. After studying the competitors, MAP surprisingly announced that an order would be placed only if the two companies co-operated in the design and

Martin Mariner I JX103, Beaumaris, 1943. (*Saro*)

34

Vought-Sikorsky Kingfisher I FN660, Beaumaris, late 1942. (*Saro*)

Short/Saro Shetland I DX166, which was eventually burnt out at its moorings.
(*Short Brothers*)

manufacture of the new aircraft. This was eventually agreed to, despite the geographical and other disadvantages, and two R.14/40 prototypes were ordered. This work involved a very close liaison between Henry Knowler and Arthur Gouge of Shorts; the two collaborated through a shuttle process until Gouge left Shorts in 1943 to join Saro as vice-chairman. Gouge's move concentrated all that was best in British flying-boat design at Cowes, and during the 1950s this partnership would yield some remarkable technical developments.

R.14/40 emerged as the Short/Saro S.35 Shetland. The aircraft was nominally a Short design, with Saro responsible for some detail design and complete wing manufacture, including flaps, ailerons, engine-mountings and wingtip floats. The Shetland components were in part tested before the prototypes were built, in scaled-down form, using the A.37 test-bed. Both Shetland prototypes were completed but the first one, DX166, did not arrive at the MAEE until late 1945, and the design was no longer needed for the war. This example was destroyed by fire at its moorings during January 1946, and the second, G-AGVD, completed as a civil variant, made onts before eventually being broken up.

Apart from this work, it was the Saro design team that created the wooden hull for the Supermarine Walrus. Study was also begun of a new type, which eventually led to the creation of Specification E.6/44. This Specification was radical; it called for a jet-propelled flying-boat fighter. The Project Office, as well as working on the Shetland, continued to create large flying-boat projects of its own, whch culminated in the Princess and the truly vast P.192.

Specialisation

Immediately after the Second World War, another period of company reorganisation began.

The starting point was the rationalisation of plant which had had to be expanded for the war. A number of the smaller works were closed, as was the larger Weybridge site. Activities of the company were again streamlined into distinct areas. Head Office, and the Project and Design Offices, were re-established on the Isle of Wight by the autumn of 1945 and an improved wind-tunnel and large enclosed towing tank were built.

At this time, there were personnel changes and promotions. R.V. Perfect had been appointed sales director in 1941, while Capt E.D. Clarke became Saro managing director in 1945. Walter Browning joined the firm as general manager and director from Shorts in 1946. Geoffrey Verdon Roe became managing director of the new postwar concern of Saro (Anglesey) Ltd. The Hon H.N. Morgan Grenville OBE became Saro chairman. In 1952, The Hon Maurice Lubbock joined the Board.

In 1945, after the withdrawal of the aircraft design facilities from Beaumaris, the site was taken over by Saunders Shipyard Ltd. As the scope of work at Beaumaris grew, the name of this concern was changed to Saunders Engineering and Shipyard Ltd and finally to Saunders-Roe (Anglesey) Ltd — SR(A) — in early 1951.

Boat-building continued as the main work of SR(A) and the new company earned a significant share of the market for the design and construction of small naval craft as well as vessels for the civil market. Work began on glass fibre boats, airborne lifeboats, and an examination into the use of aluminium alloy in the construction of motor torpedo boats. The light engineering side included work on single- and double-decker bus bodies, road tankers, torpedo tubes and pontoons. Over 1,500 bus bodies were produced, including 620 for Cuba, between July 1950 and September 1951. Others went to many parts of the world.

The marine side developed rapidly and in 1949 the first aluminium-hulled motor torpedo boat (MTB 1602) was launched, built for the Royal Navy. With three Packard engines developing a total of 3,750 hp, this craft was capable of 42 kt. In order to cope with the construction of larger craft, a new slipway was built in 1953 and a variety of boats were then produced.

During 1954 a major expansion was realised. 19 June saw the launching of *Morag Mhor*, a 72 ft Bermuda-sloop-rigged yacht built for the British Aluminium Company, and employing the first large-scale marine application of Argon arc-welded aluminium alloy to be seen in vessels of this nature. During the second half of 1954, three inshore minesweepers of 106 ft were launched. As a result of experience gleaned from the construction of MTB 1602, SR(A) was given the task of designing the Dark class of fast patrol boats for the Royal Navy. The first, *Dark Adventurer*, was launched on 28 October, 1954, the second followed in December. Others were supplied to Burma, Finland and Japan.

Another boat with which SR(A) became concerned was *Bras d'Or*, designed and built for the Canadian Defence Research Board and the British Admiralty, for research into foils. The craft was again produced at Beaumaris, but its foils were designed at Cowes. Launched on 29 March, 1957, *Bras d'Or* had a length of 60 ft and was powered by two Rolls-Royce Griffon engines. Some stability problems were encountered during tests off Anglesey and the craft was eventually taken to Canada for modifications and further trials.

Versatility was also shown at the new Folly site by Saro Laminated Wood Products (SLWP). After the war, demand for aircraft plywood fell drastically and the company was forced to look elsewhere for success. This itdid with remarkable speed, promptly diversifying into the manufacture of doors and panelling, for which there was great demand; doors for houses, hospitals, hotels and ships, decorative panels for train compartments, ships' cabins and public buildings, all were produced by SLWP. 'Medino' office partitioning with light alloy clip-together framing, was introduced in great quantity. Another product was 'Sar-Rez', a tough plastic finish for application to the wooden products. The field of plastics was widened with the development of 'Sarolite', as well as 'Saropane', transparent materials used to produce roofing sheets as a substitute for glass. Later, 'Saroy' was created, a type of plastic sheet for use as buoyancy and for refrigerator linings. During the later 1950s a series of machines were imported from the United States and full-scale production of PVC, polythene and polystyrene began.

In 1948 a new enterprise had been established, the Electronics Section, which eventually became a department distinct from other aspects of the company. This section in 1951 produced the Saro foil strain gauge. In 1954 a first analogue computer was built, for use by the newly-formed Computer Department for Aerodynamic, Hyrdodynamic and Flutter

Calculations. Over the next few years, a number of small computers were developed, some for other companies, especially de Havilland.

The test-tank side also grew. In 1950, a large free-alighting tank was built, to test the qualities of various waterborne aircraft projects. This tank became underused in its intended role but was later put to good use in assessing aircraft ditching characteristics. By 1954, this was the only tank regularly in such use in Great Britain. In 1956 a new ship tank was completed. Amongst many other activities, tests were made to help in the designs of the British challengers for the Americas Cup. All these facilities were centred at Cowes, and Beaumaris was given its own tanks.

The Unequal Struggle

The long-term effect of Sir Arthur Gouge's transfer from Short Brothers to Saro in 1943 was to concentrate postwar British flying-boat design within one company.

Two types of flying-boat were designed and built and others projected, but the time for wide-scale use of large flying-boats by airlines was coming to a close, although BOAC continued using flying-boats until 1950.

There were several reasons for withdrawing flying-boats from mainline air services. Two of the most important were the development of long-range landplane airliners in the United States, and the worldwide building of runways capable of handling the new generation of landplanes.

Many of the world's major cities are not close to water and therefore tedious surface journeys had to be made between those cities and the nearest flying-boat alighting areas. In addition, landplane operations were to prove both safer and more economic.

Although not foreseen at the time, the flying-boat could never have coped with the developments in low-visibility and automatic landings.

In spite of the disadvantages faced by the flying-boat as a commercial transport, Saro remained committed to the concept and made studies of ways in which its operation could be simplified.

Endeavour and Disappointment

After the war Saunders-Roe was free to concentrate on the development of new aircraft types, and two new test-pilots joined the company in the early postwar years, Geoffrey Tyson and John Booth. Tyson had previously been a test-pilot with Shorts and before that had been involved with in-flight refuelling experiments using Short C class Empire Flying-boats. Tyson was to fly both the SR.A/1 and the SR.45 Princess, which emerged from Cowes during the late 1940s and early 1950s. He remained chief test pilot until January 1956.

In 1949, Tyson was joined by Sqn Ldr John Booth DFC, who also came from Shorts and became Tyson's deputy at Cowes. Upon Tyson's retirement, Booth took over; it had been decided that a younger man was needed to fly the revolutionary Saunders-Roe SR.53 mixed-unit interceptor then under development. It was in the SR.53 XD151 that Booth was later to lose his life.

The first postwar aircraft from Cowes owed its origins to a wartime Specification, E.6/44. In December 1943, Saro submitted one of its new projects to MAP, involving a radical flying-boat fighter powered by two Metropolitan-Vickers F.2/4 Beryl turbojets, and able to operate from sheltered waters. After several amendments, a contract was awarded for the production of three prototypes of this aircraft, to E.6/44, which had been written round the original Saro proposals and subsequent modifications. Work on construction of the prototypes was begun at Beaumaris but mostly was done at Cowes. Designated SR.A/1 and referred to colloquially as the 'Squirt', the first prototype, TG263, flew in July 1947, creating something of a sensation. The SR.A/1 was an outstanding technical achievement and could claim several 'firsts', but a number of factors prohibited sales. The inspiration for the aircraft from the company's point of view was the island-hopping campaigns in the Pacific War, in which the type might have been very useful, though it has to be said that official enthusiasm for that role was surprisingly tepid. In any event, by the time the first SR.A/1 had flown the war had been over for two years and the armed forces had been greatly reduced. Two SR.A/1s were lost in accidents, the other performed desultory test flights until 1951 when the programme ceased. Possible use in the Korean War was briefly considered but then dismissed. TG263 is currently preserved at Duxford.

Saro SR.A/1 TG263, East Cowes, summer 1947. (*AQD, Crown Copyright*)

Princess G-ALUN, the only example to fly. (*Saro*)

The commercial failure of the SR.A/1 was undoubtedly a setback. However, a truly vast project was by the late 1940s and early 1950s overshadowing a great deal at Cowes and the firm was kept extremely busy. This project resulted in the beautiful and again technically impressive SR.45 Princess civil flying-boat, weighing 330,000 lb. The Princess, like the Bristol Brabazon, never achieved commercial success. The origins of the Princess are shown in Appendix Five.

The first Princess, G–ALUN, flew in August 1952, powered by early-series Bristol Proteus propeller-turbines which failed to provide enough power for commercial operations. Three examples were built; only the first received engines and flew. All three airframes were subsequently broken up after many years of storage.

In technical terms, the Princess was the greatest project undertaken by Saunders-Roe. As with the SR.A/1, the company which only a few years before had been engaged on sub-contracting work from other manufacturers had produced a remarkable design of its own, testimony to its small but specialist design team.

The commercial failure of the Princess was a very heavy blow to Saunders-Roe. Time and again, sales hopes were raised and then shattered as prospective customers came, and then went away again. Virtually all the aviation side of the firm had been involved to some extent with the Princess, and the workforce was rightly proud of the giant from a technical

40

point of view. Euphoria reigned in the aeronautical press when the Princess first flew, although behind this delight there were some doubts expressed over the wisdom of building such an aircraft at that time. When the Princess finally died, so too did the 1950 Duchess project, a 74-seat medium-range civil flying-boat powered by six de Havilland Ghost turbojets. For Saro a rapid change of direction became the order of the day.

It was perfectly clear to the company after this disappointment that development of subsequent flying-boats would be an extremely hazardous business even were sufficient funds obtained, which seemed unlikely. The few further waterborne projects were thus confined to theoretical studies, except for a detailed examination into the possible benefits of hydroskis (*see* Appendix Four). On a practical basis, it was understandable that the company decided to diversify its aviation products.

With Eastleigh pursuing an active role as the Saunders-Roe Helicopter Division, formed out of the take-over of Cierva in 1951, the Cowes team settled to an altogether different project after work on the Princess was well in hand. In October 1952, Henry Knowler became technical director and Maurice Brennan succeeded him as chief designer. In 1948 Brennan had been appointed technical assistant to Sir Arthur Gouge and in 1951 became assistant chief designer. Though he had worked intensively with marine aircraft while at Cowes, by the early 1950s he also provided the design team with a new breadth, for he was becoming very knowledgeable in quite a different area—rocketry.

Brennan's newly acquired expertise came to the fore after the Ministry of Supply (MoS) issued Specification F.124T during 1952, which called for a rocket-powered interceptor. Saro was not initially invited to tender but finally secured the Specification and eventually produced the SR.53, which was powered by a small turbojet and a rocket motor and was a high-altitude interceptor with an astonishing rate of climb.

Few major problems arose with the SR.53, apart from the time it took to construct the two prototypes. Meanwhile, the design was developed into

On parade: SR.53s XD145 and XD151 at Boscombe Down, spring 1957. (*A&AEE*)

the SR.177, which was bigger, heavier and incorporated a number of major refinements. The SR.53/SR.177 was another outstanding technical success for Saunders-Roe; the SR.177 was at the time of its design considered to be the best aircraft of its type in the world. Large orders seemed probable, from both the home market and abroad. However, the Defence White Paper issued during the spring of 1957 by Duncan Sandys, Minister of Defence, suddenly cancelled the programme.

Flight-testing of the SR.53 continued after the cancellation for contractual reasons but also, no doubt, in the hope of a reprieve or, better still, a new Defence Minister. Foreign interest in the programme waned, and though several SR.177s were partially constructed, none were completed. On 5 June, 1958, John Booth was killed while flying the second SR.53, and the project, which should have been a world-wide success, became a complete tragedy.

Eastleigh

At the end of the Second World War, the majority of the small Saro sites were either closed entirely or used for other purposes. The Eastleigh site was an exception. From early 1946 to mid-1948, aeronautical activity began again, with the manufacture of tools, details and some larger components for the SR.A/1 and the Princess. Later, sub-contract work was undertaken, including largescale manufacture of 760 sets of de Havilland Vampire wings, as well as elevators and fuselage bulkheads, and tailplanes and elevators for the de Havilland Venom. In addition, certain components for the Supermarine Swift and the Scimitar were produced. The company also undertook construction of 420 sets of wings for the Vickers Viscount. This work initially served to keep the site in use over a difficult postwar period and went on to provide valuable income. In late

Inheritance: Cierva W.11 Air Horse G-ALCV. The design was not developed under Saro. (*AQD, Crown Copyright*)

42

January 1951, the Saunders-Roe Helicopter Division was formed when the company took over current design commitments, the premises and most of the technical staff of the Cierva Autogiro Company, which had been based at Eastleigh for a short time.

The most promising design acquired from Cierva was a very small two-seat helicopter, the W.14 Skeeter. This existed only in underdeveloped form. The other Cierva type was the very large and unconventional three-engined helicopter, the W.11 Air Horse, but this was at a prototype stage and was not developed under Saro. The two W.11s built were doomed to failure; one crashed with loss of life, the other was eventually abandoned as unprofitable.

The Helicopter Division concentrated on improving the Skeeter. Ground resonance problems were severe and many months passed before the design was freed of this vice. Re-engined several times during development and with various other refinements, the Skeeter was eventually ordered into production for the British Army Air Corps. Also, a small number were exported to the Federal Republic of Germany. The Helicopter Division was a success; after painstaking and persistent work, sales of the Skeeter well justified the move.

Even more promising was a development of the Skeeter, begun during November 1957. This was the Saro P.531, a larger, five-seat helicopter seen as a potential replacement for the Skeeter and employing much of its

Saro Skeeter 5, possibly the prettiest variant, in its yellow and blue civil colour scheme. (*BHC*)

Progenitor of the Wasp/Scout series, Saro P.531–0 XN334 on deck-handling trials with sucker/skid undercarriage. (*Westland*)

technology. Development of the P.531 took place under the authority of T.L. Ciastula, who had been appointed chief designer (Helicopter Division). Ciastula had joined Saro as senior aerodynamicist in 1948 from RAE Farnborough. In 1952 he had transferred to the Helicopter Division as chief project engineer, in 1953 became chief technician and in 1957 chief designer. Progress of the P.531 was very rapid and by July 1958, the new helicopter made its first flight; it began a successful test programme shortly afterwards.

By mid-1959, with a long Skeeter production run and a promising replacement under way, the situation at Eastleigh appeared favourable. Unfortunately there was some debate over leasing arrangements of the site and closure became a possibility. However, in view of the success achieved by the Helicopter Division and the potential of its latest prototype, it seemed quite feasible to move the whole operation to another location should the need arise.

Final Fling

In September 1956, de Havilland Holdings acquired a 33 per cent interest in Saro and this had an important if rather short-term consequence—Saro's production of a rocket. De Havilland had supplied the Spectre rocket motor which had helped power the SR.53, and Saro's Maurice Brennan was by that time an acknowledged expert in rocket

Black Knight, the de Havilland/Saro re-entry test rocket. *(BHC)*

engine applications. De Havilland was heavily involved in the creation of a new and formidable missile, Blue Streak.

Success of Blue Streak depended on the solution of certain problems of re-entry into the Earth's atmosphere. Saro was given the task, by de Havilland but through RAE, of building a single-stage re-entry test rocket as a vehicle for the development of the warhead and certain other components of Blue Streak. The research rocket received the name Black Knight; the first was launched from Woomera in Australia on 7 September, 1958. By May 1960, when Saro was no longer an independent company, the first two-stage Black Knight had been launched.

After an examination of the relative merits of liquid oxygen (lox) and High-Test Peroxide as the suggested propellants for Black Knight, it had been decided to employ the latter, of which de Havilland had more experience. A new site for the construction and testing of Black Knight was built at High Down, near the Needles. After testing, the rockets were taken to the Woomera Rocket Range for firing trials. Black Knight, 3 ft in diameter and 33 ft tall, was powered by four Armstrong Siddeley Gamma 201 rocket motors each of 4,000 lb thrust.

Firing trials were entirely successful. The first Black Knight was fired to 300 miles and subsequent efforts realised 500 miles. Undoubtedly the experience of Saro in the field of rocketry through the interceptor programme contributed to this success and was probably one of the points de Havilland Holdings had had in mind when it acquired an interest in the Cowes firm.

However, after the results of testing had been gleaned, the Black Knight programme came to an end in 1964. Certainly, as far as Saunders-Roe was concerned, the contract was a short-term one.

Another manifestation of the company's efforts at picking up after Duncan Sandys' actions was the creation of a new enterprise, Saro Structures Ltd (SSL). This was a civil engineering concern dealing with light alloy structures, the staff for SSL being drawn from the Cowes aircraft plant and the new site established at Whippingham.

In February 1959, the close contact between Saro and Nuclear Enterprises (GB) Ltd of Edinburgh led to creation of a new firm, Saro-Nuclear Enterprises (S-NE). This concern was established to work in the fields of applied irradiation and the use of isotopes in industrial processes.

A sad event during 1958 was the death of Sir Alliott Verdon Roe, still president of Saro, on 4 January. Since 1929 Roe had overseen the growth of the company, the production of both simple and complex aircraft, the painful transition from waterborne aircraft, but after the Second World War little commercial success except with the Skeeter.

In late March 1959, Maurice Brennan resigned as chief designer. Brennan was followed by P.H. Leyton, chief rocket development engineer. Both had been bitterly disappointed over the SR.177 and the government's failure to support a British space research programme. Richard Stanton-Jones, formerly chief aerodynamicist, was made chief designer (fixed-wing aircraft) in April 1959. Slowly but surely, however, the 'old firm' personnel began to fall away.

At the same time, still more new ground was being explored by the company in an effort to keep the aircraft side occupied. In late 1956, Christopher (later Sir Christopher) Cockerell's brainchild, the Hovercraft, was proved in principle before government officials. Cockerell had experimented since 1953 with the design of a vehicle which would be wholly supported on a cushion of air. Following the 1956 demonstration, the MoS placed the whole Hovercraft concept on the Secret List because of its possible military applications. A study contract was then offered to Short Brothers and Harland Ltd, to discover how the Air Cushion vehicle (ACV) principle could best be developed. Shorts eventually declined the contract and the study was then accepted by Saunders-Roe. This was the first ever Hovercraft contract and was placed by the MoS on 31 August, 1957. With the SR.177 programme at that time facing cancellation, Saro welcomed the offer. Again, it seems that the MoS put this work in the hands of Saro as a substitute for the interceptor programme. Unlike the

SR-N1, the world's first Hovercraft, rides high on its skirt across the Solent. (*BHC*)

Black Knight programme, however, this new enterprise had very long-reaching effects.

Cockerell, Stanton-Jones and (initially) Maurice Brennan began the work which eventually led to a man-carrying prototype ACV, the SR-N1. At the same time, military interest in the potential of the Hovercraft began to fade, with the result that the concept was removed from the Secret List in September 1958. Subsequently, the National Research Development Council (NRDC) agreed to finance Cockerell's overseas patents for his ideas in return for a first option on the invention. After successful results of the studies by Saunders-Roe were made available for examination, the NRDC commissioned the firm to proceed with construction of the man-carrying prototype ACV.

The NRDC, established in 1949, was a public corporation with resources and a brief to finance new ideas held to be in the public interest. In terms of monetary support, the Cowes ACV venture was the largest yet undertaken by the NRDC. A subsidiary of NRDC was therefore established to run the operation. Hovercraft Development Ltd (HDL). HDL was founded in 1959, its task to promote Hovercraft study and hold Cockerell's patents on behalf of the NRDC.

The SR-N1 experimental ACV was finally completed at Cowes in late May 1959. Engine running with the new craft followed in early June, in conditions of secrecy. A first public demonstration was held at Cowes on

11 June, the Hovercraft being controlled by the new Saro chief test pilot Lieut-Cdr Peter (Sheepy) Lamb DSC AFC. Lamb had been appointed chief test pilot in March 1959 and went on to do most of the early testing with SR-N1, becoming the number one ACV test-pilot in Great Britain.

The test programme went very well. SR-N1 crossed the Solent on 22 June and the English Channel from Calais to Dover on 25 July, the latter trip coinciding with the 50th anniversary of Louis Blériot's historic flight. Saunders-Roe could be proud of the important part played in the development of an entirely new form of transport, in rather the same way as S.E. Saunders had been over the construction of the hull for Sopwith's Bat Boat. Moreover, the potential of the principle demonstrated by the SR-N1 could be clearly recognized; however, further development on an independent basis was not to be.

Winding-sheet

The take-over of Saunders-Roe was swift and all-embracing. Though the Saro insignia continued in use for some time afterwards, it was Westland Aircraft Ltd of Yeovil who annexed a major part of the company. Despite the potential of the Hovercraft at Cowes, company resources were at a low ebb and this helped to encourage take-over.

As part of Westland's policy of expansion, the unsettled Eastleigh Division and its promising P.531 (later the Westland Wasp/Scout) were absorbed by the Yeovil concern in August 1959. Most of the Eastleigh workforce had been moved to Yeovil by the end of 1962. Fairey Aviation Ltd and the helicopter interests of Bristol Aircraft Ltd were also acquired to form a single united British helicopter manufacturer under Westland.

With the Hovercraft showing sure signs of technical success at an early stage of development, but with financial difficulties at Cowes caused by years of failure with the aircraft prototypes, it was probable that one company or another would move to gain the principal site at East Cowes together with its facilities and staff. Westland was prepared to take the risks involved and, at the same time as the Eastleigh site was acquired, absorbed the Cowes sites, which for some time became known as the Saunders-Roe Division of Westland Aircraft Ltd.

Board changes at this time were numerous. Henry (by then Sir Henry) Knowler had retired from the company, Brennan had left. H.N. Morgan-Grenville and E.D. Clarke joined the Westland Board, Grenville having resigned from Saro; Clarke resigned from both Boards in early 1960. Sir Arthur Gouge, with the company since 1943 and finally chief executive, resigned in September 1959 and retired. Eric Mensforth, Westland chairman, became chairman of Westland Aircraft Ltd (Saunders-Roe Division) and E.C. Wheeldon, Westland managing director, also joined the new Board. Others joining included D.C. Collins (Westland works director), D.L. Hollis-Williams (Westland technical director) and W. Oppenheimer (Westland financial director). After E.D. Clarke's resignation, H.W.D. Winkworth, former Saro assistant general manager and works director, became the Saunders-Roe Division's managing director. By 1960, under Westland control, the Cowes site was continuing work on Black Knight research and development (with RAE), SR-N1 (with HDL) and SR-N2, a developed and more powerful ACV.

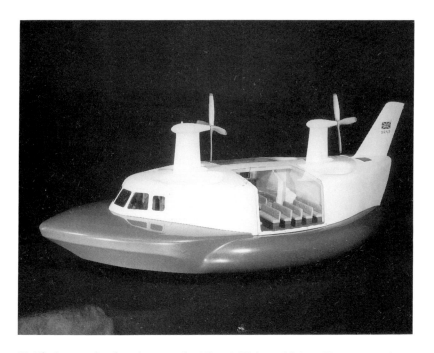

SR-N2, the second and much more refined Saro ACV, in model form. The company did not get the chance to develop it independently. (*BHC*)

The remainder of the company was also dispensed with. SLWP and SR(A) were taken over by the de Havilland Group, also in 1959, and Saunders-Roe ceased operations as an independent company. All that lingers is a name, Saunders-Roe Development (SRD), which currently exists as merely a small part of the Westland concern. SRD, with about 250 employees, is at present developing electro-luminescent products for the Westland Group.

Postscript

During late 1959, the NRDC concentrated Hovercraft development into four companies. These were Westland Aircraft Ltd (Saunders-Roe Division), Vickers-Armstrongs Ltd, Denny Brothers Ltd and Folland Aircraft Ltd. Folland was absorbed by the Hawker Siddeley Group in 1960 and Denny Brothers left the conglomerate. Britten-Norman Ltd and later Hovermarine Ltd joined it. In 1966 the group was rationalised and British Hovercraft Corporation was formed by Westland and Vickers-Armstrongs, the two major interests, with the Government retaining a 10 per cent stake through the NRDC. In 1970, Westland bought out the Vickers-Armstrongs shareholding to become 90 per cent owners of BHC. By 1980, BHC's sales figures stood at a record £23.9 million.

SR-N2, wearing Westland and HDL marks, undergoing trials on the Solent. (*BHC*)

The East Cowes site continues in use by BHC, under the Westland Aerospace banner. In addition to the manufacture of Hovercraft and marine craft research, the company designs and produces electronic and structural components for helicopters and fixed-wing aircraft. Major contracts include the centre wing section and fuselage ribs for Short Brothers' 330 and 360 aircraft, as well as the design and manufacture of composite material structures for the European space programmes. About 1,500 people are employed. The old Eastleigh site is now Southampton Airport and the former Saro premises are still extant, being used by light manufacturing concerns. Weybridge has now become largely a residential area.

East Cowes, 1983; Columbine and Medina as used by British Hovercraft Corporation.

Saunders drawing of the T.1, showing the early smoke-stack exhaust, lower mainplane cut-outs and rear Lewis gun.

Saunders T.1

The decision to produce the T.1 arose through the personal desire of Sam Saunders to market his own aircraft designs and was a measure intended to offset the effects of boat-building contracts lost during the First World War.

The first all-Saunders design, the T.1 emerged in 1917, the product of a very small team under the leadership of H.H. Thomas, recently established at Cowes. The designation T.1 derived from the surname of its designer but the aircraft never received a name. The sole example was a two-seat land-based biplane.

The T.1 had single-bay unstaggered folding wings and with wire-braced extensions to the upper wingtips. Ailerons were fitted to the upper surfaces only. Construction was of wood with a fabric covering. The tail unit was of conventional design with single fin and rudder and monoplane tailplane.

The wooden fuselage of the T.1 had Consuta copper-sewn plywood covering with no metal fittings or bracing wires. Dual flight controls were installed and all engine instruments and controls were duplicated in the rear position. The observer in the rear cockpit had a Scarff-mounted Lewis gun and the pilot a fixed forward-firing synchronised Lewis. The precise intended role of the T.1 is difficult to define. The cutaways in the lower mainplane trailing edges perhaps indicate a reconnaissance role; dual instrumentation suggests a trainer, but armament disposition compounds the problem.

It was intended that the T.1 could be fitted with either conventional wheeled undercarriage or floats. There is no evidence to suggest that floats were ever fitted. Designed to be powered by a 200 hp Hispano-Suiza engine, the aircraft eventually flew with a 150 hp Sunbeam Nubian, Saunders being unable to obtain a Hispano Suiza because production of that engine was being diverted to S.E.5a airframes for Service use.

Despite the reduced power, the T.1 is said to have performed well in the air. It was test-flown from Somerton during 1917 by a Maj Evans, an RFC pilot. The only difficulty experienced by Evans was a tendency to engine overheating. Before long, the prominent straight-through 'smoke-stack' exhaust, perhaps so configured in the hope of achieving extra horse power, was discarded for a more conventional arrangement, an indication possibly that the Nubian was adequate after all.

H.H. Thomas died in the 1918–19 influenza epidemic and his T.1 design was not developed further. Suggestions by two former Saunders employees that it was planned to convert the T.1 for civil use have not been substantiated. It appears that some time late in 1918 the Nubian was removed, but the fate of the T.1 airframe is not known.

One 150 hp Sunbeam Nubian (No. 5530).
Span 37 ft 5 in upper, 24 ft 9 in lower; length 23 ft 8 in; height 11 ft 3¼ in; wing area 335 sq ft.
Empty weight 1,795 lb; loaded weight 2,680 lb.
Maximum speed 89 mph; cruising speed 74 mph; ceiling 11,100 ft; fuel 35 gal; approximate endurance 3 hr.

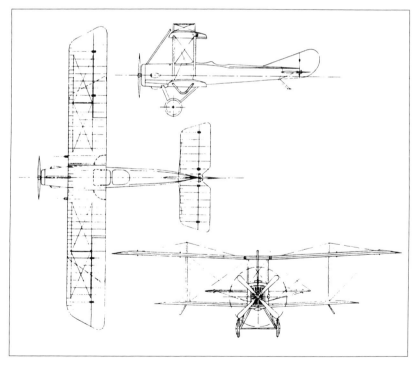

T.1

The only known photograph of the T.1, showing the large four-bladed airscrew and the adoption of a more conventional exhaust system. (*Chaz Bowyer*)

Armament: one ·303 in fixed forward-firing Lewis and one ·303 in Scarff-mounted Lewis machine-guns.

One example, X14 built under licence No. 13.

NB: 'X' numbers were issued between 1917 and 1919 to private-venture aircraft which were, nonetheless, given Government authorisation through the Licence system. These aircraft were not financed by any official contract.

Saunders Kittiwake

The Kittiwake was seen by S.E. Saunders as the start of expansion into civil aircraft production, and was designed as an entrant for the Air Ministry competition held at Felixstowe and Martlesham Heath during August and September 1920. The competition was for landplanes and amphibians.

Designed mainly by F.P. Hyde Beadle, who had recently joined Saunders from the Gosport Aviation Company, the Kittiwake was a twin-engined, four-bay biplane amphibian, the largest of its type at that time. Beadle was assisted by H.W. Gravenell and Sydney Porter, who had by that time become Saunders' aircraft superintendent as well as being in charge of boat hull designs. The necessary 6,000 drawings were completed within six weeks over the summer of 1920, and the resulting product was a remarkable aircraft, with several original features.

The Kittiwake leaves the water on its first flight from Cowes, with Norman Macmillan at the controls.

The Kittiwake was rather ugly. The three-deck arrangement of the hull, with raised cockpit and cabin, made the aircraft appear top-heavy. The hull, or 'bottom layer', was a wooden two-step Consuta-covered structure with a shallow V-bottom and tumble-home sides. It was detachable from the cockpit and cabin above, parted by a number of steel fishplate joints so that if damaged the hull could be easily replaced if necessary. The retractable main undercarriage members were situated in the hull itself, and were consequently of very narrow track. The mainwheels were raised and lowered by means of a hand-crank operated by the flight engineer. When retracted, the wheels were enclosed by two box structures inside the hull. Undercarriage doors were cam-operated by the retracting mechanism and helped preserve the hull line. Suspension was provided by coil springs and the water-rudder/tailskid was a combined unit.

The middle and upper sections of the hull served as crew and passenger cabins respectively. Accommodation was provided for two crew, pilot and engineer, and seven passengers. Entrance to the Kittiwake was made via a duralumin companion ladder fixed to the starboard side of the hull aft of the wings, leading to a doorway in the cabin. There was also an entrance hatch in the roof of the cockpit and a mooring hatch in the extreme bow. Passenger seating was arranged at the sides and front of the comfortably furnished enclosed cabin, and the raised position afforded an excellent view through side and front windows. The enclosed cockpit had side-by-side seating and partial dual control. An internal stairway connected cockpit and cabin.

The high aspect ratio wings also incorporated some novel features. The most prominent was a camber-changing mechanism which caused almost the entire leading and trailing edges of both wings to move. These leading-

The Kittiwake under construction in the Saunders East Cowes shed, summer 1920.
(*H. Hanna*)

and trailing-edge flaps were operated simultaneously from one control by the pilot's seat and activated via a series of chains, worm-gears and push-rods, which passed through the sides of the hull to the flaps themselves. Knuckle-joints, running the full span except at the tips, allowed the leading-edge flaps to droop into an unbroken wing-section when deflected. The framework of all four flaps was of duralumin but the surfaces were of Consuta, and, though the outer covering of the leading-edge assemblies were hinged to the front spars, they were free to move within the knuckle joints. The trailing-edge flaps, being separate aerofoils, were more conventionally arranged. The additional lift expected from this double-cambering was intended to offset high loading; the Kittiwake when fully laden weighed 6,200 lb, while the engines used were two 200 hp ABC Wasp Mk II seven-cylinder radials, driving two-blade wooden airscrews. Using the variable-camber, the speed of the Kittiwake was designed to range from just over 40 mph at the stall, to a maximum of 120 mph.

Because the trailing-edge cambering mechanism ran almost the full length of the wing, the balanced ailerons had to be in an intermediate position, mounted behind the two outermost wing struts. The wings were two-spar structures with spruce flanges and Consuta webs. Large box-section compression ribs connected the spars, while the Consuta covering also acted as cross-bracing. The interplane struts were of broad I-section, to dispense with the need for incidence bracing, and only single lift and landing wires were employed. The three outer sets of struts were of spruce and Consuta, while the innermost members were of duralumin and supported the ABC radials in seven-sided nacelles. They were braced to the hull with one steel-tube strut each.

The lower wing was braced by two pairs of struts attached to the hull

56

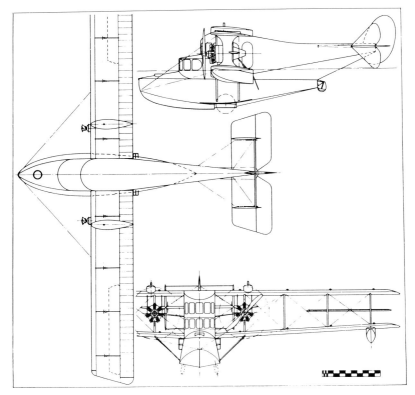

Kittiwake

slightly below the waterline. Streamlined fuel tanks were on the top surface
of the upper mainplane, one over each engine, with simple gravity feed.
These exposed tanks increased drag but were positioned to minimise risks
of fuel starvation and fire. Wingtip floats were bolted through the lower
mainplane to the outboard I struts while the upper wing was secured to
and curved with the cabin roof. The lower wing was attached to the
bottom of the middle hull tier.

The tail unit of the Kittiwake was also unusual. Mounted at the extreme
rear of the upper fuselage at a height sufficient to clear spray, it consisted
of an adjustable-incidence tailplane and divided elevators, three fins and a
central balanced rudder. The outer fins were braced at top and bottom
with tubular struts to the main central fin and, like the rest of the aircraft
with the exception of the inner I struts, the whole assembly was Consuta-
covered.

Constructional problems due to the novelty of the design hampered
progress of the Kittiwake, which was completed too late to compete in the
Air Ministry competition. However, it was felt at Cowes that the new
design might prove as good, if not better, than the competition entrants;
much was expected of the variable-camber arrangements.

Water trials of the Kittiwake, made by Norman Macmillan on the Medina and Solent, began on 11 September, 1920, with the aircraft by that time registered G-EAUD (c/n 101). During these trials it was found that the undercarriage would not fully retract and the aircraft was thus held far below hump speed. It appears that Macmillan had intended to fly the Kittiwake on its first outing, but he had to be content with engine and hydrodynamic tests alone. Water stability at the restricted speeds available was found to be good. Once ashore, the undercarriage was dismantled and inspection showed that a locking pin was missing from the retraction-operating mechanism.

The Kittiwake finally flew for the first time on 19 September, again with Macmillan at the controls. Water performance during the take-off was good, with no signs of porpoising. However, at a height of 600 ft, the inboard section of the starboard lower leading-edge flap was sucked out of its knuckle and torn from its spar. The Kittiwake then yawed violently to starboard, but this was partially corrected as a similar flap collapse occurred on the port side. Macmillan made a hasty descent with the speed kept up to avoid the consequent higher stalling speed. However, about three feet from the water the Kittiwake did in fact stall, and on touching down became holed on the reef at Egypt Point, West Cowes, a small submerged rock damaging the hull. Because of water ingress, the Kittiwake came rapidly to rest and then sank to the level of the lower wing roots.

The Kittiwake was quickly recovered and examined. It was found that almost the entire leading-edge camber mechanism had collapsed. Hull damage, though, was slight; the aircraft was repaired and the flaps

Aftermath of the first flight; the Kittiwake partially submerged off West Cowes after the accident at Egypt Point.

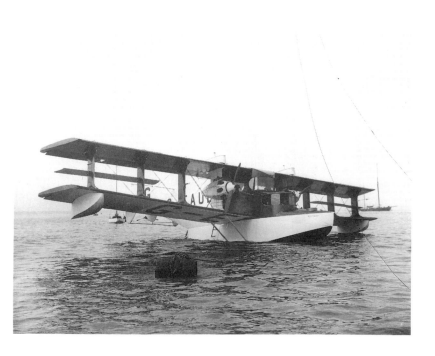

The Kittiwake at moorings, East Cowes, late 1920. (*BHC*)

reinforced with a system of tabs and wires designed to prevent the surfaces being sucked out in future. Repairs were rapid and further trials took place on 27 September, but on this occasion the engines failed to provide sufficient power for take-off.

This new fault persisted and the engines were examined. It appeared that the port engine was in some way defective and down on power, but quite why was not resolved at this stage. The struts between the hull and lower wings were removed to reduce water drag but the Kittiwake still refused to become airborne; more attempts were made on 28 and 30 September with disappointing results. When the engines were inspected more closely, it was discovered that while the starboard unit was a virtually hand-made pre-production example, the port one was a sub-contracted production motor and delivered at best 1,500 rpm. Why this had not been noticed before is unclear.

In addition to this problem, the undercarriage compression-leg springs were found to fail under static load, while it also became apparent that the interplane ailerons were rather ineffective at small angles. Further flight testing was delayed for six months while modifications to the ailerons and undercarriage took place at Cowes. During March 1921, the Kittiwake flew again, the pilot on these occasions being F. Warren-Merriam, a pre-First World War instructor.

However, the major problem with the design had not been corrected. The engines were unable to provide the Kittiwake with what later became usual: cruise at half-power to ensure economy and reliability, but sufficient power reserve for comfortable take-off, especially in poor weather. The unorthodox camber configuration did not compensate for this lack of power.

The low power/weight ratio was only one of the problems faced by the design. The Kittiwake was too experimental to be assured of instant success and it is surprising that Sam Saunders decided to produce such an aircraft as his first large venture. Because of the disappointing nature of the trials, interest in the Kittiwake from a commercial point of view was low. No orders were secured, G-EAUD remaining the sole example. During the early summer of 1921, G-EAUD crashed at Cowes while in the hands of an Air Ministry pilot unused to elevator anomalies which had also emerged as a cause for concern. The aircraft was extensively damaged and this incident did nothing to encourage confidence in the programme. In July 1921, the Kittiwake was scrapped.

Soon after this, Hyde Beadle left Saunders, and not until 1923 was a new team established at Cowes.

Two 200 hp ABC Wasp II.
Span 68 ft 3 in; length 43 ft 8 in; height 14 ft 10½ in; wing area 864 sq ft.
Empty weight 3,840 lb; loaded weight 6,200 lb.
Maximum speed 116 mph; cruising speed 92 mph; initial rate of climb 375 ft./min;
    maximum range about 340 miles; endurance 4 hr.
Design maximum speed was 120 mph.

One example, G-EAUD c/n 101.

Saunders A.4 Medina

The A.4 Medina was built at Cowes over the summer and autumn of 1925, for the Air Council, and was a distinctive twin-engined biplane flying-boat. Again, the type represented an attempt to break into the civil market, and again the attempt failed.

The Medina requirement originated from the Air Council's Research and Development Department. It was proposed in the early summer of 1924 that, if successful, the new type might operate with Imperial Airways, which was established on 1 April of that year. The new airline was the result of a merger between Handley Page Transport, Instone Air Line, the Daimler Airway, and the British Marine Air Navigation Company, as recommended by the Hambling Committee and approved by the Cabinet. It was decided that Imperial Airways would need a passenger-carrying flying-boat as part of its fleet, and Saunders undertook design and construction of the Medina in answer.

Design began during the spring of 1925, led by Bertie Thompson, who in 1923 had formed a design partnership at Cowes with Henry Knowler, as successor to the two previous design teams. The Medina was built as a commercial competitor to the Supermarine Swan, though its wing loading was greater and a longer take-off run was predicted. However, the

The Medina, at rest off Cowes, August 1927. (*H. Hanna*)

estimated top speed of the Medina was a spritely 115 mph as against the 92 mph achieved by the Swan with its Eagle IX engine.

The arrangement of the Medina was somewhat unusual. The wooden hull was of conventional two-step form, V-bottomed with mostly flat tumble-home sides. The deck, sides and hull bottom were Consuta-covered, the bottom nearly half an inch thick. Hull construction was very simple, with five main longitudinals, a number of strong bulkheads and many light spruce timbers for local strengthening of the skin.

In the extreme bow was a mooring hatch, and aft of that a side-by-side open cockpit. Only the port position had controls. Separating the cockpit from the passenger cabin was a luggage compartment to starboard, while a passageway to port connected cockpit and cabin, the latter being situated under the mainplanes. Passenger seating was for seven, three along each side facing towards the centre of the hull, with a further position forward of the main cabin by the fore luggage compartment, which doubled as a steward's position when required. Aft of the passenger cabin was a lavatory to starboard while to port was the cabin companionway, entered from a hatchway and ladder. Behind this was another luggage compartment.

The wing arrangement was unconventional. Of unequal-span, with dihedral on the outer sections of the shorter upper mainplane only, the two wings were connected by Warren Girder bracing instead of the more usual interplane struts, dispensing with the need for external bracing wires. The two 450 hp Bristol Jupiter VI nine-cylinder air-cooled radial engines were positioned slightly forward of the wings, mounted on steel engine plates slung from the front spar of the upper centre-section. The engines were supported from beneath by a complex system of struts connecting with the lower centre-section.

Behind the engines were the fuel and oil tanks, in streamlined duralumin nacelles, supported by spruce frames running diagonally upwards from the

The sole Medina, East Cowes, showing the unusual layout of the Warren girder bracing. (*BHC*)

bottom of each engine plate to the rear spar of the upper wing, while the supporting structure extended aft to reinforce the nacelles as well as the engine plates.

Both upper and lower mainplanes were fitted with ailerons, interconnected on each side by one strut. Floats were attached directly to the lower wing beneath the outer struts. The wings were almost entirely fabric-covered while the wing section employed was RAF 33, a very deep high-lift profile having a stationary centre of pressure over nearly the whole flying range. The upper surface of the lower mainplane centre section was blended with the cabin roof and was Consuta-covered to facilitate engine maintenance, being usable as a working platform. The

G-EBMG head-on, well illustrating the inverted sesquiplane layout. (*H. Hanna*)

62

The Medina on its beaching chassis, late 1927. (*Imperial War Museum*)

lower mainplane was braced to the hull on each side by two struts and the wing floats were reinforced with short struts.

A triangular-planform tailplane was mounted high on the single rectangular fin, the tailplane being braced at its leading-edge by a tubular member attached within the hull to a screw gear controlling incidence. The elevators and rudder were balanced.

Nearly all control connections were made with steel tubes, either in the form of rotating shafts or push-pull rods. All rudder and elevator connections were made by push-pull systems running from the cockpit. The tailplane-incidence handwheel drove a fore-and-aft rotating shaft through chains, sprockets and a bevel drive. The rotating shaft itself drove the tail-screw gear through a bevel gear. In the case of the ailerons, control was by means of a series of chains and sprockets driving a fore-and-aft shaft which ran down the hull to below the front wing spar, from where there were wires.

A number of interesting observations on the Medina have been gleaned from former Saunders employees and most concern the hydrodynamic performance of the aircraft. An eye-witness to its water handling trials, made in the first quarter of 1926, recalls a marked tendency to porpoise at high speeds, with a sluggish, very dirty performance at low speed. In addition, it is said that the Consuta hull covering persistently gave trouble; leaks and splitting were not uncommon. Why this should be so remains a mystery but it is a fact that the A.4 spent a considerable proportion of its life out of the water while this problem was corrected, and corrected again. No written information seems to have survived concerning the aerodynamic performance of the A.4 but a first flight was made during the spring of 1926. After a short life, during which the aircraft was tested by the RAF, G-EBMG, the sole example, was scrapped at Cowes during 1929. No orders were placed by the Air Council and the Medina passed into obscurity. Such was the disappointment at Cowes that Bertie Thompson left the team and Henry Knowler was made chief designer.

Two 450 hp Bristol Jupiter VI.
Span 52 ft upper, 58 ft lower; length 49 ft; height 16 ft; wing area 1,007 sq ft.
Empty weight 8,060 lb; loaded weight 11,560 lb.
Maximum speed 115 mph; cruising speed 90 mph; range 360 miles at cruising speed; endurance at cruising speed 4 hr.

One example, G-EBMG c/n A.4/1. N214 allocated for Service Trials.

Saunders A.3 Valkyrie

Built to Air Ministry Specification 22/24, which called for a large general-duty/patrol flying-boat, the A.3 Valkyrie was Saunders' third marine design, and Henry Knowler's first for the company. The A.3 was seen as a contender for a share of the market for the big military types dominated in the late 1920s by Shorts, Supermarine and Blackburn. However, the Valkyrie did not enter production as it was in some ways a poor performer.

Saunders tendered for 22/24 in October 1924 and was eventually awarded a contract for the construction of one A.3 in February of the following year. However, in December 1924 the Air Ministry had announced dissatisfaction with the projected hull design and development of the original design slowed. During April and May 1925, testing of the hull in model form was observed by the Air Ministry. Results showed a tendency to instability in pitching and yawing moments. In view of this, a certain amount of redesigning had to be undertaken, which caused a marked slowing of the programme. Though it is not certain exactly when the Valkyrie first flew, the date is probably early June 1926, the test-pilot being Frank Courtney.

As a design, the A.3 was fairly conventional, especially by comparison with some of Saunders' other designs. A large three-engined biplane flying-boat, the Valkyrie was handsome enough to suggest an atmosphere of purpose and capability. This was deceptive.

As an example of the difficulties encountered, the flexible hull was found to be weak where it joined the rigid hull centre-section and had twice to be reinforced, once at Cowes in January 1927 and again at MAEE before trials in the following spring.

The wooden hull adopted for the A.3 was of two-step monocoque Consuta-covered circular flexible type, after the flexible principle introduced by Linton Hope and previously used in the design of the Phœnix Cork, in which Henry Knowler had played a part. However, the

The handsome Valkyrie on the Cowes slipway, early 1927. The beaching trolley was designed to allow launching side-on to the water, and was so arranged because of lack of space. (*Saro*)

A.3 hull had no bulkheads as these were found in the Cork's case to concentrate water loads which invariably seeped through to some extent. The hull was therefore an almost completely elastic structure designed to be shock-absorbing during take-off and alighting. Only a rigid section directly beneath the mainplanes was conventionally constructed. No water rudder was fitted but two drogues assisted water manoeuvring.

Accommodation consisted, in the extreme nose, of a bow gunner's position, behind which was the two-seat tandem cockpit. Below and behind the rear cockpit were the radio and navigation positions. Aft of the mainplanes two further defensive Scarff-mounted machine-guns were mounted in staggered offset positions. Bunks and living quarters for the crew of five were in the rigid section beneath the mainplanes. Both cockpits and all defensive positions were open. Full dual-control was provided and the control system was similar to that of the A.4 Medina, employing jointed metal rods in place of the usual stranded wires.

The 97 ft equal-span wings were slightly staggered, and the upper and lower centre-sections were connected by three sets of steel tube V-struts, between which were the engine mountings. The extremities of the bottom centre-section were braced to the hull with large N-struts of tubular steel, and the outer wings were each connected by two pairs of wooden interplane struts. The lower mainplane was lifted slightly above the hull on a single wide pylon running the full length of the chord. Construction was of the usual wooden spars and ribs, with fabric covering except for the lower centre-section which was Consuta-covered to facilitate engine maintenance. Balanced ailerons were fitted to all four planes, and lateral stability on the water was by means of large wingtip floats. Offensive armament, consisting of two 520/550 lb bombs, was carried on two mountings, one under each lower wing root.

The tail unit was of normal monoplane layout with a single fin and

65

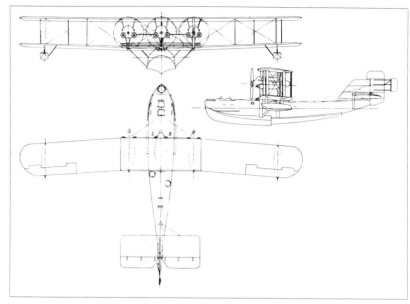

A.3 Valkyrie

rudder. In order to clear spray, the strut-braced tailplane was carried high up on the fin. The rudder itself featured a large and distinctive servo rudder mounted on outriggers.

The three 680 hp Rolls-Royce Condor IIIA twelve-cylinder vee water-cooled engines were mounted side by side on the centre-section V-struts. Fuel and oil were contained in tanks mounted abaft each engine; engines and tanks were fully-faired with duralumin sheet. The main fuel supply was carried in four 138 gallon tanks in the hull.

Serialled N186, (c/n A.3/1), the Valkyrie arrived at the MAEE for trials in March 1927. By the end of April, these were complete. After arrival, but before tests began, the joints between the flexible hull structure and the rigid wing-bearing section were reinforced, because substantial leakage had been experienced. This was after the problem had already been dealt with at Cowes, but apparently not thoroughly enough. After this episode, there was no further leakage experienced from this source, though the wooden hull continued to soak up water to an extent.

The MAEE's conclusions on the performance of the A.3 were not favourable. Though the hull design and layout received some praise, N186 suffered from slight porpoising and a rather dirty take-off until up on the step. The latter fault was thought to be a problem of aerodynamics rather than a hull design deficiency. Water handling was found poor at low speeds because the (air) rudder did not become effective until the centre engine was running at fairly high rpm.

Because of the main fuel tank arrangement, the hull was considered larger in beam and cross-sectional area than would have been necessary had the tanks been wing-mounted. MAEE considered it dangerous for the

66

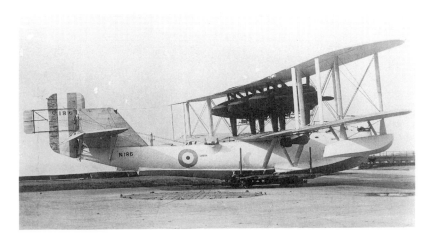

N186 on its beaching trolley at MAEE Felixstowe during type trials, May 1927, showing the large servo-rudder. (*RAE, Crown Copyright*)

main tanks to be within the hull and the point was made that the area set aside for this could be better used should the A.3 be employed on long-range patrols. It was intimated that the entire fuel tankage might be moved to wing-mounted positions before production (if any) took place.

The biplane arrangement was assessed as constructionally good but the integral nature of the engine support structure with the wings was criticised as a less serviceable arrangement than relative independence might have allowed. As first flown at Felixstowe, the A.3 suffered from severe tail flutter, but rectifications during the trials by Saunders personnel entirely cured this. Servicing arrangements generally were held as good and practical by MAEE.

However, the A.3 revealed at Felixstowe certain flight characteristics and poor aspects of performance which aggravated an already disappointing report. Though N186 was quite manoeuvrable for an aircraft of its size, handling was affected by a tendency to fly port wing low which was not cured even by the most strenuous rigging adjustments while at Felixstowe. Also, aileron control was found rather heavy and despite various efforts to rid the A.3 of this vice, the problem was never entirely resolved.

Though longitudinal stability was adequate, laterally the Valkyrie was quite a handful and would start to roll to port if not held. Early aileron modifications at Cowes had only reduced this vice slightly and in fact the aircraft had to return to Cowes for a brief period for corrective measures.

Despite the MAEE's criticisms, some good points did emerge. A strong point in favour of the A.3 was that, with one engine stopped in flight, the aircraft remained controllable, though it would not leave the water in this state. Height could be maintained with either outboard engine idle and N186 could climb at about 80 ft/min with the centre engine idle. Maximum speed was 119 mph at sea level, though this was reduced significantly at the

Another view of N186 at Felixstowe, showing the bomb-mounting position and the distinctive hull 'hump' on which the lower mainplane was mounted. (*RAE, Crown Copyright*)

service ceiling of 9,600 ft. Endurance was a very useful 9 hr 20 min. The trolley on which N186 sat while ashore was praised as having good centring arrangements, and allowed frequent hull inspections to take place, which again drew promising conclusions; though the Consuta stitching tended to harbour dirt, soakage appeared to be surprisingly limited, the timber having been specially impregnated with a proprietary chemical.

However, the series of problems that emerged through the trials prompted a condemnation of the A.3 as a poor performer. This seems a little harsh in view of some of the more favourable aspects of the design, and indeed it was decided to continue with further tests, alterations and theoretical studies; had the aircraft been as disappointing as MAEE made out, it seems there would have been little point in continuing tests.

Starting immediately after the trials, in April 1927, the new tests began with an assessment of performance with engine cowlings removed. This showed (not surprisingly) that both speed and climb became impaired, but there is no record of why such tests were made. It seems possible that some cooling problem had emerged but, at any rate, the cowlings were eventually refitted. By May, before these trials were concluded, the starboard engine had failed seriously and the tests were suspended.

Also by May, the effect of gap/chord ratio on drag had been studied theoretically at RAE Farnborough, with the intention of improving top speed. However, wing-gap tests were uninspiring The reduction of induced drag when the wings were set further apart was found to be offset by the increase in drag caused by necessary lengthening of the interplane struts and, in model form, results revealed that setting the wings further apart would have no beneficial effect on top speed. Because of the disappointing

68

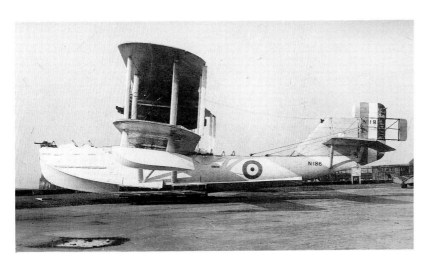

The A.3 at Felixstowe. (*RAE*)

nature of the gap tests, the Valkyrie remained as it was. During July, N186 returned briefly to Cowes, where finally the tendency to fly port wing low was rectified through drastic rigging alterations.

On 12 August, 1927, the A.3, having returned to Felixstowe, left on a 9,400 mile goodwill tour of the Scandinavian capitals, in company with Blackburn Iris N185, Short Singapore I N179 and Supermarine Southampton I N218. This cruise was made by the Flying Boat Development Flight. In command was Sqn Ldr C.L. Scott, and 28 other people were carried, including Sir Samuel Hoare, the Secretary of State for Air, who was to visit the Copenhagen Air Traffic Exhibition. On 30 August, the A.3 was forced to alight off Königsberg with the starboard engine giving trouble, and was towed into port; at Copenhagen, it was damaged on take-off, which caused some delay, but eventually arrived back at Felixstowe on 28 September. The Southampton was also delayed, breaking down with mechanical trouble at Danzig.

One of the objects of this cruise was to compare the durability of the wooden hull with the metal variety. The impregnated Consuta covering employed on the Valkyrie hull in fact absorbed quite a lot of water over the course of the cruise. Provision and use of the trolley during the Felixstowe tests, as well as the speed at which the trials were made, had tended to hide this unfavourable trait before the cruise took place. It seems that Saunders' water-repelling chemical was unsuccessful over the long term.

The metal hull was eyed with favour by the Air Ministry. It would not rot, or soak up water and thus become heavier as would a wooden hull, and its sole disadvantage was the corrosion aspect which if monitored would not be a severe handicap. It was also stronger than the wooden hull. The Short S.2 had proved this satisfactorily. Thus the Air Ministry turned away from the Valkyrie and other wooden hulled flying-boats. Further

69

N186 over the Solent, its long equal-span mainplane configuration shown to effect. (*BHC*)

tests with the A.3 were made by the MAEE after the cruise, but these were of a secondary nature. Development of a metal hull for the Valkyrie was briefly considered, but rejected because of the other problems exposed by MAEE, which would have compromised the usefulness of such an undertaking. It was felt at Cowes that too much work was required on the Valkyrie before it might find favour with the Air Ministry, and the programme stopped. N186 was eventually dismantled at Cowes during 1929.

Three 680 hp Rolls-Royce Condor IIIA.
Span 97 ft; length 65 ft 6 in; height 18 ft 5½ in; wing area 1,967.5 sq ft.
Empty weight 17,851 lb; maximum weight on MAEE trials 25,000 lb; maximum overload weight 26,600 lb.
Maximum speed 119 mph; cruising speed 95 mph; alighting speed 60 mph; initial rate of climb 585 ft/min; service ceiling 9,600 ft; endurance 9 hr 20 min.
Armament: three Scarff-mounted ·303 in Lewis machine-guns in bow and midship positions; two 520/550 lb bombs.

One example, N186 c/n A.3/1. Contract No. 543186/25 of February 1925.

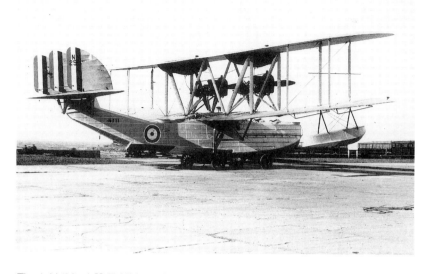

The A.14 'Metal Hull' N251 on its custom-built trolley at Felixstowe during trials in the spring of 1930, its simple slab-sided hull shown to advantage. (*Crown Copyright via A.S.C. Lumsden*)

Saunders A.14 'Metal Hull'

An important stepping-stone toward Saro hull forms adopted during most of the 1930s, the Saunders A.14 was built to prove a principle. Colloquially known simply as the 'Metal Hull', the sole example, N251, tested a new type of hull which was subsequently used in the designs of the Saunders/Saro A.7, the Saro Cutty Sark, Cloud, Windhover and London, and in the fuselage of the Spartan Cruiser series.

By the mid-1920s the metal hull looked set to replace the wooden variety in the design of waterborne aircraft. This changeover was led in Britain by Short Brothers with their S.2 of 1924. The S.2 consisted of a Felixstowe F.5 superstructure combined with a hull of Short-patented monocoque metal construction. The S.2 was a great success; it eliminated the problem of water soakage, which could put several hundred pounds of unwanted weight on a large wooden-hulled flying-boat, while providing much greater strength and resilience in the event of harsh treatment. Because the S.2 represented such an advance in flying-boat design, the Air Ministry rapidly lost interest in wooden-hulled 'boats. This is one of the reasons why the Saunders A.3 Valkyrie was a failure. After this successful development by Shorts, the other manufacturers of waterborne aircraft were forced to change to metal hull construction or become uncompetitive. Each

71

developed its own methods of producing metal hulls over the next few years.

At Cowes, this was far from straightforward to accomplish. By the late 1920s, the company was in an uneasy financial position. It had produced a series of unsuccessful aircraft prototypes, and had faced increasing competition from manufaucturers of marine aircraft. Available funds provided for only limited resources to be placed at the disposal of Henry Knowler, whose job it became to design a metal hull for the company. The main criteria for this project were cheapness, because of the financial problems, and simplicity of construction.

The Cowes labour force was traditionally a group of highly skilled boat-builders, and the boats were of mainly wooden construction. Previous aircraft construction had also involved principally the use of wood. The workforce had therefore only limited experience of working with metal. Of course, it was possible to employ extra labour familiar with metal-working techniques, but it was necessary to keep costs down. Knowler's hull had thus to be constructionally simple as well as inexpensive, so as to ease the workforce into the ways of extensive metal-working.

Under these circumstances, Knowler did well. It was decided in 1927 to build, if possible, only a hull rather than a complete prototype. An attempt to find a ready-made set of flight surfaces was made, in much the same way as Shorts had built their S.2. This search was successful, and in co-operation with Supermarine, Contract 826424/28 was issued during April

Detail of the A.14 forward hull showing the corrugated method of construction that became widely used by Saro through the early and mid-1930s. (*Crown Copyright via A.S.C Lumsden*)

1928, ordering Southampton N251 to be fitted with a new (metal) hull designed and built by Saunders. The Southampton superstructure and engines were retained and the aircraft became known as the Saunders A.14.

Henry Knowler's famous 'corrugated' hull principle stemmed from the A.14. The hull form employed straight-line frames, the simplest form to manufacture and avoiding extensive panel-beating. During the early years of flying-boat development it had been found that a plain V-bottom was apt to be dirty; water was thrown high into the air unless deflected by suitable curvature of the hull. Thus the curved V-bottom was introduced, the V at the keel being gradually flattened out as the chine was approached. The resultant shape of the bottom planking necessitated a certain amount of double-curvature, but Knowler developed a simpler method of achieving a similar arrangement. The lines of the bottom frames were kept straight, but instead of pointing them toward the chine, Knowler directed them to a point a short distance inboard. Where this straight line cut the horizontal though the chines, a gap occurred. This gap was covered by a narrow strip of horizontal planking which served to keep down the water in much the same way as conventional curved bottoms of other hulls did. The beauty of Knowler's method was that, except in localised instances, double-curvature was avoided and thus metal-beating tasks were made easy or eliminated. Simple straight-line frames could be used extensively with this design method.

Having simplified construction to that extent, Knowler continued by considering the problem of the longitudinal stringer. Stringers usually required a great deal of riveting to the hull planking and, if continuous over any distance, the hull frames had to be cut out to accommodate them. If this was not done, it became necessary to interrupt the stringers where they intersected the frames and provide gussets to attach the two. The scheme Knowler evolved was to create longitudinal corrugations in the hull planking itself, a few inches apart. By the stiffness these introduced, the corrugations replaced the conventional riveted stringer and a structure requiring a minimum of riveting resulted. For aircraft of low performance, where speed was not an essential, the extra drag imposed by the corrugations (which were external) was felt to be of little consequence. The corrugations were sealed at their extremities by small end-caps. Hull weight became significantly reduced. Knowler's principle was patented in 1929.

The assembly of N251 began at Cowes during the summer of 1928 and brief trials were made towards the end of the year. The cockpit had tandem dual controls. Three defensive positions were provided: bow and two offset dorsal machine-gun posts. It is doubtful whether armament was actually fitted until late in the life of N251, if at all. Structure was of duralumin with Alclad plating. All went well at first and the new principle was included in the design of the forthcoming A.7 Severn. The A.7 of course was not successful, due in part to hull weakness directly attributable to the 'corrugated' principle. Initial testing of N251 had, however, been rather fleeting and had failed to reveal any tendency toward fragility. Certainly the new hull was roomier than that of the equivalent Southampton Mk II, having a wider beam, and that was something in its favour though it required its own custom-built beaching chassis as a result.

Typical of damage suffered by the 'corrugated' types; distortion to the planing bottom corrugations just forward of N251's step.

N251 finally arrived at the MAEE for full testing during March 1930. Only in the following summer, when the A.7 was also being tested, did the A.14 start to show any sign of frailty. By July, N251 had completed only 47 hr 20 min flying time since receiving the Saunders hull, which seems a minimal amount bearing in mind the infancy of the principle involved. The hull first started showing signs of distortion during mid-July, around the area immediately forward of the main step, on the port side. The buckling could be detected at that stage only by slight curvature apparent in the discontinuity of the hull corrugations in the planing bottom near the chine.

In mid-October N251 was again examined, after a further 27 hr 40 min flying. The significant increase in its use over the summer of 1930 perhaps indicates the concern felt by the company over possible weaknesses. The October examination revealed these fears as not unfounded. Over the summer, the buckling had increased considerably on the port side of the planing bottom and had started on the starboard side. Though N251 had been used fairly rigorously over the summer, making take-offs and alightings while overloaded to 16,000 lb and 18,000 lb, it was undoubtedly treated gently in comparison with routine Service use. That the decision to build the A.7 was taken without first testing the A.14 thoroughly seems surprising.

The hull distortions were subsequently rectified and the affected areas reinforced with local internal stringers. The aeroplane had done its job; it

The A.14 at the MAEE, the tandem cockpit and offset dorsal machine-gun posts are in evidence. (*Crown Copyright via A.S.C. Lumsden*)

was merely a test-bed. No production orders were expected or placed. It had exposed the problems that might arise with subsequent 'corrugated' hulls. The A.14 performed well in the air according to eye-witnesses. In any event, the performance of the aircraft as a whole should be seen as secondary in importance to that of Saunders' first metal hull. Water performance was very clean indeed, especially after hump speed had been achieved, though there was a slight tendency to plough through waves at low speeds.

Thus the problems of the new metal hull were eventually exposed. Despite this, the frailty persisted to varying extents in the construction of most 'corrugated' Saro flying-boats and only the A.27 London was free of such weakness. Nevertheless, the principle remained until the last London was delivered from Cowes in May 1938.

Two 500 hp Napier Lion VA.
Span 75 ft; length 48 ft 8 in; height 18 ft 7 in; wing area 1,448 sq ft.
Empty weight 8,870 lb; normal loaded weight 14,000 lb; maximum tested overloaded weight 18,000 lb.
Maximum speed 97 mph; cruising speed 87 mph; initial rate of climb 390 ft/min; absolute ceiling 8,400 ft; range 600 miles; endurance 6½ hr.
Armament: three Scarff-mounted ·303 in Lewis machine-guns in bow and dorsal positions; 1,900 lb bomb load.

One example, N251. Contract No. 826424/28 of 5 April 1928.

Saunders/Saro A.7 Severn

The A.7 Severn, the last waterborne design to emerge from Cowes under S.E. Saunders, did not fly until after the company was reconstituted and was found to perform well in the air and on the water.

Knowler designed the A.7 in response to Specification R.4/27 for a large, multi-engined metal-hulled flying-boat for maritime patrol duties. The Saunders patented method of metal-hull construction, involving longitudinal corrugations which dispensed with the need for riveted stringers, was adopted for the Severn, the first application of the principle to an intended production flying-boat.

It is interesting to note that the 'corrugated' hull method had not been proven through thorough testing of the A.14 by the time design work began on the A.7, but despite this, the principle was incorporated in the Severn from its inception.

In July 1927 the A.7 design was begun and detail work followed almost throughout 1928. Smaller than the A.3 and considerably more angular in appearance, the only serious doubt which appears to have been raised was over the choice of the engines. Both the Armstrong Siddeley Jaguar VI and the Bristol Jupiter XIFP were considered and finally the Jupiter was chosen. Progress on the prototype was, however, very slow.

The new firm of Saunders-Roe put great effort into the design of its own

The Severn over the Solent, summer 1930. (*BHC*)

76

N240 off Cowes. The A.7 engine arrangement was very clean, with marked airscrew clearance, but the aircraft required significant trim changes between engines on and off. (*Saro via W.F. Murray*)

new aircraft, with the result that the leftovers from S.E. Saunders tended to suffer some neglect. Nevertheless work on both the Severn and the A.10 fighter continued. Neither achieved production status, and the new Saro directors must have reflected during the early 1930s that it might have been wiser to abandon the old Saunders designs altogether, and start afresh.

Construction of the A.7 was almost complete by late 1929. Engines were delivered from Bristol a little before Christmas and the aircraft, serialled N240 (c/n A.7/1) was launched from Cowes during the following year. Two former Saro employees emphatically put the date of launching as early spring 1930, but MAEE Report F/F/6, issued on 6 June 1931, gives the launching date as 10 July, 1930. It is generally agreed that the first flight took place within days of launching.

Company flying and water trials were made by Flt Lieut Stuart Scott before N240 was sent to Felixstowe for official trials. During the firm's tests, it had become apparent that the A.7 was severely under-elevatored and very heavy on the rudders. New and larger elevators were fitted and servo-rudders on outriggers installed before N240 left Cowes.

This was Sam Saunders' last attempt at a successful flying-boat and like its predecessors, the A.7 was by no means a modest design. A three-engined sesquiplane flying-boat, it was intended from the outset to operate as an independent self-contained unit on long-range patrol duties. The A.7 hull was similar in principle to that of the A.14, an all-metal two-step structure with tumble-home sides. The system of external longitudinal corrugations pressed into the skin dispensed with the need for

77

conventional riveted stringers, giving a substantial weight saving, reducing man-hours spent on manufacture and thus cutting production costs. The absence of beaten sections was noticeable, made possible by Knowler's skill, especially round the planing bottom.

Accommodation provided for a crew of five: pilot, co-pilot, engineer, wireless-operator and gunner. In the extreme bow was mounted a Lewis gun on a Scarff ring which was able to slide aft to facilitate mooring and towing operations. Aft of this was the side-by-side dual-control open cockpit and, behind it, the engineer's position, navigation and wireless room and sleeping quarters. Further aft was a mess area, galley, dining table, couch and lockers. From this area an elevated platform led to the dorsal gun position, from which the tail gun position was entered, both mounting Lewis guns. No water rudder was fitted but two drogues were installed to aid water manoeuvrability.

The wings, of unequal span and chord, were of RAF 31 section, had duralumin structures and fabric covering. Frise-type ailerons were fitted only to the upper wing. Substantial inverted V-struts ran from the lower wing roots to the centreline of the upper wing and took the loads of the centre engine which was just forward of and below the upper leading-edge. A second inverted V was positioned on the centreline near the trailing edges. Single main struts supported the outer engines with splayed-out struts further aft. There were full-chord fairings, attached to the upper wing, behind each engine. Outwardly splayed interplane struts ran from near the lower wingtips. Strut-braced wingtip floats were adopted.

The engines were 490 hp Bristol Jupiter XIFP nine-cylinder air-cooled units. They were uncowled and drove two-blade wooden airscrews. The engines were gravity-fed from tanks in the upper wing and oil tanks were placed aft of each.

The tailplane was mounted on the rear of the hull, to which it was strut braced and carried twin strut-braced fins and rudders, each of which carried a servo rudder although these were not fitted initially.

Defensive armament was intended to consist of three Lewis guns,

The Severn on its trolley at the MAEE. The testing authorities praised the on-land ease of movement, often a problem for the large flying-boat not equipped with any form of bolt-on chassis. The navigator's position is just behind the cockpit, by the leading window. (*RAE, Crown Copyright*)

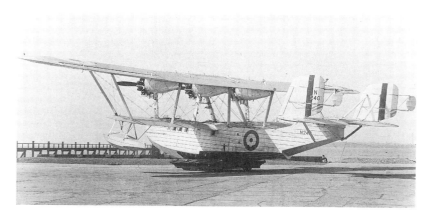

N240 at Felixstowe. The sesquiplane layout is shown to advantage, as well as the distinctive tail configuration. The rear defensive position is unarmed. (*RAE, Crown Copyright*)

though the tail position of N240 was not armed until very late in its life. Provision was made for the carriage of eight 230 lb or four 500, 520 or 550 lb bombs on underwing racks.

N240 finally arrived at Felixstowe for trials during late July 1930, and began an extensive test programme in the following month. The interim was spent trying to cure unsatisfactory elevator control when alighting, caused by excessive longitudinal stability. The tailplane area was finally reduced by 25 per cent in order to overcome this, though longitudinal stability remained marked. The MAEE found much to praise.

In normal flight, rudders and ailerons were found to be light and responsive, though elevator control was somewhat heavier. Control at low speeds was easy with no vices near the stall. Manoeuvrability was found to be good for an aircraft the size of N240, which could be flown with either outboard engine throttled fully back, the rudder load remaining light with good control. With the centre engine throttled back, height could be maintained at 21,550 lb and, though this was not possible with either outboard engine throttled back, the rate of descent was gentle.

Take-off was very clean and easy, with a minor tendency to swing easily corrected by a small amount of rudder. Because of the heavy elevators, alightings were made easier by adjusting the tailplane to its full negative angle. No sign of on-water instability was found up to the maximum tested weight of 25,750 lb, and manoeuvrability on the water was good. Even in choppy water taxi-ing was clean. N240 was indeed tested several times in a chop, with winds of up to 35 mph, but handling remained good with minimal roll. No difficulties were experienced when towing direct from the bow was undertaken.

Nor was performance lacking. At the tested weight of 22,150 lb, N240 achieved 126 mph at sea level. Take-off runs were in the order of 450 yd at Felixstowe, and took a creditable average of 23 seconds. Economical cruising speed at 22,000 lb was 96 mph. MAEE found, then, that the Severn incorporated both good flight and water characteristics and had very few vices in performance. These qualities were, however, seriously offset by the unduly light construction of the A.7, which caused a constant succession of structural failures. Though most of these were not severe, they were nonetheless irritating and the A.7 in this form could not have withstood Service use. MAEE succinctly pointed out that performance would deteriorate if appropriate modifications were made, the result of the consequent weight penalty.

During the spring and early summer of 1931, the initial series of failures was corrected. All three carburettor air-intakes failed at welding points during MAEE tests. They were replaced by modified types, but these too failed at a later date. The hull structure had been damaged at Felixstowe by dinghies moored to the port side in the area of the cockpit. MAEE suggested that local strengthening be incorporated to cure this drawback. In addition, after 80 hr flying and 800 hr at moorings from the time of delivery to Felixstowe, severe corrosion was found along the chine angle plates, along the lines of stainless steel hull bolts and at the main step. Also, a large number of cracks had developed in the hull, mostly at the corners of the panels formed by the corrugations and the bolts holding the plating to the transverse bulkheads, and leakage occurred at some of them. Other cracks were found along the corrugation bases. All plating was therefore cleaned, repaired, locally strengthened and then repainted.

Carburettor heater pipes had also failed and were repaired or replaced several times. The centre engine mountings failed seriously, and, later, failure became advanced on the rear mountings of the other engines. After the oblique stays at the top of the centre engine mounting were reinforced, another mounting failed; MAEE promptly recommended complete redesign of the entire engine mounting facility, but it seems the structure

Its slab sides well illustrated, N240 taxi-ing at the mouth of the Medina.
(*Saro via W.F. Murray*)

continued to be strengthened when appropriate, rather than being replaced.

Slight leakage was experienced from places other than the hull cracks; the scuttle frames and control exit points posed some problems. During the trials, N240 had flown slightly port-wing low and no amount of rigging adjustment seemed to cure this. Remarkably, performance did not seem to be impaired. In the spring of 1931 the aileron spars were inspected and found to be distorted. A large number of fittings failed at regular intervals throughout the trials; minor supporting brackets, fairing clips, cowling clips and, more seriously, upper wing inspection flaps, all tended to fly off. Floor fastenings failed in many places and engine nacelles began to crack. All these and other faults were repaired during the summer.

Yet N240 had been treated gently compared with what might have been expected had the A.7 entered Service use. Small wonder that the MAEE decreed extensive modification. On the other hand, performance qualities seemed to justify further tests being made. It was agreed that as soon as N240 could be rendered sufficiently serviceable, it should go on a proving cruise to the Near East.

Before this journey, N240 was thoroughly overhauled at Felixstowe by Saro personnel. Engines were removed, serviced and re-installed on their modified mountings. All nacelles were strengthened. Further corrosion of the chine angle plates, main step and the keel was treated. Fittings throughout the hull and control system were repaired or modified. Before the cruise, the air intakes were altered to allow either a direct open position or a facility to draw in air heated by the cylinder walls, a shutter control being added.

The cruise was made by the Flying Boat Development Flight. N240 left Felixstowe for Mount Batten (Plymouth) en route for Aboukir on 15 August, 1931, in company with Short Singapore N246. The A.7 was commanded by Flt Lieut C.H. Cahill, and there were six other crew members. The outward flight as far as Malta was uneventful except for some difficulty experienced with starting after heavy rain at Lac d'Hourtin (near Bordeaux) and small leakage problems at the same place. Oil temperatures between Etang de Berre (near Marseilles) and Malta rose somewhat but were easily rectified by higher altitude. Two days were spent at Malta making minor repairs to engine speed indicators, ASI and the exhaust heater muff of the central carburettor of N240. The presence of the Singapore was used to advantage after the Saro 'boat's Zwicky pump gave trouble at Malta, where N246's pump was used for both aircraft. In view of high oil temperatures experienced by N240, oil squirts fitted between trials and cruise were eventually removed at Aboukir.

Flying via Port Sudan, the A.7 arrived at Lake Timsah in the Canal Zone for speed trials, two-engine tests and further assessment of climb performance. A maximum speed of 120 mph was reached, at an all-up weight of 22,410 lb and a height of 5,000 ft. Minimum rate of descent with the starboard engine throttled fully back was found to be 60 ft/min, while, with either the centre or port engine in this condition, the rate was some 75 ft/min. After these tests, on 8 September, N240 returned to Aboukir and on the following day left for Malta. Take-off from Malta for Gibraltar on 11 September was one of the longest and most difficult of the cruise, lasting 79 sec in a two-foot swell.

N240 undergoing overhaul at the East Cowes shed. (*BHC*)

Due to a strong headwind on the flight to Gibraltar, a diversion was made to Algiers before darkness. During the night of 15 September, while N240 was moored at the Algiers civil seaplane base, a very severe gale struck, with winds reaching 60 mph. The Severn rode the storm remarkably well, however; damage was caused only to the elevator leading-edges. The seaworthiness of N240 was shown to its greatest advantage. During the storm, several fishing boats were sunk in the harbour and three French submarines parted their mooring cables.

After repairs to the elevators, N240 left for Gibraltar on 15 September and then returned home via Cape Finisterre, the Bay of Biscay and Ushant. Forty miles off Plymouth the port engine failed. It has been said that this engine was stopped deliberately, in order to demonstrate the capabilities of the A.7, but in fact there had been no choice in the matter. On inspection at Mount Batten, the port engine pump filter was found to contain small pieces of steel. Also, the centre airscrew was found to be badly split longitudinally. This damage was thought to have occurred after a heaving line had become ensnared shortly after take-off from Gibraltar. Of course, the fact that N240 was able to continue the journey in that condition does it credit. Mount Batten was finally reached as the sun set on the night of 16 September. A total of 6,530 miles had been flown.

However, despite continuing high quality of water and air performance, N240's cruise revealed persistent frailty. The Zwicky pump failed many times, and hull leakage had reached an unacceptable rate by the time the A.7 arrived at Aboukir, filling to a depth of 8 in in any 12 hr moored. The port engine exhaust-pipe stay failed in the air between Malta and Aboukir, as did a carburettor air intake and the mechanic's platform to the centre engine. In tropical conditions it was found difficult to start the engines; this

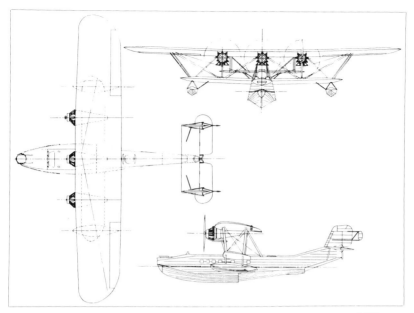

A.7 Severn

problem arose from choking caused by an over-rich mixture provided by a Ki-gas starter with no provision for adjustment.

Other problems also emerged. Towards Port Sudan, two rib failures occurred in the top mainplane. On alighting, a servo-rudder kingpost was found to be broken. Inadequate trim control was revealed on Lake Timsah, when take-off took 64 sec in a flat calm, with the whole crew having to move as far forward as possible before N240 would grudgingly leave the water. More problems included a sticking port outer petrol-tank gauge which finally cleared itself, more difficulties with engine speed indicators, a broken port engine mounting, a lost centre engine carburettor heater and a blocked starboard-outer service tank. This is by no means a full list. It was also noted that dazzle from the forward decking tended to inflict blinding headaches on the pilot and co-pilot.

At Mount Batten a new port engine and two new airscrews were called for, the engine arriving from Bristol on 18 September. Two four-bladed airscrews also arrived. After repairs had been made, N240 passed again to MAEE, where a complete inspection was made. The hull structure at least was found to be generally intact apart from the leakage points. However, some of the upper (and later, lower) mainplane ribs were found to have weakened, as had the hull floors in places not previously reinforced. The bow foot rail had been fractured. De-briefing revealed that oil cooling in tropical conditions had never been adequate and N240 had frequently had to be flown above desirable operational height, which hampered navigation and reduced range.

Corrosion was minimal during the cruise and this was one good point.

N240 moored off East Cowes works, 1930. (*BHC*)

However, various panels had continued to drop off at frequent intervals. Altogether, the Near East cruise seemed to spell the end for the A.7. Detail work, as well as some major structural features, was undoubtedly flimsy and poor, and this more than offset the good performance qualities. The Air Ministry understandably took the view that even if the A.7's performance was acceptable, it had so many defects that it was of little practical use. At the same time, R.4/27 was becoming a middle-aged Specification. Had N240 been strengthened, the increase in weight would inevitably have penalised performance. No production order was given and, finally, Saro reluctantly took the decision to abandon the A.7 and start on a new design to R.24/31. This new type incorporated some of the broad design features of the A.7, though it was considerably stronger, and emerged as the A.27 London.

Surprisingly, in the meantime N240 was used by No. 209 Squadron for maritime patrol. No. 209 had experienced difficulty in building up strength and the Severn was passed to them as an interim measure in February 1932 after MAEE had finished with it.

Together with the military version of the A.7, a projected civil variant was also abandoned. This was to feature the same engines and a similar airframe. Accommodation was planned for 21 passengers, two pilots and a steward. Loaded weight was to have been 20,900 lb and normal range 575 miles. The serial N245 was allotted to a Severn and this was probably for the civil variant which was not in fact built. The sole Severn continued in Service with No. 209 Sqn until the summer of 1932, being lost in the Channel on 13 July of that year.

Three 490 hp Bristol Jupiter XIFP.
Span 88 ft; length 64 ft 6 in; height 19 ft 3 in; wing area 1,557 sq ft.
Empty weight 14,800 lb; normal loaded weight 22,000 lb; maximum overloaded weight tested 25,750 lb; maximum permissible flying-weight 27,100 lb.
Maximum speed 126 mph; cruising speed 96 mph at 22,000 lb and 2,050 ft; alighting speed 58 mph IAS; initial rate of climb 590 ft/min; service ceiling 8,930 ft; absolute ceiling (estimated) 10,800 ft; endurance 6 hr.
Armament: three ·303 in Lewis machine-guns in bow, dorsal and tail positions; four 500, 520 or 550 lb or eight 230 lb bombs.

One example, N240 c/n A.7/1. Contract No. 839664/28.

Saunders/Saro A.10 'Multi-gun'

The development of the A.10 single-seat biplane fighter represented a distinct design departure for S.E. Saunders. Only one previous landplane design had originated from the company. However, lack of any orders for the firm's waterborne types through the 1920s prompted Saunders to look at the possibility of building a private-venture landplane fighter.

First proposals for the A.10 design were shown by Henry Knowler to the Air Ministry Technical Staff during January 1927. Prominent characteristics included the sesquiplane arrangement, broad interplane I-struts and very large, 9 ft 6 in diameter, four-bladed airscrew. Perhaps the most significant aspect was the projected armament: a four-gun fuselage-mounted arrangement, at a time when the majority of fighters employed only two machine-guns. Proposed powerplant was the Rolls-Royce F.XI in supercharged form.

During September 1927, Saunders received a copy of Specification F.20/27, which the company felt could be met by the new design, though certain revisions were made in the light of the requirements. Saunders asked the Air Ministry for the loan of an F.XIS engine and instruments, and meanwhile a mock-up of the A.10 was begun at East Cowes.

F.20/27 called for an interceptor fighter with the ability to climb rapidly to 20,000 ft and then overtake an enemy aircraft flying at 150 mph. Design of the A.10 was altered somewhat to comply with F.20/27, but retained the use of the F.XIS inline, rather than adopting the specified Bristol Mercury air-cooled radial. Though only two machine-guns were required, the A.10 retained a four-gun configuration at some small sacrifice to endurance and a slightly higher stalling speed than that laid down in F.20/27. The heavy armament was justified by the company as a very powerful offensive capability.

Manufacture of the A.10 prototype was delayed while Saunders negotiated for the use of an engine during November. The Air Ministry was unable to provide a supercharged F.XI and, after some provisos, offered instead an unsupercharged model which was accepted by letter on 2 December and delivered shortly afterward. Construction then began in early 1928 and the prototype was completed for inspection by November of the same year.

The airframe of the A.10 was all-metal, as laid down in F.20/27. Duralumin was used extensively in the production of the wing spars and

The A.10 in January 1929, Cowes. At that time it had unbalanced ailerons. The triangular fuel tank bays and ground-out centre-section are apparent.

fuselage members, while the engine mountings were of tubular steel. The fuselage consisted mostly of bolted-together tubular components which almost completely obviated the need for welding while easing the task of rebuilding in the event of damage.

Emphasis was placed on good view for the pilot. The upper mainplane was placed at eye-level and the lower mainplane incorporated cut-outs in the trailing edges for improved downward view. The mainplanes were of RAF 31 section, with the exception of the upper mainplane centre-section, which was of thinner RAF 30 section. The ailerons were initially unbalanced. A pair of triangular-shaped gravity-feed 60 gal fuel tanks were incorporated in the upper centre-section. An unusual device was the 'lattice' arrangement of the radiator shutters, the radiator itself being underslung beneath the heavy-gauge engine bearers.

One pair of ·303 in Vickers machine-guns was situated in the upper fuselage decking, the other in flank positions, and all breeches were accessible from the cockpit. A total of 2,400 rounds of ammunition was carried. Wireless, specified by F.20/27, was not fitted, however. While both wings were fabric-covered, the forward fuselage was faired with duralumin. The monoplane tail unit, with single fin and rudder, and the rear portion of the fuselage, were all fabric-covered.

It was because the Air Ministry was interested in comparing the performance of the private-venture A.10 design with other (two-gunned) submissions to F.20/27 that a contract had been placed with Saunders for the manufacture of one prototype in December 1927. This was placed with some provisos as the Air Ministry was concerned with the short moment arm of the tail surfaces. In fact the engine was lent on condition that the fuselage was lengthened and the area of the tail surfaces increased.

86

When the A.10 (frequently referred to at the time as the Saro 'Multi-gun') finally emerged from Cowes, it differed somewhat from the original studies, partly as a result of revisions made after September 1927 when F.20/27 had been received. One of the visually obvious points was the substitution of conventional interplane struts for the original I type. The longer fuselage reduced the 'thick-set' appearance of the first studies, while the airscrew finally adopted was two-bladed. The area of the nose around the low-slung radiator was of a more curvaceous appearance than that of the original arrangement. Provision was made for the carriage of 2,000 rounds of ammunition.

The official Air Ministry inspection of the A.10 at Cowes noted a roomy and well appointed cockpit but found fault with the armament arrangement. The port deck gun was staggered in relation to its starboard counterpart and the port ammunition feed-pawls were not easily accessible from the pilot's seat. Also, the port flank gun was placed so close to the fuselage side that clearance of the loading mechanism was insufficient. These faults were duly corrected before a first flight was made, early in the following year.

The A.10 (c/n A.10/1) flew for the first time on 27 January, 1929, piloted by Herbert Broad, de Havilland's chief test pilot. The flight lasted just ten minutes and, when Broad landed, he complained of heavy ailerons. Before the next flight, on 16 March, the ailerons were lightened and

The A.10 by July 1929 with balanced and lightened ailerons. The 'roller-blind' radiator shutter was novel. (*BHC*)

balanced by means of Frise inset hinges. However, it was August before the Aeroplane and Armament Experimental Establishment (A&AEE) at Martlesham Heath received the A.10 for testing.

Meanwhile, in July, the newly-reconstituted firm of Saunders-Roe announced that in addition to F.20/27, the A.10 would be submitted to F.10/27. This called for a fighter armed with two Vickers guns in the fuselage and four wing-mounted Vickers or Lewis guns firing clear of the airscrew disc. Requirements were heavy volume of fire, high rate of climb, good manoeuvrability and maximum possible top speed.

The A&AEE received the A.10, as yet unserialled, during August 1929, and tested it until mid-September. The company's intention to submit the A.10 for both F.20/27 and F.10/27 seems to have caused some confusion at that point. At the A&AEE weigh-in, all four guns were *in situ* (double the number required for F.20/27 but insufficient for F.10/27), but wireless equipment specified by F.10/27 was not fitted. The engine is described in test reports as a Rolls-Royce F.XIS, so perhaps the supercharged version was fitted after all. These papers also mention the A.10 fitted with only two guns, which complied with F.20/27, while to add to the confusion, they state that the aircraft was tested in connection with F.10/27.

By contrast, the A&AEE's conclusions on the A.10 were clear-cut. No. 22 Squadron, which at that time was responsible for the A&AEE's performance testing, was very unimpressed by the new aeroplane. While diving, the aircraft was found to be very difficult to keep at a steady airspeed, which also proved virtually impossible to maintain in partial climbs up to 12,000 ft. Longitudinal stability was lacking and, if the

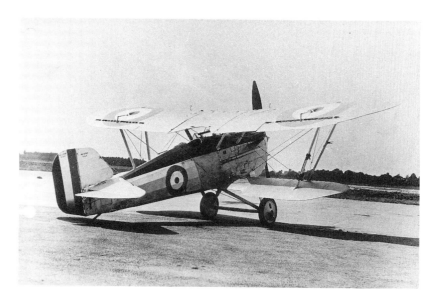

Still with no markings, the A.10 at Martlesham Heath, 1929. The flank guns have been removed.

control column was released, the aircraft would drop violently, reaching excessive speeds and showing no inclination to return to the original pace. The A.10 was also accused of hunting badly in fast dives, and on landing was said to skid savagely. Ground manoeuvrability was claimed to be very difficult, but this has been vigorously denied by Sqn Ldr Leslie Ash, a Saro test pilot, who flew the A.10 on a number of occasions. Though he recalls that the aircraft was rather under-ruddered (this was later corrected) Ash used to take the aircraft up for fun.

It might be suggested then, that the A&AEE exaggerated some of the faults, especially the ground-handling vices. Moreover, had the A.10 really suffered from all the in-flight anomalies described by the A&EE, it seems reasonable that Ash would recall at least some of them and would not have picked such a poor performer for stunting around the Solent.

After the A&AEE's unflattering comments, the A.10 was duly modified. Certainly the tailskid load was too great and the main undercarriage was moved 3 in aft. It was suggested by the A&AEE that all tail surfaces be enlarged, and this was also done.

F.20/27 trials were terminated at the end of January 1930, the remaining competitors being the Hawker Hornet, Fairey Firefly IIM and the Westland Wizard. All these aircraft were powered by the F.XIS, provision for which had been subsequently inserted in F.20/27. Though the A.10 was therefore no longer required by the A&AEE, Saro intended to make

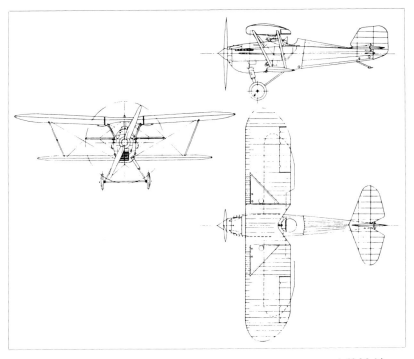

A.10 Multi-gun

89

The A.10 as K1949, during firing trials at the A&AEE. (*RAF Museum*)

another attempt to cure the defects, and then send it back. Meanwhile, the aircraft lost its engine, which returned to Rolls-Royce for modifications. It was September 1930 before the aircraft returned to the A&AEE. In the interim, the Air Ministry had remained unconvinced by the modifications Saro had in mind and by mid-May had finally selected the Hornet as the winner of F.20/27. This type was put into production and became the Fury.

After new company trials starting on 15 May, the A.10 was again evaluated by the A&AEE, during September. Modifications included those to the undercarriage position, a further 1 ft 9 in fuselage extension, and new tailplane, elevators and extended fin and rudder. Still the aircraft appears to have handled badly. Longitudinal stability was again judged inadequate, except when gliding at about 75 mph IAS with engine throttled back. The A.10 remained very difficult to trim to fly level 'hands off' even with only a small amount of power. The tailplane incidence adjustment wheel had to be positioned with extreme care in order to produce this ability at all. When speed was increased there was still a decided tendency to dive, which could only be corrected by use of the control column. When trimmed to fly level at full throttle, a 10 mph disturbance either side of full-throttle speed produced hunting instability. Even gradual reduction of speed frequently led to a stall and dive that was again curable only through use of the control column. The A&AEE, from whose reports these remarks come, concluded that the A.10 would make a very unsteady gun platform.

Moreover, the A&AEE continued to find fault with the performance of the A.10 on the ground. However, subsequent observatons by Ash have led to the impression that the A&AEE's comments were again somewhat harsh. Nevertheless, the aircraft was considered unsatisfactory and the Air Ministry showed no interest in ordering further examples, either to F.20/27 or F.10/27. In any case, the type was not wholly suited to F.10/27, having insufficient armament and no wireless equipment.

In 1931, the A.10 at last acquired a Service serial number; K1949. Before this allocation, the Class B marking L2 had been used. Together with the Gloster SS.19 J9125, which had also competed for F.20/27 (as the SS.18) and F.10/27, the A.10 was used during this year for trials examining the fire-effect of multi-gun aircraft. These trials were concluded by November 1931. Interestingly, though the SS.19 was found to be the steadier gun platform, the A.10 was described in the concluding papers as good from that point of view. This seems to confirm that the A&AEE was far too vigorous in its earlier criticisms of the A.10. The Air Ministry of course had digested the official reports and accordingly showed no interest.

Further tests were considered but the A.10 went unserviceable with a radiator defect in early December. As for comparative purposes it had been decided to use two different aircraft for the tests, they were postponed. Trials restarted in the summer of 1932 and continued into 1933, K1949 being used to examine the relationship between density and range of multi-gun fire. The information gleaned was held to be of great use.

It must have been something of a consolation to Saunders-Roe to know

The B Mark L2 was allotted during 1930. The A.10 is seen at Martlesham with a lengthened fuselage. (*RAF Museum*)

91

that the aircraft was of any use at all. The A.10 was finally struck off charge from the A&AEE on 20 November, 1933, and was swiftly forgotten by the new board at Cowes.

One 480 hp Rolls-Royce F.XI.
Span 32 ft; length 24 ft. 5 in, later 26 ft 2 in; height 9 ft 9 in; wing area 273 sq ft.
Empty weight 2,674 lb (F.20/27), 2, 694 lb (F.10/27); loaded weight 3,467 lb (F.20/27), 3,598 lb (F.10/27).
Maximum speed 200 mph; landing speed about 70 mph; service ceiling 29,000 ft.
Armament: two ·303 in Vickers machine-guns each with 600 rounds (F.20/27), four ·303 in Vickers machine-guns each with 500 rounds (F.10/27).
Preliminary estimates were: maximum speed 170 mph at sea level, 192.5 mph at 18,000 ft; service ceiling 31,600 ft; absolute ceiling 32,900 ft; maximum weight 3,235 lb.

One example, L2/K1949 c/n A.10/1.

Saro/Segrave A.22 Meteor

The Meteor was a beautifully streamlined four-seat twin-engined low-wing cantilver monoplane designed by Sir Henry Segrave and built by Saunders-Roe.

Segrave, a First World War fighter pilot, was a well known racing driver

The sole Saro A.22, shortly after its completion, over Cowes aerodrome, 1930. (*BHC*)

and, at one time, holder of the world land speed record. In July 1929 a number of important financial interests formed the Aircraft Investment Corporation (AIC) to help finance British commercial aviation and this concern obtained substantial interests in Saunders-Roe and the Blackburn Aeroplane & Motor Co. Segrave was, until he was killed, technical director of the Aircraft Investment Corporation. In 1930 Saunders-Roe was asked to undertake detail design and construction of the Meteor, to which it gave the designation A.22.

The one-piece wooden wing tapered in chord and thickness, was ply-covered and incorporated long-span inset ailerons. The fuselage was of very clean design and contained a well glazed cabin with two pairs of side-by-side seats. The side windows could be slid open while those on the port side hinged to give access to the cabin. There was a baggage compartment behind the cabin, a detachable control column could be fitted for the right hand front seat, and the rear seats could quickly be removed for cargo carriage.

The tail surfaces, with adjustable incidence tailplane and balanced rudder, were of metal construction with fabric covering.

The main undercarriage was of the divided type with rubber-in-compression main legs and steel-tube V-struts attached to the fuselage centreline. A tailskid was provided.

The two 120 hp de Havilland Gipsy III four-cylinder inverted inline air-

The very clean nose and engine cowling lines of G-AAXP, at Cowes during 1930. (*BHC*)

93

G-AAXP at Cowes during the spring of 1930. Apart from the non-retractable undercarriage, the impression is that the Meteor belongs to a much later period. (*BHC*)

cooled engines were carried on steel-tube mountings built into the wing leading-edge, were neatly cowled and drove two-blade fixed-pitch wooden airscrews. A fuel tank was located in the inboard section of the wing on each side.

In designing the Meteor, Segrave attempted to produce the ideal touring aeroplane with high performance and maximum safety. It was designed to be capable of climbing at 350 ft/min at maximum weight with either engine inoperative, have a stalling speed of about 60 mph, and a top speed of 140 mph. The initial rate of climb on two engines was 1,000 ft/min.

Painted in a distinctive scheme of all-white, and registered G-AAXP, the Meteor first flew, from Somerton, on 28 May, 1930, in the hands of Saro test-pilot Stuart Scott. Although officially named the Saro/Segrave Meteor, the new aircraft was referred to in the aeronautical press as the Segrave Meteor Mk I. By June, when wheel-brakes had been fitted, a Certificate of Airworthiness had been awarded at Martlesham Heath. Tests there were marred by problems of fuel starvation. Also, a small amount of tail flutter was discovered. The Saro-built Meteor had a wire-braced tailplane, but in later examples a variable-incidence cantilever tailplane and a modified rudder horn balance were introduced to alleviate the problem.

Production of subsequent Meteors was undertaken by Blackburn under an AIC directive. Two more Meteors, incorporating an all-metal stressed-skin semi-monocoque fuselage, were completed by 1931. In this new form, the type became known as the Blackburn Segrave I, and the two examples were registered G-ABFP and G-ABFR. Construction of a third example, G-ABZJ, was started but never completed. Sir Henry's death in the motor-boat *Miss England IV* caused an inertia from which the Meteor programme did not recover. Also, Blackburn became gradually preoccupied with military orders for its own aircraft, and Saro needed its available space for the manufacture of Clouds and Cutty Sarks.

94

G-AAXP's first public appearance was as an entrant in the 1930 King's Cup Race. This was a bold move on behalf of Segrave and Maj Andrew Holt, the mainspring of the AIC, for the Meteor was then a brand new type and virtually untried. Though Segrave had designed the Meteor, it was entered for the race by Maj Holt and must have looked a formidable aircraft alongside some of the other entrants; Moths, Bluebirds and Avians abounded. Interestingly, Capt H.H. Balfour MC (later the Rt Hon the Lord Balfour of Inchrye PC MC) and Lieut-Col L.A. Strange also entered, flying a Spartan Arrow and a Simmonds Spartan respectively.

Flt Lieut R.L.R. (later Air Marshal Sir Richard) Atcherley and Flt Lieut G.H. Stainforth, the well-known Schneider Trophy pilots, formed the crew of G-AAXP for the race; the aircraft bore racing number 10 and was by that time painted maroon overall. For several days before the event, the starboard engine had started to misfire when opened out wide. Though the port engine behaved perfectly, the trouble with the starboard was not cured by the day of the race and, shortly after starting the course, the Meteor was forced to return to Hanworth, its starting point. The race was won by Winifred Brown, flying Avian G-EBVZ. Miss Brown won the Siddeley Trophy in addition to the King's Cup itself.

Later in 1930, with the starboard engine rewired, G-AAXP was flown to Italy by T. Neville Stack. There, it was demonstrated to the Italian Air Force and flown by General Italo Balbo. The advanced configuration impressed the Italians and two Meteors were later built under licence by Piaggio as the P.12.

In 1932, G-AAXP was acquired by J.G.D. Armour and operated from Hanworth as a light tourer, the role originally conceived for the design. Armour entered the Meteor in the 1932 King's Cup but again the aircraft developed a fault, problems arising from a broken fuel pipe that necessitated a forced landing at Filton. However, this time the course was

The A.22 seen in its later colour scheme of overall maroon, the livery worn for the 1930 King's Cup Race.

95

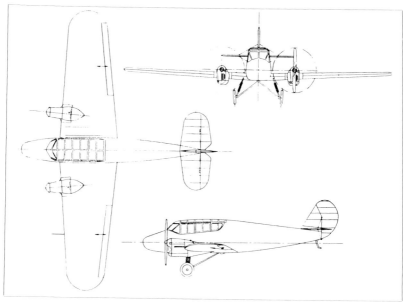

A.22 Meteor

at least completed, with the aid of a replacement pipe, at an average speed of 131 mph.

Saunders-Roe was also responsible for construction of the wings for the two Blackburn Meteors, as well as for some minor fuselage components. The single Saro/Segrave Meteor was eventually cannibalised at Brough during September 1932, after spares for the other examples became difficult to obtain. Its registration was not cancelled until September 1938.

Two 120 hp de Havilland Gipsy III.
Span 39 ft 6 in; length 28 ft; height 7 ft 6 in; wing area 230 sq ft.
Empty weight 1,725 lb; loaded weight 2,750 lb.
Maximum speed 140 mph; cruising speed 125 mph; initial rate of climb 1,000 ft/min; ceiling 17,000 ft; normal range 340 miles; maximum range 450 miles; endurance 4 hr.

One example, G-AAXP c/n 1.

Saunders-Roe A.17 Cutty Sark

The first design under the reconstituted concern of Saunders-Roe Limited, the A.17 Cutty Sark, was viewed by the company as a basis on which to build its business. Of moderate scope and size, twelve examples were produced and helped stabilise the Saro aircraft interests during the early 1930s.

Design work on the A.17 started during March 1929 as a private

Cutty Sark A.17/1 G-AAIP was initially fitted with small-diameter four-bladed airscrews, but these were soon discarded. The amphibious undercarriage has yet to be added. (*C.A. Sims*)

venture, with exhibition at the forthcoming Olympia Aero Show in mind; this was due to take place during the coming summer. Under the supervision of Henry Knowler, much of the work was done during overtime hours and the main drawings were assembled in one month. The prototype Cutty Sark was completed in four months by the summer of 1929, well in time for the Aero Show in July and its first public appearance.

Interestingly, the first A.17 did not incorporate the Saro patented method of 'corrugated' hull construction, though all other examples did. By the summer of 1929, full trials of the A.14, with the prototype metal hull, had not been completed. It was perhaps because of some uncertainty over the full success of that hull that G-AAIP, the A.17 prototype, was designed with a conventional single-step hull of frame and stringer construction, over which the Alclad plating was riveted. Very little double curvature was in evidence, beating being confined to the chines and a number of small plates in the extreme bow.

Provision was made for two crew and two passengers, both pairs seated side by side. Dual control was fitted in the fully-enclosed cockpit and the passenger cabin was situated just ahead of the wing. A mooring hatch was provided in the bow and the glazed cockpit roof could be opened to provide an entrance hatch, though this was generally used in conjunction

97

with the forward hatch for mooring. The main entry hatch was in the upper hull over the wing trailing edge. The hull itself was divided into five watertight compartments, that aft of the cabin being used as a large luggage area. Construction of the hull was all-metal and the few external fittings were of stainless steel.

The mainplane was a deep-sectioned Avro-Fokker watertight cantilever design of all-wood construction, with two box-spars, spruce flanges and three-ply webs and ribs. The plywood skinning was stiffened in the vicinity of the engines to provide walkways. The wing was of sufficient buoyancy to support the aircraft in the event of the hull being flooded, and was bolted to the gunwales at four points. This wingform was subsequently used in almost identical form in the A.19 Cloud and A.21 Windhover. The wing design had been taken to Cowes through the introduction of A.V. Roe, John Lord and Harry Broadsmith to the company from Avro. In the case of the A.17, narrow-chord unbalanced ailerons were fitted. The absence of rigging minimised maintenance of all three types and, if the wing became damaged, replacement was simple.

All but one A.17 were of twin-engined configuration. The first, G-AAIP, had two 105 hp Cirrus Hermes Is four-cylinder inline air-cooled engines, mounted on pylons high above the wing in order to clear spray, and the nacelles were toed slightly outward to minimise offset thrust when flying on one engine. The position of the engines allowed optional

A.17/2 VH-UNV with Matthews Aviation badge on the rudder; the first of the 'corrugated' Cutty Sarks.

Cutty Sark G-ACDR off AST's base at Hamble, 1935. (*British Powerboat Co*)

powerplants to be used, and this was later taken full advantage of. Two fuel tanks, each of 20 gal capacity, were contained within the wing, providing a range of 340 miles. Oil tanks were in the nacelles aft of the engines. Compressed air starting was employed.

The tail unit was of normal monoplane arrangment. It was constructed of welded steel and fabric-covered. The tailplane was high-mounted to avoid the water. Tailplane incidence was adjusted by means of a screw-jack operated from the cockpit and the rudder and elevators were horn balanced. The fin was built integral with the hull and the tailplane was strut-braced to the hull and fin. Stepless wing-floats provided lateral stability on the water and were situated rather close to the hull on short strut attachments.

G-AAIP (c/n A.19/1), provided a basis not only for subsequent Cutty Sarks but also for the later Cloud and Windhover, both of which were structurally very similar. G-AAIP first flew from Cowes on 4 July, 1929, piloted by Flg Off Chilton. Flt Lieut Stuart Scott, the Saro test-pilot, also flew it. A visit to the MAEE followed where C of A trials were made on 30 and 31 August. The MAEE unfortunately holed G-AAIP but the damage was slight and was swiftly repaired. Testing revealed good airborne characteristics with light and responsive controls. However, during these tests, G-AAIP flew slightly starboard wing low; this lack of trim was

99

passed over and not rectified at the trials because of the short time available. Though the Cutty Sark was laterally stable it tended to hunt, especially in bumpy weather, and aileron vibration was noticeable throughout the tests. Water performance was found to be dirty until about halfway onto the step, and choppy water threw spray over the whole cockpit area. The absence of a windscreen wiper was criticised by the MAEE. G-AAIP also showed a tendency to porpoise with the centre of gravity in the forward position, though this was greatly reduced if it was moved to the aft extremity; vibration arising from the engine mountings was also minimised. The aircraft could be quite effectively trimmed over the flying range in either CG position so the faults were cured simply by moving it aft.

G-AAIP was duly presented to the public at Olympia in July 1929. Curiously, the stand on which it was presented was labelled 'Saunders' without the 'Roe', though by the time of the exhibition the company had changed its name as well as ownership. There was also an S.E. Saunders advertisement in the catalogue. A dainty little aircraft, the Cutty Sark endeared itself to all who visited Olympia. It was painted light blue for the Show and priced at £3,500; a land undercarriage was offered as an optional extra for a further £250.

After its public debut, Chilton took G-AAIP to La Baule Seaplane Rally on 14 September, 1929, in company with Sir Sefton Brancker, Director of Civil Aviation. On its return to Cowes, G-AAIP was fitted with an

A.17/3 at Cowes, spring 1930, with B Mark L3, armed with bomb racks and a machine-gun operated from the mooring position. (*BHC*)

G-AAVX in flying-boat form, summer 1930, Cowes.

amphibian undercarriage, designed to give greater versatility. This arrangement consisted of two compression legs and two steel-tube V-struts, which hinged the bottom ends of the compression legs to the hull sides. A worm gear was positioned at the top of each leg and actuated by a threaded cross-tube passing through the hull to the cockpit. When the tube was rotated, the top ends of the legs were drawn inwards, thus retracting the wheels. Wheel brakes were fitted on some Cutty Sarks, though G-AAIP does not appear to have had them installed initially. Suspension was through oil-operated oleo legs and high-tensile steel springs.

In its amphibious form, G-AAIP was sold in April 1930 to Norman Holden and based at Selsey Bill, where it was flown by E.G. Horden. In May it was acquired by Messrs S. Kirston and R. Mace and used as a small passenger transport between Woolston (Southampton) and St Helier harbour in Jersey.

During early 1931, G-AAIP again returned to Cowes for modification, two closely-cowled 120 hp de Havilland Gipsy II engines replacing the Hermes Is and improving performance somewhat. Stuart Scott then took G-AAIP on a European tour between 26 March and 23 April, 1931, in search of buyers. Capt H.H. Balfour, of Whitehall Securities and recently elected to the Saro board, travelled with Scott, sharing some of the flying. First stop was Brussels, where the undercarriage and a float were damaged by a wire fence running along the perimeter of the aerodrome. After repairs, Zagreb was reached on 7 April, after flying via Cologne, Würzburg, Linz and Vienna. At Zagreb the Cutty Sark was serviced and, to its credit, needed only cleaning and some lubricating. The aircraft was

101

demonstrated to, among others, the Commander in Chief of the Yugoslav Navy. Flying via Dubrovnik and Sarajevo, Belgrade was the next destination and G-AAIP was again demonstrated, this time before the managing director of the Yugoslav airline Aeroput, as well as members of the Belgrade Aero Club. The return journey to Cowes was flown in mostly poor weather and the Danube was followed at 50 ft from Budapest to Vienna. Via stops at Linz, Nuremberg, Frankfurt, Cologne and Brussels, Lympne was reached on the evening of 23 April. Cowes could have been reached later the same evening but the Cowes customs official had already locked up for the night. The journey had covered nearly 3,000 miles and no mechanical problems at all had developed, apart from some difficulties with the compass.

In June 1931, Scott took G-AAIP to the Stockholm Exhibition and in January 1932 the aircraft was bought by Capt Campbell Shaw and Flt Lieut Tommy Rose, who had between them formed Isle of Man Air Service. G-AAIP was used to carry passengers between Liverpool and Douglas harbour, though if the seas were rough it was usual to land at Ronaldsway instead. After varied and useful service, G-AAIP was eventually scrapped during 1935.

Meanwhile, the eleven subsequent Cutty Sarks had been manufactured at Cowes. All these incorporated the Saro patented method of 'corrugated'

G-AAVX in its later, amphibious, form, Cowes aerodrome, autumn 1930. (*BHC*)

102

hull construction, though internal hull arrangements remained similar to those of the prototype. A variety of engines were adopted for the later A.17s, most of which were built with the amphibian undercarriage. The second example, c/n A.17/2, was initially L1 (Class B) and was powered by two de Havilland Gipsy IIs. Later, as VH-UNV it was sold to the Australian Matthews Aviation Pty for its short-lived services across the Bass Strait. It passed to Qantas Empire Airways and was destroyed in an accident at Pinkenba on 5 April, 1938.

Also Gipsy II-powered, the third example (A.17/3) was used by the Governor-General of New Zealand. It was based at RNZAF Station Hobsonville and serialled '3'. In November 1937, this example was taken out of service and used as an instructional airframe. VH-UNV and '3' were constructed during the early months of 1930. The fourth Cutty Sark, G-AAVX, was launched from Cowes in May 1930. This was initially a pure flying-boat and it was intended for the Hon A.E. Guinness, but Guinness bought a Cloud instead. In December 1930 G-AAVX went to the Royal Singapore Flying Club, for taxi and club work. It became VR-SAA in October 1934, but after the climatic conditions had caused warping of the wing, it was finally scrapped in 1935.

A.17/5 emerged from Cowes in July 1930 as G-ABBC and was sold in January 1931 to Francis Francis, who based it at Heston. In March 1932, it was purchased by British Amphibious Air Lines Ltd and named *Progress*. While operated by this concern, G-ABBC flew in competition with G-AAIP. Both aircraft shared Douglas harbour and Ronaldsway, but G-AAIP flew from Liverpool and *Progress* from Squires Gate, also picking up passengers from Blackpool seafront. By April 1935, G-ABBC had returned to Cowes and because no further purchasers were found for it was put into store. It was finally destroyed at Cowes during the May 1942 air raid.

The sixth Cutty Sark, S1575, was launched during November 1930 and passed briefly to the Seaplane Training Flight at Calshot before going to

G-ABBC *Progress*, 1932, possibly taken at Squires Gate, Blackpool.

The Cutty Sark example considered by the Seaplane Training Flight and the MAEE for use as a military trainer, S1575, late 1930. (*BHC*)

the MAEE for assessment as a possible Service trainer. The MAEE's reports followed in January and February 1931. At that time this Cutty Sark was powered by two Gipsy II engines and had accommodation for two pilots and a navigator.

It was found that manoeuvring on the water was straightforward in calm conditions but in a chop the aircraft required careful handling. Performance tests at 3,750 lb in choppy water revealed that the hull leaked badly in several places; the port wing float rear supporting struts were also damaged. At a weight of 3,700 lb, the height reached in three minutes from rest was 1,000 ft, rather less than the minimum requirement for civil aircraft.

The flying qualities were generally good, the controls being light and responsive, though there was a significant tail-heavy change of trim with engines off, and this was considered very undesirable in a training aircraft. Alighting was straightforward but had to be done at a rather high speed because elevator control was lost before the stall occurred. Another criticism was that under full throttle when climbing, vibration was felt throughout the entire control system. Although the aircraft was judged to be a better performer than G-AAIP, MAEE could not recommend S1575 for Service use at an all-up weight greater than 3,700 lb, which would have meant reducing either the fuel load or the crew.

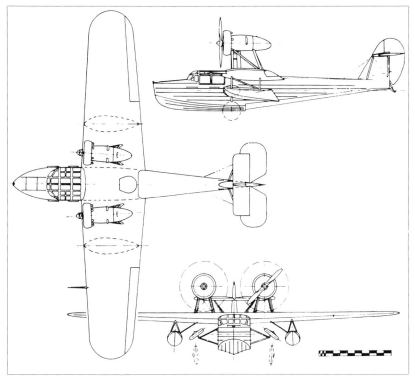

A.17 Cutty Sark

S1575 was subsequently re-tested by the MAEE, using Gipsy IIIs in lieu of Gipsy IIs—the report on its handling was issued during April 1934. It was found that flying performance was slightly improved but a strong tendency to swing to starboard after alighting was experienced; the cause was not discovered. The performance with the new engines was not sufficiently improved for MAEE to recommend Service use.

One of the more disconcerting faults experienced during these tests was the collapse of the planing bottom suffered by S1575. The lateral stiffeners along the planing bottom tended to deflect inwards if subjected to heavy treatment. If the deflection happened to be in the area below the control column, this could cause the control column to jam. The deflecting weakness was obviously serious and occurred in other 'corrugated' Saro aircraft. Only the A.27 London was free of such a vice; for the rest, it was a matter of finding that a trouble-spot had occurred after construction, and applying local strengthening, usually in the form of angle-strips. S1575 was reinforced in such a way. It appears to have been the only A.17 to have suffered from such a serious failure (though general dents in the hull skins were not unknown), which came at a highly inconvenient time.

While the first six A.17s were variously engined, the remaining examples

"SARO CUTTY SARK."   SAUNDERS-ROE, COWES,

A.17/8, Cowes aerodrome, the example which eventually became G-AETI after its return from China.

were with one exception powered by the 140 hp Armstrong Siddeley Genet Major I five-cylinder air-cooled radial. The seventh, A.17/7, and the eighth, A.17/8, were both shipped to Hong Kong. A.17/7 became VR-HAY and was used by the Far East Flying School for instructional purposes for about three years, after which its fate is uncertain. A.17/8 remained in its crate unregistered, after its sale to the Kwangsi Air Force in China had fallen through. Both these aircraft were equipped with overload tanks which gave an endurance of seven hours. A.17/8 was returned to the United Kingdom in late 1936, was registered to Air Service Training as G-AETI, in February 1937, and impressed in 1939. It served with No. 3 EFTS and was struck off charge on 1 April, 1942.

The ninth Cutty Sark, c/n A.17/9, was unique in being the only single-engined example. Registered G-ABVF in March 1932, it was built as a pure flying-boat and was powered by one 240 hp Armstrong Siddeley Lynx IVC. It was tested at Cowes during late March, where it was found that the elevator control was more effective than that of the twin-engined A.17s, though the water handling was more difficult with a single engine and the rudder was slightly heavier. No water rudder was fitted to either the Cutty Sark or the later A.21 Windhover. In May 1932, G-ABVF was sold to the Japanese round-the world pilot Yoshihara, for a flight from San Francisco to Japan.

G-ACDP (A.17/10) and G-ACDR (A.17/11), became familiar sights along the south coast of England during the 1930s. Both were sold to Air

106

G-ABVF, the sole single-engined Cutty Sark, moored by the west bank of the Medina, Cowes.

G-ACDP, one of three Cutty Sarks used by AST, 1935. (*C.A. Sims*)

Service Training of Hamble, where they were used for training. G-ACDP arrived on 11 April, 1933, and was followed on 24 April by G-ACDR.

It was here that the Cutty Sark found its vocation. Though the A.17 was envisaged by Saro as a multi-purpose type, its strong point was undoubtedly the ability to operate as a trainer. It was cheap to purchase and run, and easy to fly provided care was taken during the approach to avoid a slight inclination to stall. Four examples, including VR-HAY, were operated in this role and a fifth, S1575, was tested as a possible Service trainer. The three AST aircraft were retained through the 1930s. G-ACDP was finally withdrawn following its C of A expiry in April 1939, though it was later impressed using spares from G-ACDR, which had been dismantled during the previous year.

G-ADAF (A.17/12) went to San Domingo where by February 1935 it had been acquired by R.H. Kulka Ltd.

Span 45 ft; length 34 ft 4 in; height 11 ft 2 in; wing area 320 sq ft.
Normal range 340 miles (Hermes), 300 miles (Gipsy II), 315 miles (Genet Major).

	Engines	Weights, lb				Performance			
		Total hp	Tare	Fuel Pilot	Payload	Loaded	Maximum mph	Cruise mph	Climb ft/min	Service ceiling ft
A.17A*	Two Hermes I	210	2,430	590	680	3,700	100	82	550	10,000
A.17b	Two Hermes I	210	2,600	590	510	3,700	96	78	520	9,000
A.17C*	One Lynx DD	215	2,400	550	750	3,700	102	85	550	10,000
A.17D	One Lynx DD	215	2,570	550	580	3,700	97	82	500	9,000
A.17E	One Lynx IVC	240	2,490	530	680	3,700	112	90	600	10,000
A.17F	One Lynx IVC	240	2,600	530	610	3,740	104	83	550	9,500
A.17G	Two Gipsy II	240	2,500	620	730	3,850	103	85	570	9,500
A.17H	Two Gipsy II	240	2.670	620	560	3,850	102	82	550	9,000
A.17J	Three Genet	240	2,545	625	530	3,700	105	90	550	9,500
A.17K	Three Genet	240	2,715	625	360	3,700	103	85	500	9,000
A.17L*	Two Genet Major I	280	2,570	720	610	3,900	115	96	500	9,500
A.17M	Two Genet Major I	280	2,725	630	510	3,865	107	93	500	9,000
A.17N*	Two Gipsy III	260	2,430	520	550	3,500	114	97	580	9,600
A.17P	Two Gipsy III	260	2,430	590	680	3,700	104	92	540	9,200
A.17Q	Two Gipsy II	240	2,600	590	510	3,700	106	90	580	9,850

*Flying-boats, the others were amphibian designs.

Though all these variants were offered by the company, not all were built:

G-AAIP c/n A.17/1. Ff 4.7.29, Flg Off Chilton. To MAEE 8.29 for C of A. 1929 Olympia Aero Show, to La Baule Seaplane Rally 9.29, to Cowes late 1929, to Norman Holden 4.30, based Selsey Bill, to Kirston and Mace 5.30. Early 1931, to Cowes (mods). European tour 26.3.31 – 23.4.31. To Stockholm Exhibition 6.31, to Isle of Man Air Service 1.32. Scrapped 1935; L1 c/n A. 17/2. 'B' Mark initially allotted but to Matthews Aviation Co as VH-UNV. Crashed 5.4.38; L3 c/n A.17/3. 'B' Mark initially allotted but to RNZAF Hobsonville, serialled '3'. Became instructional airframe 11.37; G-AAVX c/n A.17/4. Launched 5.30. To Royal Singapore Flying Club 12.30 as VR-SAA. Scrapped 1935 due to warped wing; G-ABBC c/n A.17/5. Ff 7.30. To Francis Francis 1.31, to British Amphibious Air Lines 3.32, to Saro (storage) 4.35. Destroyed in air raid, Cowes, 5.42; S1575 c/n A.17/6. Launched 11.30. To Seaplane Training Flight Calshot 12.30, to MAEE 12.30, to Cowes 4.31, to MAEE 1.34. Returned Cowes c5.34 and subsequently scrapped; VR-HAY c/n A.17/7. To Hong Kong for use by Far East Flying School. In service three years; G-Aeti c/n A.17/8. To Hong Kong, but remained in storage and not registered there. To Britain late 1936 and reg'd G-AETI. To AST Hamble. Impressed and to 3 EFTS 1939. SOC 1.4.42; G-ABVF c/n A.17/9. Reg'd 3.32. C of A test at Cowes by MAEE pilot, 24.3.32. To Japanese long-distance pilot Yoshihara 5.32 and subsequently crashed by him; G-ACDP c/n A.17/10. To AST Hamble 11.4.33. Wdn after C of A. expiry 4.39 but subsequently impressed and to 3 EFTS 1939. SOC 1.4.42; G-ACDR c/n A.17/11. To AST Hamble 24.4.33. Dismantled 1938. Later cannibalised in order to resurrect G-ACDP, between April and December 1939; G-ADAF c/n A.17/12. To San Domingo 2.35, operated by R. H. Kulka.

Saunders-Roe A.19 and A.29 Cloud

The second design started under the reconstituted firm of Saunders-Roe was the A.19 Cloud; it was of similar general configuration to the A.17 Cutty Sark. Design work began in the summer of 1929 but the first example was not launched until 16 July, 1930.

The Cloud was larger than the Cutty Sark but embodied a similar wooden Avro-Fokker cantilever wing except that the centre-section was of parallel chord. Pylon-mounted, toed-out engines were once again employed, as was localised strengthening of the wing to facilitate engine maintenance. The two 100 gall fuel tanks were within the wing beneath the engines. Eight types of engines were used in Clouds, including three models of the Armstrong Siddeley Serval.

Again, the Saro method of 'corrugated' hull construction was used, though the Cloud had two steps rather than the single step of the A.17. Also, a water-rudder/tailskid was provided. The tail configuration of the Cloud was similar to that of the A.17 while the amphibian undercarriage retracted to the same position, just clear of the waterline.

There was a bow compartment for the storage of marine gear, complete with sliding hatch, behind which was a fully-enclosed, side-by-side dual-

Cloud A.19/1 G-ABCJ on C of A trials at Felixstowe, July 1930. (*RAE, Crown Copyright*)

control cockpit. The main passenger cabin, seating six to eight people, was beneath the wing. To the rear of this was a large luggage compartment and a lavatory. Entry was made through a hatch aft of the wing in the top of the hull and via a companionway to the cabin, while a sliding hatch in the foredeck and a hinged windscreen gave access to the cockpit.

The Cloud was initially aimed at the civil buyer, whether for taxi-work, private flying or short-range airline operations. The first Cloud (c/n A.19/1) was completed during July 1930 and carried the Class B marking L4. It was launched on 16 July and undertook trials from Cowes flown by Flt Lieut Stuart Scott, before receiving a C of A from the MAEE at the end of the month as G-ABCJ. Its flying qualities were praised by the MAEE, G-ABCJ being easy to control for long periods and quite capable of being trimmed to fly 'hands-off'. The only real criticism made was that the tailplane incidence operating gear was not designed to be adjusted readily in flight, and slight tail buffet was experienced near the stall. Behaviour on the water was found to be good and take-offs were fairly clean. This commendable water performance was somewhat spoilt, however; due to the buoyancy of the tyres it was found almost impossible to lower the undercarriage while the Cloud was on the water. In fact, while still at Felixstowe, it suffered an undercarriage collapse while on the water, when the hoisting gear failed and the main wheels dropped from a re-tracted position to water level. G-ABCJ's C of A was issued subject to the hoisting gear being reinforced. It was also recommended that the watertightness of the hull and floats be improved, as slight leakage had been experienced while at Felixstowe.

G-ABCJ with Napier Rapiers, Cowes, early 1934. (*Saro*)

The first Cloud was powered by two 300 hp Wright Whirlwind J-6 nine-cylinder air-cooled radial engines. It was purchased by Capt Robert Holt and was taken in December 1931 to Canada, where it became CF-ARB. It was re-purchased by Saro in January 1934 for various experiments and re-engined with two 340 hp Napier Rapier IV sixteen-cylinder H air-cooled engines. The revised c/n A.19/1A was allotted and on the Cloud's return to Cowes the registration G-ABCJ was reinstated. In its new form it appeared at the 1934 and 1935 Hendon SBAC Shows and was loaned to Jersey Airways Ltd in August 1935. G-ABCJ was finally withdrawn from use in December 1936.

The second civil Cloud (c/n A.19/2) was also an amphibian and was ordered by the Hon A. E. Guinness in mid-1930, after he had looked at a Cutty Sark and considered the possibility of waiting for a Windhover. In the event, he bought the larger of the currently available 'boats. C/n A.19/2, registered G-ABHG, was test-flown in December 1930, the Saro pilot being Leslie Ash. G-ABHG had three 215 hp Armstrong Siddeley Lynx IVC seven-cylinder radials instead of the normal twin configuration. However, before delivery finally took place and receiving its C of A in late July 1931, two Pratt & Whitney Wasp nine-cylinder radials of 425 hp had been installed. Despite becoming a twin-engined aircraft, G-ABHG retained a great deal of originality, in that by the time of its C of A, twin fins and horn-balanced rudders had been fitted, together with a smaller third rudder situated below the tailplane. These modifications were intended to reduce slight problems of directional control experienced just before alighting. MAEE had not noted this problem with G-ABCJ, but praised the new arrangement as satisfactory, and also remarked on the improved watertightness of G-ABHG over A-ABCJ.

In addition to these modifications, G-ABHG had at the same time

111

Cloud A.19/2 G-ABHG in original form with three Armstrong Siddeley Lynx IVC engines, Cowes, late 1930. (*BHC*)

G-ABHG in revised form, early summer 1931, with two 425 hp Pratt & Whitney Wasps, an auxiliary aerofoil and three rudders. (*C.A. Sims*)

received a large auxiliary aerofoil mounted above the engine nacelles, which gave it a most distinctive appearance. This was designed to improve elevator control at low speed, but the improvement was only rather slight; early Clouds would suddenly drop if allowed to, and only after substantial research by the company was this problem eased. The MAEE certainly *had* remarked on this vice when testing G-ABCJ, but had not formally demanded that something be done about it. G-ABHG's extra aerofoil was the beginning of an attempt at a cure, and was at the same time unique—no other Cloud flew with three engines or the auxiliary aerofoil.

Named by Guinness *Flying Amo*, G-ABHG was based at Eastleigh. Passing through the hands of Brian Allen Aviation Ltd, it was sold in November 1939 to Imperial Airways, and delivered to Hythe on Southampton Water on 29 December, 1939, where it was used for basic marine instruction until June 1940, though it had come under BOAC ownership on 1 April. By September 1940 it was based at Poole for crew training but its C of A expired during December. By May 1941, G-ABHG was at Hythe once more, but it was considered not worthwhile to overhaul her and during the following month she was written off. From August 1943 the hull was used as a rest area for BOAC staff but by 1952 it was at St Leonards, near Ringwood in Hampshire, in use as a caravan.

The third civil Cloud was G-ABXW *Cloud of Iona* (c/n A.19/4) launched on 15 July, 1932. Like G-ABCJ in its original form, G-ABXW had Whirlwind J-6 engines, it received its C of A later in July. It was then sold to British Flying Boats Ltd and operated an experimental Stranraer-Belfast service on 14 August before operating a Greenock-Belfast Service for a week during that month. In September 1934 it went to Guernsey

A.19/4 G-ABXW *Cloud of Iona* in Guernsey, 1935, (*Bob Wealthy*)

113

A.19/5 G-ACGO in original form, Cowes, summer 1933. (*Bob Wealthy*)

A.19/5 in revised form as OK-BAK, with Walter Pollux radials and deflectors behind the nacelle struts. (*BHC*)

114

A.19/3 as 12, on type trials at the MAEE, December 1931. (*RAE, Crown Copyright*)

Airways but on 31 July, 1936, was lost off Jersey with the loss of all ten occupants.

The last Cloud to be built for the civil market was G-ACGO (c/n A.19/5), which first flew in mid-July 1933. It was powered by two 340 hp Armstrong Siddeley Serval III ten-cylinder radials, and acquired its C of A in late July. It was then taken on an extensive sales tour of Europe by Flt Lieut Scott, returning to Cowes on 10 August. However, the Cloud had impressed the Czechoslovaks before whom it was demonstrated outside Prague on 8-9 August. Representatives of both the Czechoslovak Air Force and the civil aviation authority had watched G-ACGO and its amphibious qualities were appreciated.

Ceskoslovenské Státní Aerolinie (CSA) purchased G-ACGO, but before delivery in July 1934, the Servals were replaced by 300 hp Walter Pollux radials. The Townend rings were not increased in diameter, however, and consequently the Pollux rocker gear was allowed to protrude through slots in the rings themselves. After satisfactory tests with the new engines at Cowes, G-ACGO became OK-BAK, serving with CSA until the German invasion of Czechoslovakia when it was dismantled and put into store. After the war, the wing could not be found, but the hull was put to good use. With the tail unit and rear section of the hull removed, and a marine engine installed, OK-BAK became a motor launch named *Delfín* (Prague licence number PO2-21) and was used on the Vltava until the mid-1960s.

G-ACGO was the last of the civil Clouds, but the Air Ministry had shown an interest in the Cloud for possible use as a navigational trainer and a prototype for that purpose had been built. C/n A.19/3, K2681, made its first public appearance as '12', in the 1931 Hendon SBAC Show. Though this example retained the designation A.19, Saro designated subsequent military Clouds A.29.

Though generally similar to the civil type, the military Cloud differed greatly in its interior layout. Developed as a flying and navigational trainer, the large cabin space allowed a number of pupils to be taught navigation simultaneously, while the dual-control side-by-side cockpit was ideal for flying training. The optional teaching layouts allowed for six pupils plus wireless, other electrical equipment, navigational instruments and signalling apparatus, or for four pupils plus similar equipment and increased tankage to allow an endurance of up to $5\frac{1}{2}$ hr. Gun rings could be fitted in the bow and aft compartments and four 50 lb bombs could be carried on underwing racks, though it is probable that armament was fitted in only a few cases.

The military prototype was used for experimental work for most of its existence. Dual control was not fitted although provision was made for installation if required. A.19/3 differed from the eventual A.29 production batches in that it had two uncowled Armstrong Siddeley Double Mongoose II ten-cylinder radials. Launched from Cowes on 20 July, 1931, after its visit to Hendon it went to the MAEE for evaluation. Once there, things began to go wrong.

While at Felixstowe, a failure similar to that of G-ABCJ occurred when A.19/3's undercarriage collapsed; the tyres were also found to be over-buoyant. The oil tank mountings behind the engines also failed, as did the

A.29 K2681 with Monospar wing, and without engine strut fairings, Cowes.

116

nacelle pylon fairings. The military Cloud was praised for generally good flying qualities and ease of water handling, but it was again commented that ease of landing particularly could be much improved by increasing elevator control. This combined with the problem of frail fittings to postpone a decision on whether the type would be fit for Service use. In the interim, A.19/3 went to Calshot where it joined the Seaplane Training Flight for a short spell. Here, another problem emerged when STF commented on a tendency toward tail shuddering (as well as loss of elevator control) when it was stalled with engines off.

On its return to Cowes, several modifications were made to the military prototype. Townend rings of 12 in chord were fitted for the first time and the engine mountings were given stiffening plates to reduce recently observed flexing. The elevators were slightly enlarged and static balance weights were fitted in the forward part of the horn balances. The tailplane was given additional external bracing and the front of the fin was stiffened. The aircraft then returned to the MAEE during the spring of 1932, where it was found that the shuddering had been reduced. After further modifications consisting of stiffening the upper part of the fin, the rudder-bar bracket and the addition of a stiffened main balance rib to a further refined rudder, the shuddering was overcome.

However, by June 1932, problems had arisen with failures of the hull and float structures. Principal areas involved were the planing bottom

Cloud 12 in modified form with Townend rings, early 1932. (*BHC*)

117

Cloud 12 on the Solent, 1932. This example became K2681. (*BHC*).

transverse members, the bulkhead over the rear step and the vertical supporting members on the hull sides, all of which showed signs of buckling. The forebody plating of the wing floats also suffered with similar troubles. Because of this, tests with A.19/3, by that time flying as K2681, were suspended by the MAEE. The Cloud returned once more to Cowes, during early June, for more modifications entailing local strengthening of the affected areas.

By October, K2681 had returned again to Felixstowe, via the A&AEE where landing and wheel-brake tests had been made. As a result of these, the military prototype had its brakes modified to reduce the landing run by one third; the originals had been judged inadequate. At MAEE, new and experimental Townend rings were fitted and found to improve slightly the sluggish elevators. K2681 spent much of the rest of the year at Felixstowe for tests on control locking devices, parachute dropping and with various airscrews, being subsequently used in the development of the Saro A.33.

By late 1932 the Air Ministry had ordered sixteen military Clouds for pilot and navigator training, at a purchase price of £5,000 each. These were ordered in three batches; K2894—K2898, K3722—K3729 and K4300—K4302, to Specification 15/32, and all were powered by Armstrong Siddeley Servals of various marks, Serval being the new name for the Double Mongoose. The first to emerge from Cowes, K2894, was

Cloud A.29 K2894 at Felixstowe for comparative trials with K2681, May 1933. (*RAE, Crown Copyright*)

tested at Felixstowe during April 1933 for comparison with the prototype. It incorporated the modifications developed on K2681, as well as several other alterations. The fuel system was changed to allow either engine to be fed by either tank. Townend rings of increased chord were fitted. The interior was rearranged for greater utility. Emergency exits were provided in the form of readily removable aft windows. The dorsal cabin exit was altered from a lifting to a sliding configuration.

Compared with the prototype, the performance of K2894 was slightly inferior: a small reduction in maximum speed and 65 ft/min less in rate of climb. However, this was not a major disadvantage. K2894 showed a slight inclination to porpoise at all-up weight but this was avoidable with careful handling at take-off and by sufficiently fast alightings, an essential in any event because of the persistent elevator problem.

The first production batch of military Clouds was supplied with hulls similar to that of K2681, though significantly reinforced, as was the second batch. However, to make sure, the third batch was supplied with some-what redesigned hulls so as to cure the slight porpoising experienced with K2894, and experiments were undertaken once again with the prototype. By August 1933, MAEE officials had tested K2681 at Cowes. The proto-type's hull had been altered in a number of ways. The main step had been cut forward to form a more pronounced taper while the aft hull bottom was extended 23 in increasing the length between front and rear steps by the same amount. Also, the top of the hull was raised six inches at the

First of the second batch of Clouds, A.29 K3722 at Felixstowe for type trials, January 1934.
(*RAE, Crown Copyright*)

G-ABCJ with Rapiers and a deflector behind the engines. It is also without engine strut fairings.

leading edge of the fin. The bow was raised and faired into the cockpit area. K2681 in this form did not experience porpoising.

The first of the second A.29 production batch, K3722, was tested at Felixstowe in January 1934 and not surprisingly appeared similar in characteristics to K2894. The following month, G-ABCJ, by that time re-engined with 340 hp Napier Rapier IVs, began its own trials. Retained by Saro after returning from Canada, G-ABCJ suffered from the suspect elevator control similar to that experienced by contemporary Clouds. In an attempt to rectify the partial stall which was at the centre of the trouble, a deflector was fitted above the wing, aft of and extending just outboard of the nacelles. The engine strut fairings were also removed, to provide a more satisfactory flow. The deflector succeeded in unstalling the central region of the wing. From then on, a further series of modifications took place.

G-ABCJ in its original form appears to have retained the deflectors. By the time G-ACGO became OK-BAK, but before delivery to CSA, it too had received deflectors. These took the form of two separate units, the middle section between the nacelles having been omitted. In conjunction with RAE Farnborough, Saro made a series of tests during the summer of 1934, using faired and unfaired nacelles in a variety of positions, various

Cloud OK-BAK served with the Czechoslovak airline CSA and was powered by Walter Pollux engines.

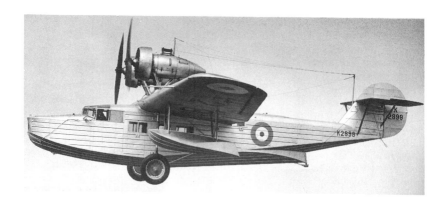

A.29 K2898, with engine strut fairings removed.

deflectors, and sometimes omitting engine strut fairings. The combinations were tested in model form in the RAE wind-tunnel.

Parallel to these tests, K2895 arrived at Felixstowe via Cowes and STF Calshot. At the MAEE it was flown with faired and unfaired engine strut fairings; without these, it was found that elevator control was ample up to the stall, that post-stall control was easy to regain and that elevator control was available throughout the approach and alighting. K3726, also tested at this time, retained the strut fairings and the adverse characteristics. This led to the fairings being discarded. There appears to have been no hard and fast application of the lesson learned, but by late 1935 many A.29s were being flown without fairings. Deflectors were more commonly adopted for the civil variants, which also tended to lose their fairings.

The first production A.29 joined 'B' Flight at Calshot in August 1933. Cloud production finally ceased in January 1935, the last delivery being made in the same month. In addition to STF, A.29s served with the School of Air Pilotage at Andover, with No. 48 Sqn at Bircham Newton and Manston, Calshot's 'A' Flight, the School of Air Navigation and No. 9 Elementary and Reserve Flying Training School.

Several Service Clouds were involved in accidents. In February 1934 negligence led to a mishap: Cloud K3722 was severely damaged at Andover when, left unattended, it blew backwards into a hangar door during a freak wind. In August 1936 K4302 grounded off Manston after an undercarriage collapse which ripped the hull open. The following month, K3723 dropped a wing while alighting, lost a float on impact and though it did not sink, two of the crew were injured. In April 1937, K2895 was destroyed, when having just taken off from Calshot, it dropped a wing after a very early right-hand turn. The wing touched the water and K2895 crashed with the loss of three lives.

During January 1937, K2897 nosed over on the slipway at Calshot while taxi-ing and damaged its bow and planing bottom. In September 1938, K3723 crashed in a field at Walsgrave, near Coventry, sustaining Category 'C' damage. One episode worth recording is the fate of a diligent if

122

A.29 K2897 over the south of England.

ungifted pupil flying a blind navigation exercise in the cabin of an A.29. After a routine flight, the aircraft alighted in very choppy waters off Calshot. At this stage, the pupil had his position as some 30 miles inland over open country, and interpreted the bumpy run as a forced landing in a ploughed field. Thinking it safer not to be aboard at the end of the run, the pupil leapt smartly out and provided the Calshot rescue boat with some work.

The Cloud undoubtedly found a niche in Service life, performing essential training duties until struck off in July 1939. Though the civil variant found only a limited market, Specification 15/32 had provided an opening and badly needed orders after Saunders' financial reorganisation. The decision to build a 'family' of small aircraft led to total orders for 35 examples, no mean feat for the small Cowes firm. The Cloud in particular helped lay the foundations for company prosperity in the late 1930s, which extended until after the Second World War.

Clouds K3729 and K3725, with No. 48 Squadron. (*Bob Wealthy*)

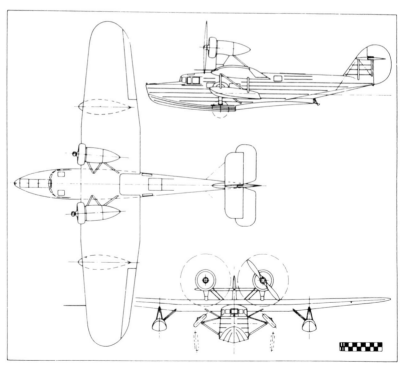

A.19 Cloud

Two 300 hp Wright Whirlwind J-6; three 215 hp Armstrong Siddeley Lynx IVC; two 425 hp Pratt & Whitney Wasp C; two 340 hp Napier Rapier IV; two 300 hp Walter Pollux; two 340 hp Armstrong Siddeley Double Mongoose II; two 340 hp Armstrong Siddeley Serval I (A.29s c/n 1-6) and 340 hp Serval III (A.19 G-ACGO and A.29s c/n 7-16).
Span 64 ft; length 47 ft 9 in (A.19s and A.29s c/n 1-9), 48 ft 8 in (A.29s c/n 10-16 and modified A.19/3); height 13 ft 2 in; wing area 650 sq ft.
Empty weight 5,500 lb Whirlwind; 6,075 lb Lynx; 5,687 lb Wasp; 6,450 lb Rapier; 6,500 lb Double Mongoose; 6,845 lb Serval I; 6,970 lb Serval III. Loaded weight 8,100 lb Whirlwind; 9,000 lb Lynx; 10,000 lb Wasp; 9,700 lb Rapier; 9,500 lb Double Mongoose; 9,530 lb Serval I; 10,090 lb Serval III.
Maximum speed 120 mph (Whirlwind and Lynx); 125 mph (Wasp); 121 mph (Rapier); 118 mph (Serval). Cruising speed 95 mph (Whirlwind); 96 mph (Lynx); 98 mph (Wasp); 102 mph (Rapier); 94 mph (Serval). Initial rate of climb 520 ft/min, production A.29s 455 ft/min. Service ceiling (A.29) 7,630 ft. Absolute ceiling (K3722) 9,430 ft. Endurance about 4 hr, G-ABHG 5 hr 25 min.
Armament: two ·303 in Lewis machine-guns or two camera-guns in bow and dorsal positon; four 50 lb bombs.

21 Examples. C/ns A.19/1 (as 1A)–5, A.29/1–16.

A.19

A.19/1 G-ABCJ, to CF-ARB, to A.19/1A G-ABCJ; A.19/2 G-ABHG; A.19/3 K2681; A.19/4 G-ABXW; A.19/5 G-ACGO/OK-BAK.

A.29

Batch One (5). K2894 c/n A.29/1– delivered 2.4.33, to MAEE, to B Flt Calshot, to 1255M 2.39; K2895 A.29/2 – 20.4.33, to STF, to MAEE, to B Flt Calshot, to STF. Crashed on take off at Calshot 6.4.37; K2896 A.29/3 – 1.5.33, to B Flt Calshot, SOC 6.1.38; K2897 A.29/4 – 19.5.33, to B Flt Calshot, to STF, to 938M 1.37; K2898 A.29/5 – 8.6.33, to B Flt Calshot, to School of Air Navigation (SAN), to 1203M 12.38.
Batch Two (8). K3722 A.29/6 – 5.12.33, to MAEE, to School of Air Pilotage (SAP), to 48 Sqn, to 9 Elementary and Reserve FTS (ERFTS), SOC 15.11.38; K3723 A.29/7 –5.12.33, to SAP, to 48 Sqn, to 9 ERFTS. Crashed at Walsgrave, near Coventry, 22.9.38, Cat C; K3724 A.29/8 – 8.12.33, to SAP, to 48 Sqn, to 9 ERFTS, SOC 7.39; K3725 A.29/9 – 16.4.34, to 48 sqn, to 9 ERFTS, SOC 7.39; K3726 A.29/10 – 28.2.34, to A Flt Calshot, SOC 7.39; K3727 A.29/11 – 20.3.34, to B Flt Calshot, SOC 16.12.38; K3728 A.29/12 – 28.3.34, to B Flt Calshot, SOC 28.10.38; K3729 A.29/13 – 3.5.34, to 48 Sqn, to 9 ERFTS, SOC 7.39.
Batch Three (3). K4300 c/n A.29/14 –14.12.34, to 9 ERFTS, SOC 7.39; K4301 c/n A.29/15 – 14.12.34, to A Flt Calshot, SOC 7.39; K4302 c/n A.29/16 – 7.1.35, to 48 Sqn, to 939M.
The delivery date follows the c/n.

Saunders-Roe A.21 Windhover

The Windhover was perhaps the prettiest of the series of three related flying-boats and amphibians produced by Saro in the early 1930s. In that sense it is sad that only two examples were built. The design did not suffer from any real defects and only the observation that perhaps the added complexity of the third engine deterred potential customers can be put forward as an explanation for the lack of orders.

Windhover A.21/1 ZK-ABW over the Solent, late 1930. (*BHC*)

Intermediate in size and weight between the earlier A.17 Cutty Sark and the A.19 Cloud, the Windhover was of very similar general configuration. The A.21 was evolved after Saro had considered the possibility of fitting a Cutty Sark with a third engine. This proved impractical; in model tests, payload dropped, owing to the restriction placed by the limited wing surface. The Windhover was therefore created as a larger type more suited to commercial work, but without the higher running costs of the large Cloud.

General design and construction of the A.21 was almost identical to that of the A.17 and A.19, with the exception of the A.17 prototype G-AAIP. Again, the Saro-patented method of 'corrugated' hull construction was employed, with a cantilever Avro-Fokker type wooden wing and a similar tail unit. Three 120 hp de Havilland Gipsy II four-cylinder inline air-cooled engines were mounted on struts above the wing. Fuel tanks giving an endurance of 4 hr were situated in the wing between the float mountings and the hull sides. A fully-enclosed, side-by-side dual-control cockpit was provided, together with a cabin extending beneath the wing and capable of seating four in comfort or six with reduced space. Access to the accommodation was similar to that of the Cutty Sark. Aft of this area was situated a large luggage compartment, and in the extreme bow a mooring hatch. The hull itself was of single-step layout and the wing was bolted to

Windhover ZK-ABW at Felixstowe for C of A trials, late October 1930.

the hull at four main attachment points. Strutted mounted floats provided lateral stability on the water and a land undercarriage was optional. Both aircraft were supplied with fittings so that a semi-retractable land chassis could be attached.

Windhover c/n A.21/1 was launched from Cowes on 16 October, 1930, being tested and flown by Stuart Scott on that day and the next. It was found that the new design could maintain height and control on any two of its three engines. On 22 October, this aircraft, registered ZK-ABW, flew to Felixstowe as a pure flying-boat, for C of A trials.

Tests were interrupted due to buckling of the hull plating just forward of the step, which indicated a definite weakness of the hull structure in that region, for only normal take-offs and alightings had been made, albeit in rather choppy weather. ZK-ABW returned to Cowes where repairs were made and stringers added locally as reinforcement. C of A trials were then completed at Cowes.

Conclusions were favourable. The flying qualities of the new type were found to be very good, with light and well harmonised controls. Take-offs were clean with no sign of porpoising and on-water manoeuvrability was straightforward. The only faults found were a slight tendency for the wing-tips to touch the water when turning tightly and a problem encountered in level flight at full throttle near sea level, when the airscrews gave engine speeds in excess of the maximum permissible. Saro duly fitted floats of about 35 per cent increased buoyancy, together with airscrews of increased pitch, and the first Windhover gained its C of A at the end of October.

It was intended that ZK-ABW should go to New Zealand for operation by Dominion Airways; but it was delivered instead to Matthews Aviation Pty, in Hobart, Tasmania, and registered VH-UPB. In amphibian form, it flew until destroyed off King Island, Bass Strait, in mid May 1936. From

127

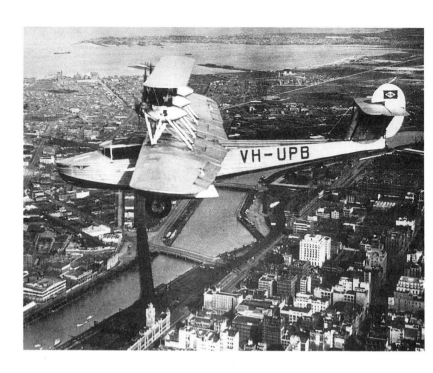

A.21/1 as VH-UPB, under the ownership of he Matthews Aviation

23 January 1933 until February 1934 it worked the Melbourne—King Island—Launceston weekly service.

The other Windhover produced, G-ABJP c/n A.21/2, arrived at Felixstowe for certification at the beginning of July 1931, beginning trials on the 4th. G-ABJP was built with a land undercarriage. C of A trials were held at Martlesham Heath to begin with, water qualities being assessed at Felixstowe. Apart from suffering a slight tendency to yaw and a low initial rate of climb, rather sluggish control was experienced near the stall. Because of the handling anomaly between engines-on and -off, a small auxiliary winglet was later fitted to both Windhovers, to restore flow over the tail and increase lift, though at the cost of increased drag.

G-ABJP was sold later in July to Francis Francis, who based it at Heston; but by September, Gibraltar Airways had bought it for use on its experimental Gibraltar-Tangier service which began on 23 September and ceased on 3 January 1932 after 117 return flights. The Windhover was named *General Godley*. By July 1932 the aircraft had again changed hands when the Hon Mrs Victor Bruce bought it, naming it *City of Portsmouth*, for an attempt on the world flight-refuelled endurance record.

City of Portsmouth was duly modified. Fuel capacity was much increased, arranged as a 75 gal tank in the mainplane, together with two tanks of 84 and 75 gal in the fuselage beneath the mainplane. Hand fuel

128

G-ABJP in the East Cowes shop, early summer 1931. (*BHC*)

pumps and a wind-driven pump were installed. A specially-prepared catwalk and safety harness was fitted, designed to allow basic in-flight engine maintenance. To save weight, the undercarriage was removed. Newly fitted jettison valves enabled all fuel to be dumped in under one minute.

When Mrs Bruce began her first attempt from Clarence Pier, Southsea, the endurance record was held by the Hunter brothers of New York. The first attempt by Mrs Bruce failed after two hours, when G-ABJP was forced to alight for various adjustments. The second was foiled after 15 hr 40 min after fog had formed, preventing contact with the tanker aircraft, the specially converted Bristol Fighter G-ABXA. However, during 9–11 August, G-ABJP stayed in the air for 54 hr 13 min, when refuelling took place over Suffolk to avoid more fog before excessive oil temperature forced the aircraft to land. It was nonetheless a creditable performance, even though it did not capture the record, which remained at 553 hr 41 min. It was also one of the few flight-refuelling operations of the time not handled by Sir Alan Cobham.

Mrs Bruce sold G-ABJP in May 1935 to Jersey Airways; while operating with the new owners, tankage was once again standard and the amphibian undercarriage replaced. The second Windhover was eventually withdrawn from service during 1938.

129

G-ABJP in the Cowes shop, illustrating the unusual auxiliary aerofoil addition eventually adopted for both examples. (*BHC*)

The Windhover was also offered with three 105 hp Cirrus Hermes or one 340 hp Armstrong Siddeley Double Mongoose engines.

Three 120 hp de Havilland Gipsy II.
Span 54 ft 4 in; length 41 ft 4 in; height (as amphibian) 12 ft 6 in; wing area 450 sq ft plus winglet 72 sq ft.
Empty weight 3,650 lb flying-boat, 4,180 lb amphibian; loaded weight 5,500 lb flying-boat, 5,700 lb amphibian.
Maximum speed 110 mph (108 mph); cruising speed 90 mph (87 mph); initial rate of climb 600 ft/min (510 ft/min); absolute ceiling 10,020 ft (9,680 ft); endurance 4 hr (both versions). Figures in parentheses for amphibian.

Two examples, ZK-ABW/VH-UPB c/n A.21/1 and G-ABJP c/n A.21/2.

Spartan Cruiser

The origins of the Cruiser series of passenger-carrying aircraft can be traced back to the Saro-Percival Mailplane built at Cowes during 1931. Designed by Edgar Percival, the Mailplane was built by the Cowes firm as a joint project under Percival's supervision.

G-ACDW over the Isle of Wight, summer 1933. (*BHC*)

The Mailplane was a low-wing cantilever monoplane of wooden construction with ply-covered fuselage and wing. It was powered by three 120 hp de Havilland Gipsy III engines, two mounted on the wings and one in the nose. Behind the fully-enclosed single-seat cockpit was a large mail-carrying compartment with a loading hatch in the upper section of the fuselage above the mainplane. There was a braced tailplane, divided elevator, single fin and horn-balanced rudder. Test-flights, made by Flt Lieut Stuart Scott of Saro, and C of A trials, took place in early 1932, the sole A.24 bearing the registration G-ABLI. Percival sold his share in the project during the spring of 1932 and the aircraft was then redesignated Saro A.24 Mailplane. When Spartan moved to the Isle of Wight, it became linked, through Whitehall Securities, with Saunders-Roe, and the decision was made to let the companies continue building landplanes and waterborne aircraft respectively. Thus, development of the Mailplane passed to Spartan, the name once again changing, this time to Spartan A.24 Mailplane.

Under Spartan the single fin and rudder was replaced with twin fins and rudders, whilst cramped provision was made in the forward area of the mail compartment for two passengers, and two small circular windows were let into the fuselage sides for their benefit. On 15 June, 1932, the mail-plane set off on a publicity flight to India, in an attempt to demonstrate the usefulness of the type on long-range mail routes.

131

The sole Saro-Percival Mailplane, G-ABLI, in its Spartan A.24 Mailplane guise with twin fins and rudders, Cowes, late spring 1932. (*BHC*)

Flown by T. Neville Stack and named *Blackpool*, G-ABLI reached Karachi in an elapsed time of 5 days 23 hours and 50 minutes, after which it was demonstrated before the Indian Director of Civil Aviation. During the tour, Stack presented Sirdir Khan, a chaukidar at Karachi aerodrome, with Great War medals for which he had been patiently waiting almost 17 years, redeeming a promise made some twelve months earlier. The Mailplane's flight was marred only by a forced landing in Greece with an oil leak.

Though Percival's design was in itself perfectly sound, from a commercial point of view the concept of a pure mail-carrier was thought questionable at Cowes. In the light of this, the decision was made to alter the role of the aircraft to that of passenger carrier. The work was undertaken by Spartan under the direction of the larger Cowes firm (and Henry Knowler in particular) and Saro also undertook a certain amount of component manufacture.

The result of this conversion of the Mailplane design was the Spartan Cruiser I G-ABTY. Successful trials were made by Lieut-Col L.A. Strange of Spartan during May 1932 and a C of A awarded at Martlesham Heath in the same month. The Cruiser I retained most of the basic features of the Mailplane, including the cantilever wooden wing and the three-engined configuration. However, the Cruiser I incorporated an entirely new, metal fuselage and a tail similar to that of the Mailplane in its original form. The

The sole Cruiser I, G-ABTY, Cowes, summer 1932. (*BHC*)

wing was built in one major piece, using two box-spars with spruce flanges and three-ply ribs and webs. The whole wing was ply-covered. The spars passed through the lower part of the fuselage and the wing was attached by four bolts mounted in the bottom longerons. There were narrow-chord inset ailerons.

The new fuselage, from which the Cruiser gained the modified designation A.24M, was of rectangular section and constructed in the same way as contemporary Saro flying-boat hulls. Longitudinal 'corrugations' ran along the fuselage sides, dispensing with the need for riveted stringers. As usual in Saro's 'corrugated' method of construction, double curvature was kept to the absolute minimum in order to simplify production. The change to a metal fuselage was carried out under the overall supervision of Percy Taylor after Knowler had drawn up the broad design study.

The tail unit was a duralumin structure with fabric covering, the tailplane had adjustable incidence, and the rudders and elevators were horn balanced. The undercarriage was of the divided type with the front leg of each V incorporating steel-spring suspension with oil damping. Wheel brakes were standard, the main wheels were normally spatted and a tailwheel was fitted.

Like the Mailplane, the Cruiser I was powered by three de Havilland Gipsy IIIs mounted two immediately forward of wing and one in the nose.

Cruiser II fuselage at East Cowes, showing the nose engine mounting-point, longitudinal corrugations and the large cutaway to accommodate the wing. (*BHC*)

The two fuel tanks were situated inboard of the wing engines and had a total capacity of 120 gal. The tanks were interconnected and so arranged that any combination of tanks and engines could be used in an emergency. Oil tanks were located behind each engine.

Accommodation consisted of a side-by-side enclosed cockpit with provision for full dual control if required. The passenger cabin, with seating for six, was extensively glazed and was situated above the wing. In a manner reminiscent of the Saro-Segrave Meteor, the cabin roof was partially glazed. Aft of the cabin was a large stowage area, and this could be increased to provide a maximum of 140 sq ft of space if the cabin furnishings were removed. Access was by hinged panels on the port side of the fuselage. Both Percival and Saro/Spartan (as indeed had Segrave with the Meteor) made safety a dominant criterion; both the Mailplane and the Cruiser series could climb on any two of the three engines.

The new Cruiser I was demonstrated at the first Hendon SBAC Show, in June 1932, and at Heston on 30 August, where it was joined by the Mailplane. On 22 September, G-ABTY flew from Sunningdale to Croydon, piloted by L.A. Strange and carrying HRH The Prince of Wales, and two days later ferried the Lord Mayor of London from Heston to Maylands, where he opened the Essex Air Display.

On 14 October, Strange took the Cruiser I to Paris in atrocious weather,

Cruiser II G-ACJO, later purchased by Aeroput, when it became YU-SAN. (*Bob Wealthy*)

The second Cruiser II sold to Aeroput, G-ACMW/YU-SAO. (*Bob Wealthy*)

135

on the first leg of an extended sales tour which took him as far as Belgrade. On 19 October, it was shown to representatives of the Yugoslav airline Aeroput where the ability to climb on any two of its three engines was demonstrated, as well as controlled flight on one engine only at a loaded weight of 5,500 lb.

Continuing via Salonika, the Cruiser flew to Athens where, on 22 October, it was again demonstrated, this time before the Greek Air Ministry and civil authorities. The Cruiser then began the return trip via Brindisi, Lyons and Paris, and Heston was reached on 25 October. Altogether, 3,593 miles had been covered, at an average speed of 113 mph. The only real mishap Strange had encountered throughout the entire journey was a forced landing on the outward journey just before Munich, again in extremely bad weather. Though the tour was undoubtedly a technical success, only minimal orders resulted. Yugoslavia purchased two aircraft and a licence to build further examples; however, only YU-SAP, registered in 1935, was built in Yugoslavia.

In the event, the Cruiser I served as a prototype for the refined version, the Cruiser II. This model retained the wingform of its predecessor but the fuselage, while remaining the same length, was modified somewhat. Passenger windows were made smaller for structural reasons and the

First of the Cruiser IIs, G-ACBM, wearing its Iraqi markings as Y-AAA. (*Bob Wealthy*)

Cruiser II G-ACNO, Cowes, early 1934, without markings but en route for Bata. (*BHC*)

pilot's windscreen altered to a vee-shape to improve vision. Conventional access by a port-side cabin door replaced the previous folding upper fuselage panels. Spats were usually omitted and cabin arrangements revised. Optional facilities within the new cabin provided for six, seven or ten passengers, luggage space being modified accordingly.

The careers pursued by the Cruiser IIs involved much shuttling between one operator and the next. G-ACBM, the original Cruiser II, was first flown during February 1933 and subsequently passed to Iraqi Airwork, who used it for a trial route between Baghdad and Mosul, along the Tigris. During this period it was registered YI-AAA, delivery to Iraq having been made by Neville Stack. It was powered by three Hermes IVs, but the majority of Cruiser IIs had Gipsy Majors. In June of 1934, YI-AAA arrived back in Britain where it reverted to G-ACBM for operations with Spartan Air Lines during the 1935 season. When Spartan Air Lines was taken over by British Airways Ltd in October 1935, G-ACBM was duly transferred and began operations from Eastleigh, before eventually being sold to Airwork at Heston.

Five Cruiser IIs were sold abroad, two being purchased by Aeroput and two more by the Bata Shoe Company at Zlín. The first Czechoslovak example, G-ACNO (later OK-ATQ) was delivered in March 1934 and was powered by Gipsy Majors. During March and April 1934, OK-ATQ was used on a lengthy business tour of Europe, the Near East, Sudan and South Africa, a distance of 21,900 miles eventually being covered. For this

Cruiser II G-ACOU at Cowes; this example was sold to the Bata Shoe Company. (*BHC*)

tour the Cruiser was named *Cape of Good Hope*. The second Bata example, G-ACOU (later OK-ATM) was delivered in July of the same year, with Czechoslovak Walter Major IV engines. The fifth export Cruiser went to the Maharaja of Patiala and the registration G-ACKG changed to VT-AER for the passage to India in November 1933. This example was powered by Hermes IVs, the three remaining export examples receiving Gipsy Majors.

It was Spartan Air Lines who made the greatest use of the Cruiser. After the formation of the new airline in February 1933, operations began on 12 April. G-ABTY, the sole Cruiser I, was the first of the Cruiser series to operate with the airline. It remained in service until late January 1935, when it passed to the Hon Mrs Victor Bruce and was used on a route from Croydon to Le Bourget run by Commercial Air Hire. G-ABTY was eventually lost in the Channel off Le Tréport on 11 May, 1935.

Cruiser IIs G-ACDW and G-ACDX *Hampshire* were commissioned in May and June 1933 respectively and went straight into operation with Spartan Air Lines on London-Isle of Wight Services. After the operating season ended on 2 October, G-ACDW was chartered by Lord Apsley MP and Capt W.P. Crawford Greene MP for a flight to Australia which covered 32,000 miles. For this expedition, the Cruiser was named *Faithful City* and flown by Capt P.W. Lynch-Blosse, Spartan Air Lines' chief pilot. The aircraft left Perdiswell, Worcester, on 9 October. The following day, a

Cruiser II G-ACDW in Spartan Air Lines livery, Cowes. (*Bob Wealthy*)

real start was made from Lympne and by 27 October G-ACDW had arrived at Wyndham in Western Australia. Sydney was reached three days later. On the return via India, where Capt Greene left the expedition, and with the last stop at Lyons, G-ACDW eventually arrived home on Boxing Day. Due to poor visibility, Britain was not sighted until the Cruiser was over Clacton, and because of the bad weather, a landing was swiftly made on St Osyth beach in Essex.

This charter flight appears to be one of the longest ever made and it is a tribute to the reliability of the Cruiser design that no serious mishap resulted. G-ACDX operated with Spartan Air Lines until being transferred on loan to United Airways during April 1935, flying between the Isle of Man, Carlisle and Blackpool.

Further Cruiser IIs, G-ACSM (later named *Sussex*) and G-ACVT, were commissioned by Spartan Air Lines in June and August 1934 respectively. They were later joined by G-ACBM, returned from Iraq, by September. By April 1935, G-ACDW had been sold to Misr Airwork in Cairo, where it was registered SU-ABL, and worked the Cairo-Jerusalem-Haifa route. The penultimate Cruiser II was delivered to Spartan Air Lines in late 1934 as G-ACYL, but by 1935 it was on loan to United Airways, operating between Heston, Blackpool and Ronaldsway until going to British Airways in October of that year. The last Cruiser II, G-ACZM, was built for Spartan Air Lines but by April 1935 it too had passed to United.

By May 1935, the Spartan Cruiser III had made its first public

139

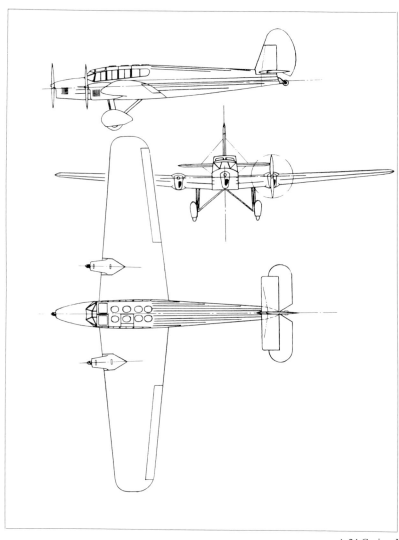

A.24 Cruiser I

appearance. The new variant was refined in several ways. The mainplane remained similar to that of previous Cruisers but six fuselage fixing points for the wing were included. The fuselage, slightly lengthened, was of straight metal panels at the front wherever possible, in order to minimise beaten work. However, the process of longitudinally corrugated skinning was abandoned; the rear fuselage of the Cruiser III was of welded steel tube covered with fabric over light metal fairings. The rudder was substantially enlarged, but the most obvious change was the inclusion of a

140

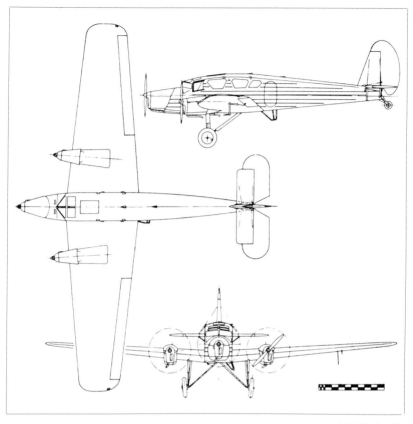

A.24 Cruiser II

heavily trousered cantilever undercarriage. Seating was generally for eight passengers and the chosen engine remained the de Havilland Gipsy Major.

The first cruiser III, G-ACYK, made its debut at the Heathrow Garden Party of the Royal Aeronautical Society, on 5 May, 1935. By June, all three examples built had joined Spartan Air Lines, the others being G-ADEL and G-ADEM. In October 1935, all three were transferred to British Airways.

During October 1935, Spartan Air Lines was absorbed by Allied British Airways (soon renamed British Airways) and the remaining British-registered Cruisers were transferred to their new bases at Eastleigh (Southampton), Stanley Park (Blackpool) and Renfrew (Glasgow). These were Cruiser IIIs G-ACYK, G-ADEL and G-ADEM, and Cruiser IIs G-ACBM and G-ACVT, all of which went direct from Spartan to British Airways. United Airways had also been absorbed by British Airways in October and their Cruisers were also transferred G-ACDX, G-ACSM, G-ACYL, all on loan from Spartan Air Lines since the previous April,

First of three Cruiser IIIs, G-ACYK.

together with G-ACZM, which United had bought at the same time. In this way, the remaining Cruisers were bought together as part of the Whitehall Securities-backed British Airways.

Most of the British Airways' 1935 fleet was an inherited one. Aircraft came from Spartan Air Lines, United Airways, Hillman's Airways and British Continental Airways. Gradually the Cruisers were redistributed, some going to Northern and Scottish Airways, three eventually being impressed and one being sold to Airwork. During early 1936, some British Airways Cruisers operated in its southern area centred at Gatwick, wearing the livery of Railway Air Services. RAS had maintained a financial interest in Spartan Air Lines. By June, most of these had gone to Northern and Scottish Airways.

The Cruiser series was an undoubted success. That more were not produced is not due to any major fault in the design itself; the 23,000-miles voyage of Cruiser II G-ACDW underlines the type's robust nature. During January 1933 the Spartan design team had been absorbed into Saunders-Roe, though it continued to concentrate in the short term on the Cruiser series. It proved impractical to keep Spartan and Saunders-Roe as separate units and an effective merger was completed by the spring of 1933, though aircraft bearing the name Spartan were produced after this date. By late 1935, even the name had disappeared. Saunders-Roe concentrated on the production of waterborne aircraft and the subordinate Spartan facilities

142

Cruiser III G-ADEL over the Isle of Wight, showing the revised forward fuselage. (*BHC*)

helped them do this, neglecting the Cruiser in the meantime, production of which ended with Cruiser III G-ADEM.

A.24 Mailplane
Three 120 hp de Havilland Gipsy III.
Span 56 ft; length 41 ft 6 in; height 9 ft; wing area 470 sq ft.
Empty weight 4,425 lb; loaded weight 5,645 lb.
Maximum speed 122 mph; cruising speed 105 mph; initial rate of climb 500 ft/min; ceiling 11,500 ft; range 400 miles.

Cruiser I
Three 120 hp de Havilland Gipsy III.
Span 54 ft; length 39 ft 2 in; height 10 ft; wing area 436 sq ft.
Empty weight 3,400 lb; loaded weight 5,500 lb.
Maximum speed 135 mph; cruising speed 110 mph; initial rate of climb 600 ft/min; ceiling 13,000 ft; range 660 miles.

Cruiser II
Three 130 hp de Havilland Gipsy Major, Cirrus Hermes IV or Walter Major IV.
Dimensions as Cruiser I.
Empty weight 3,650 lb; loaded weight 6,200 lb.
Maximum speed 133 mph; cruising speed 115 mph; initial rate of climb 630 ft/min; ceiling 15,000 ft; range 310 miles.

Cruiser III

Three 130 hp de Havilland Gipsy Major.
Span 54 ft; length 41 ft; height 9 ft 6 in; wing area 436 sq. ft.
Empty weight 4,010 lb; loaded weight 6,200 lb.
Maximum speed 135 mph; cruising speed 118 mph; initial rate of climb 600 ft/min; ceiling 15,000 ft; range 550 miles.

Mailplane. One example. G-ABLI, c/n A.24/1. Scrapped 1933.
Cruiser I. One example. G-ABTY, c/n 24M. C of A 5.32.
Cruiser II. Twelve UK-built and one Yugoslav licence-built. G-ACBM, c/n 2. Scrapped 11.37; G-ACDW/SU-ABL, c/n 3; G-ACDX, c/n 4, *Hampshire*. Damaged beyond repair in forced landing at Gosport 9.10.35 after engine failure; G-ACJO, c/n 5. To Aeroput as YU-SAN 9.33; G-ACMW, c/n 6. To Aeroput as YU-SAO 4.34; G-ACKG, c/n 7. To Maharaja of Patiala as VT-AER 11.33; G-ACNO/OK-ATQ, c/n 8. C of A 26.2.34. Believed scrapped 1938; G-ACOU/OK-ATM, c/n 9. C of A 14.7.34. Walter Major IV engines; G-ASCM, c/n 10. *Sussex*. Impressed as X9433, o/c 6AACU 7.4.40, o/c 7AACU 3.5.40, SOC 4.7.40; G-ACVT, c/n 11. Damaged beyond repair after skidding into a dyke on landing at Glanbrittle, Skye, 25.7.36; G-ACYL, c/n 12. Impressed as X9431, o/c 6AACU 30.4.40, o/c 7AACU 3.5.40, SOC 11.41; G-ACZM, c/n 14. Withdrawn from use 9.1.40.
C/ns 1 and 13 not used.

Cruiser III. Three examples. G-ACYK, c/n 101. Crashed on hillside near Largs 14.1.38 in poor weather, while returning after delivering films for a cinema. Remains, mainly the forward fuselage, recovered for Royal Scottish Museum by RN Sea King HAS. 1, 25.7.73 and now preserved at the Museum of Flight, East Fortune; G-ADEL, c/n 102. Impressed as X9432 and o/c 6AACU by 7.4.40, o/c 7AACU 3.5.40, SOC 26.7.40. G-ADEM, c/n 103. Crashed into hangar while taking off from Blackpool in fog, 20.11.36. Capt O'Connell and sole passenger killed.

Licence-built Cruiser I. YU-SAP, c/n 1. Built in Yugoslavia during 1935. Believed the sole licence-built example.

Saunders-Roe A.27 London

Built as a response to Air Ministry Specification R.24/31, the A.27 London was the last Saro design to employ the patented method of 'corrugated' hull construction. Though derived from certain aspects of the earlier A.7 Severn, the London incorporated refinements of strength and serviceability not present in the Severn. This ensured that the company did not meet with a barrage of complaints over frailty and poor detail design, as had been the case with the A.7, and the London is the only Saro 'corrugated' flying-boat against which no structural problems stemming from this particular hull type are recorded.

R.24/31, issued during 1931, called for a twin-engined general-purpose coastal patrol flying-boat of tough but simple construction, with low

London prototype K3560, Cowes, April 1934, the only example with servo-rudders. These were discarded before type trials at Felixstowe.

maintenance costs. High speed was to be made secondary to these aspects, but range was to be 1,000 miles and flight maintained on one engine while carrying 60 per cent of the fuel load. Knowler's team began type studies at the beginning of 1932 and by March 1934 a prototype had emerged. This was the A.27 London K3560. The new design engaged in company sea and air trials from April until June, made mostly by Stuart Scott and Leslie Ash, before departing for MAEE Felixstowe for type trials on 6 June.

The A.27 prototype was a medium-range sesquiplane flying-boat, powered by two 820/875 hp Bristol Pegasus IIIM3 nine-cylinder air-cooled radials, driving two-blade wooden airscrews. The upper mainplane was built in three sections and the lower in four, of which the two outermost portions could be easily removed or replaced in the event of damage, without dismantling any of the strut assembly. The appropriate joints for this operation were situated at the base of the outer interplane struts. Construction of the fabric-covered wings was of duralumin and stainless steel. Ailerons were fitted to the upper mainplane only and had external wires running underneath the wings. The wings for the prototype London were Saro built; those of most later examples were constructed by Boulton Paul of Norwich and supplied in knock-down form. The wing construction of the London was similar to that of some contemporary Boulton Paul aircraft, with spars formed from lock-joint tube-booms surrounded by open tubes, these having flanges for riveting to the laterally-corrugated spar webs. Ribs were of Warren-type in anodised duralumin.

The upper wing contained four fuel tanks in the centre-section, each of 137 gal capacity. These fuel tanks were aerodynamically blended with the upper wing top surface, and created a distinctive bulged appearance. Pump-assisted gravity-feed supplied the engines, and two 16 gal oil tanks were mounted on the front spar booms adjacent to and on the inboard side of the engine mountings. The engines were in nacelles attached to the underside of the top mainplane centre-section, and were faired by nine-sided cowlings with exhaust collectors in the leading edges.

The two-step hull had pronounced tumble-home sides. Construction was of Alclad and duralumin, apart from local highly-stressed fittings which were of stainless steel. Again, the absence of beaten, double-curvature sections was noticeable, designed to simplify construction and repairs. Unlike previous 'corrugated' Saro flying-boats, the London proved successful because it was strengthened locally from its inception.

These reinforced areas consisted primarily of the planing bottom, the chine forward of the main step and the main step itself. With these additions to the basic structure, the hull was undoubtedly the most service-able of its type to be produced at Cowes. Accommodation for the crew of five provided for living on board, with bunks and a stove included. In the extreme bow was a multi-role mooring, gunnery and bomb-aiming position. The Lewis gun was mounted on a Scarff-ring, which was able to

K3560, without servo-rudders but otherwise in its original form, at the MAEE for type trials, October 1934. Note the nine-sided cowlings, stepless wingfloats and early beaching chassis arrangements. (*RAE, Crown Copyright*)

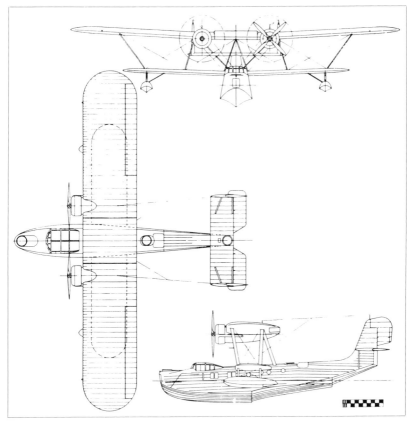

A.27 London

slide aft so as not to hinder mooring operations. A hinged door in the nose opened forward and upward to give a free view for using the bomb-sight. A side-by-side dual-control fully-glazed cockpit was provided, the pilots' seats being on a raised platform so that the glazing took on a form of 'bubble' shape, giving excellent all-round view. This raised system proved so successful that it was later adopted for the Saro A.33.

Aft of the cockpit was situated the officers' wardroom, with two bunks on the starboard side, while on the port side was the navigator's table and instruments, beside a large window. Under the centre section and extending to the dorsal gunner's post, was the crew cabin, with the engineer's instrument panel by the forward bulkhead to starboard and the wireless position to port. The dorsal gunner's position was again on a raised platform, with the firing step doubling as a workbench, complete with vice. Aft of the dorsal gun was substantial stowage space for a spare (two-bladed) airscrew, maintenance platforms, a collapsable dinghy, spare bunks, bedding and other loads. Aft of this was a narrow, low gangway which led to the tail-gunner's positon, which gave a wide field of fire impeded only by the tail unit.

The tail consisted of twin endplate fins and horn-balanced rudders strut-braced to an adjustable tailplane which carried horn-balanced elevators. K3560, the A.27 prototype, had servo-rudders when first constructed, akin to those of the A.7, but by the time it arrived at Felixstowe these had been replaced by tabs. Tail construction was also of duralumin and stainless steel, with fabric covering.

Armament comprised three defensive Lewis IIIB machine-guns, one each in bow, dorsal and tail positions, and all Scarff-mounted. Midships and tail positions were partially covered by foldaway 'perambulator' hoods for protection against slipstream and bad weather. Offensive loads were on two 50–550 lb universal carriers on the underside of each bottom wing, and two 50–250 lb carriers slightly outboard of these. Light series carriers were placed inboard of the bomb mountings, near the wing roots.

K3560 was tested very thoroughly by the MAEE over the summer of

K3560 over the south of England, 1934. (*BHC*)

148

1934. It proved a great success. General construction was praised; at no time did any structural failure occur, and the hull was described as sturdy. Flying weight for most of the trials was 18,280 lb, at which K3560 achieved 133.5 mph at 5,000 ft, a minimum cruising speed of 99 mph at the same height, a service ceiling of 14,700 ft and a take-off run of about 380 yards over 22·5 seconds. Up to 5 October, 1934, when it left the MAEE for Service trials, K3560 had completed 122½ hr flying, and 881 hr at moorings, all without incident.

The flying qualities of the prototype London were virtually viceless. The MAEE extravagently reported that it was 'pleasant and easy to fly . . . and the controls are light and effective over the whole speed range'. Though the rudders were found to be a little lighter than the other surfaces, no objection was raised to this. At an overload weight of 22,000 lb, the controls were deemed a little less effective than at the normal testing weight of 18,280 lb, but this was passed over. Control remained good right down to the stall, with no tendency for a wing to drop. Little trim change was necessary from engine-on to engine-off and K3560 could be taken off, flown level and then landed all with the same tailplane setting and without any difficulty. It would maintain lateral and longitudinal trim for long periods even if the pilot left his seat. It could not maintain height on one engine, however, even at the low weight of 16,740 lb, though directional control with either engine shut down was good and required little use of rudder. Take offs were very easy, with no real tendency to swing, and

Spare engine stowage position of K3560 but typical of all Londons. (*RAE, Crown Copyright*)

149

Torpedo stowage position on the rear deck of K3560 and adopted for other Londons. (*RAE, Crown Copyright*)

alighting was also straightforward; it was possible to make a tail-down alighting in an emergency without then developing a violent forward pitch on the water.

Most Londons, including the prototype, had provision for the carriage of extra loads (a spare engine, a torpedo, overload tanks or a spare air-screw) mounted on the decking aft of the cockpit and between the wings. Such stowage was found not to change perceptibly the flying behaviour, even in a shallow dive.

Water qualitites were found to be equally good. K3560 did not swing into the wind as rapidly as did most other flying-boats. This peculiarity was felt to be advantageous because taxi-ing control at different angles to the wind was more uniform. Downwind taxi-ing in particular was found easier in comparison with most contemporary flying-boats. No difficulties in control during take offs or alightings were reported. The hull was found to be reasonably clean during tests.

The wingtip floats afforded good lateral stability. Though rough-sea tests were not made at this stage, Saro need not have worried; subsequent poor weather failed to impair stability or performance to any marked extent.

Maintenance was found to be straightforward. The controls were easily accessible, a surfeit of inspection doors and hatches being provided. The hull suffered from some corrosion during the time at the MAEE. It had been unsuccessfully treated with an experimental Cellon anti-corrosion coating but after its removal at Felixstowe and the application of standard material only very limited corrosion occurred, mainly around the keel, and it was decided that this could be contained during normal overhauls.

After the main tests, the fuel jettison system of K3560 was examined. This was found satisfactory in principle though too slow. It was required that all fuel should be jettisonable in under two minutes, and this was not possible with the outlet pipes and jettison valves fitted to K3560. These units were therefore enlarged to achieve increased jettison rate.

Finally, before K3560 left Felixstowe, major 'ease of maintenance' trials were held. Times in terms of man-hours were calculated for the replacement of various components, such as rudder, airscrew, aileron, wingtip float and fuel tank. Trials took place on both land and water. It was found that accessibility of most airframe components likely to require removal either from wear or accidental damage was very good. The engines were also found fairly easy to work on, though of course maintenance platforms had to be used.

The prototype London was thus deemed a success by the MAEE, though it was noted that the requirement of R.24/31 that level height was to be maintained on one engine with 60 per cent fuel was not met. The only structural failure that occurred at Felixstowe was a collapse of one of the exhaust collector cowlings, both of which were later reinforced. Altogether K3560 was a very successful aircraft, with good air and water characteristics and many sound facets which the Air Ministry found most attractive. On 5 October, 1934, K3560 left Felixstowe for Service trials.

The Air Ministry ordered an initial production batch of seven London

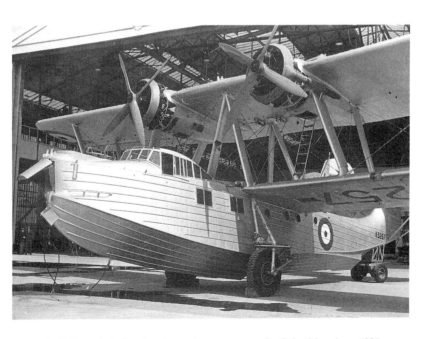

K5257, first of the London Is, at the entrance to the Columbine shop, 1936.

151

Mk Is in March 1935, serialled K5257 to K5263. Supermarine had also tendered for R.24/31, with an improved Scapa, but their submission was rejected.

Though there was no great difference between the prototype London and the first production batch, when K5258 was tested at Felixstowe between June 1936 and February 1937, it was found to be longitudinally unstable due to overbalance of the elevators at certain angles. Whether this problem was peculiar to K5258 is not certain, but former London pilots recall their old mounts with enthusiasm, remembering them as easy and comfortable to fly.

The first production batch, all London Mk Is, were issued mostly to RAF Calshot and No. 201 Squadron, from the spring of 1936, replacing Supermarine Southamptons in most cases. All were powered by Pegasus IIIs, though circular cowlings were adopted and four-blade airscrews fitted. The exhaust system was altered from the original overwing arrangement to a long, underwing configuration. Though K3560 had stepless wing floats, all production aircraft had the carvel-built stepped variety with a revised strut assembly which was found easier to maintain than the original. Other departures from the prototype included a slight revision of the forward turret mooring position, increased tare and all-up weights, a greater military load, slightly increased wing-loading and take-off run, and marginally reduced service ceiling.

The only appreciable trouble encountered with the London was high oil temperatures. K3560 was fitted experimentally with three- and four-blade airscrews, and the inlet and outlet oil temperatures exceeded the maximum

London Is under construction in the brand new Columbine shop, Cowes, 1936. The far right example is K5258, the others are unmarked. (*BHC*)

152

London I K5258, second of the first production batch, at Felixstowe for type tests, early 1937.

permissible in both cases. The number of fins on the coolers was increased and Bristol-type air intakes fitted. New Pegasus IIIs were installed in the late spring of 1935. Over the summer, K3560 was subjected to climb trials at full throttled and throttle level flight trials; air inlet and outlet temperatures, oil pressures and engine speed were monitored. Still the oil tended to overheat. Investigations at the MAEE continued into the summer of 1936 using K5258 with four-blade airscrews, revised oil tanks and Vickers 'U' coolers in place of the standard Air Ministry type used by K3560. Again, conclusions were disappointing, with both oil inlet and, this time, cylinder temperatures rising above the limit set. K5258 stayed at Felixstowe until February 1937 and its ring cowlings were eventually cut back. This reduced cylinder temperatures but did not bring down oil temperature. In fact, experiments into the problem of these high temperatures continued until the autumn of 1938, using Londons K5259 and K6928 as well as those previously mentioned. The trouble was never terribly serious but it did mean that operating in hot weather was made unnecessarily taxing. The oil temperature problems were eventually cured by the installation of a 'hot-pot' rather than constant circulation of all the oil; even smaller engine cowlings and careful use of mixture helped also to keep engine temperatures down. These modifications were introduced during the latter stages of 1938. Subsequently, there were some reports of oil loss, but this leakage was easily traced to the control operating the partial circulator and was duly corrected.

While these problems had arisen and been overcome, the development of the A.27 had escalated at Cowes. A new Specification, R.3/35,

K3560, modified to London Mk II standard, photographed at Felixstowe, autumn 1938.
(*RAE, Crown Copyright*)

essentially an updated R.24/31, had given rise to the London Mk II. The modifications that produced this variant were straightforward: 915/1,055 hp Pegasus X engines in place of the Pegasus III, driving four-blade airscrews, though these were by late 1938 replaced by the three-blade metal variety fitted with spinners. The underwing exhausts were retained for a short while, but were later replaced by shorter overwing pipes. Circular Townend rings were retained for the Mk II version. The London Mk II was judged to meet R.3/35 adequately and went on to be the major RAF variant, a total of 23 examples being produced.

K3560, thus modified, served as the prototype London II, and remained mainly at Felixstowe from November 1936 until the end of its life, undergoing type trials and then various water trials. Flight and water qualities remained sound while performance was improved by the increased power, giving a maximum speed of 155 mph at 6,000 ft, a service ceiling of 18,000 ft and a maximum rate of climb of 950 ft/min at 3,800 ft. Gradually, the London Is were returned to Cowes for modification to Mk II standard. The first production batch of London IIs consisted of six aircraft, K5908–K5913. These were issued mostly to No. 204 Squadron, between October 1936 and May 1937. Subsequent batches were K6927–K6932, delivered from June 1937, K9682–K9686, delivered from September 1937, and L7038–L7043, which arrived at their Squadrons between January and May 1938. While the London Is were undergoing conversion at Cowes, production of Mk IIs progressed steadily until May 1938, when the last

154

London K5258 in 'late' Mk II guise with three-bladed metal airscrews and spinners, late 1938.

order was fulfilled. In all, one prototype, seven Mk I and 23 Mk II aircraft were completed.

Individual aircraft careers were varied and some were retained for an almost indecently long time by the RAF, well after war started, due in part to the severe shortage of patrol flying-boats at that time. K5258 had a particularly interesting career. After its stay with DTD Felixstowe, it became the only London to be used by No. 228 Squadron, which was expected to re-equip with Stranraers after its re-formation in December 1936. The arrival of the Stranraers was delayed, however, and 228's first flying-boat was a Scapa. By April 1937, the Squadron operated three Singapore IIIs, single examples of the Scapa and Stranraer, and K5258. By August 1938, Stranraers had become the sole equipment. K5258 continued in use, like many of its type, until after the outbreak of war, being struck off during April 1941.

In line with contemporary RAF thinking on long-range training flights, No. 204 Squadron took five Londons, K5910, K5911, K5912, K6927 and K6930, on a cruise to Australia and back, between December 1937 and July 1938. This cruise was organised as the RAF representation honouring

155

London II K5911 at East Cowes for overhaul, 1939.

K6927 on Columbine apron, mid-1939. Note late airscrew/spinner arrangement and overload fuel tank.

the 150th anniversary of Sydney University, and a distance of some 30,000 miles was covered. These aircraft were in fact fitted with three-blade air-screws before the others, and also carried large cylindrical overload tanks with pump feed, mounted on their decks under the upper mainplanes, range being increased from 1,740 miles to 2,600 miles. In fact, even after the return to Britain, these tanks were left *in situ*, to provide greater patrolling range in expectation of war.

The tour had gone smoothly, and the odd incidents which arose served only to illustrate the London's durability. On both occasions K6927 was involved. On 15 December, 1937, 52 miles from Akyab and over the Bay of Bengal, K6927 put down with fuel starvation problems, only to damage a wingtip, float and airscrew on alighting. It was subsequently towed into Akyab by the steamer *ss Jalagopus*, with a drogue behind the 'live' engine, at an average speed of three knots. At Akyab, the aircraft was repaired, but on the return flight via Singapore it again alighted prematurely, this time off Rangoon, where rough seas damaged the lower mainplanes. K6927 again had to be made airworthy.

The London went on to fly leisurely patrol duties, although some mishaps, a few of them serious, occurred throughout its career. During November 1936, K5908, newly arrived with No. 204 Squadron and taxi-ing in Fowey harbour, was struck and damaged by a mud-barge. During March 1937, K5910, also of 204 Squadron, caught fire when starting up at Mount Batten, after an engine backfire. A year later almost to the day, K6928, based at the MAEE and at that time on flare trials, suffered an elevator control failure and struck the water very hard, but only damaged the port tailplane. More serious was a collision between K5262, then with 204 Squadron, and a Short Sunderland N9028 at Mount Batten in July

London II K5262 engaged in mooring operations, its forward defensive turret ring retracted aft.

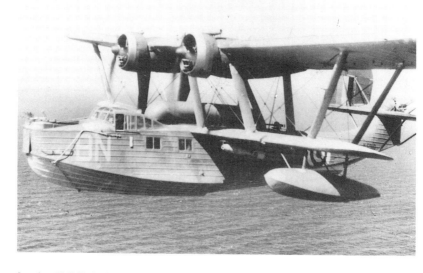

London II K6910 with No. 240 Squadron over the North Sea during the first half of 1940.

1939. The London struck the Sunderland while both were moored, swinging on its ropes due to the tide, and K5262 was extensively damaged.

At the start of the war, the London, Singapore and Stranraer were all in service to varying extents. Three London Squadrons existed; No. 202, based in the Mediterranean, and 201 and 240 (which also operated Stranraers) for North Sea patrol. No. 204 had by September 1939 all but exchanged its Londons for Sunderlands, and 240 received some of its Londons from this source. All Squadrons continued patrol work, but the accident and casualty rate increased. In February 1940, K6927 was lost while alighting in fog at Holyhead Harbour, when it fell heavily into the sea and sank. During August, K5260, with No. 202 Squadron, suffered an engine failure off Gibraltar while on anti-submarine patrol, and made a forced alighting, and while on tow, the hull plates opened up and the aircraft sank.

In fact it was No. 202 Squadron at Gibraltar which suffered the most London casualties. During February 1941, K5909 was wrecked on the foreshore; in the same month, K5263 was lost while on tow after an engine failure; in April, K6930 sank at its moorings during a storm; K6931 and K5257 were damaged when they collided with HMS *Wellington* in Gibraltar Harbour, also during April. Just before this, K5911 had been damaged when it hit a catamaran after taxi-ing toward (but missing) the harbour hoist.

158

Despite the age of the design by the time war began, one London at least proved that the type was still capable of offering resistance if attacked. During mid-December 1939, K5911 of No. 240 Squadron encountered nine Heinkel He 111s of KG26 off Lerwick in Shetland. Attacked by one of the enemy aircraft, the gunners managed to hit and damage the Heinkel's starboard engine, but K5911's pilot was killed in the exchange. The co-pilot succeeded in landing K5911 in very heavy seas, and after 20 min, managed to take-off again and return to base, testimony to the strength of the design as well as the ability of the crew.

By 1941 the London was being phased out of front-line duties. A number of Londons went to No. 4 (Coastal) Operational Training Unit between April 1941 and June 1942. A few served with FBTS at Stranraer. K9683 was lost while with 4(C)OTU when during May 1942 it dived into the Irish Sea and sank off Portpatrick, the cause never being ascertained. K9685 and K5257, also by 1942 with 4(C)OTU, were damaged in a collision near Stranraer during unauthorised formation flying, and both were eventually scrapped. The surviving examples gradually returned to Cowes, where they were broken up.

The Saro London performed essential if largely undramatic patrol duties in peace and war. The war provided an extended lease of life, and the type rose well to the challenge. It is surprising how many Londons eventually made their way back to Cowes for dismantling during 1942.

A.27 London prototype

Two 820/875 hp Bristol Pegasus IIIM3.
Span 80 ft; length 57 ft; height 20 ft 3 in; wing area 1,427 sq ft.
Empty weight 11,920 lb; loaded weight 18,930 lb; maximum overloaded weight 22,000 lb.
Maximum speed 145 mph at 4,500 ft; economic cruising speed 99 mph; initial rate of climb 965 ft/min; time to 5,000 ft—6 min 9 sec; service ceiling 14,700 ft; absolute ceiling 16,400 ft; normal range 1,740 miles; normal endurance 8 hr; overload endurance 13½ hr.
Armament: three Scarff-mounted Lewis machine-guns and 1,600 lb load of bombs, mines or depth charges.

A.27 London Mk I

Two 820/875 lb Bristol Pegasus IIIM3.
Dimensions as prototype.
Empty weight 12,285 lb; loaded weight 19,000 lb; maximum overloaded weight 22,000 lb.
Performance as prototype except initial rate of climb 758 ft/min; time to 5,000 ft—7 min 22 sec; service ceiling 14,050 ft; absolute ceiling 16,000 ft.
Armament: as prototype except 2,000 lb bomb load.

A.27 London Mk II

Two 915/1,055 hp Bristol Pegasus X.
Dimensions as prototype and Mk I.
Empty weight 12,800 lb; loaded weight 19,300 lb; maximum overloaded weight 22,000 lb.
Maximum speed 155 mph at 6,000 ft; economic cruising speed 106 mph; initial rate of climb 850 ft/min; time to 5,000 ft—5½ min; service ceiling 18,000 ft; absolute ceiling 19,700 ft; range and endurance as prototype and Mk I.
Armament; as Mk I.
Overload deck tank capacity 318 gal and maximum range, all aircraft, 2,600 miles.

Production batches

Batch	Serial nos	Type	Quantity	Delivery dates	Spec
1	K3560	Prototype (later Mk II)	1	6.34	R.24/31
2	K5257–K5263	Mk I (later Mk II)	7	4.36–10.36	R.24/31
3	K5908–K5913	Mk II	6	10.36–5.37	R.3/35
4	K6927–K6932	Mk II	6	6.37–9.37	R.3/35
5	K9682–K9686	Mk II	5	9.37–12.37	R.3/35
6	L7038–L7043	Mk II	6	1.38–5.38	R.3/35

K3560 prototype, launched 3.34. Company tests 4–6.34, DTD Felixstowe 6.6.34, DTD 209 Sqn 5.10.34, DTD Felixstowe 20.7.35, to 210 Sqn 17.9.35, DTD Saro 18.9.35, to 210 Sqn 4.10.35, DTD MAEE 9.1.36, DTD Saro 13.1.36, DTD MAEE 26.11.36, MAEE 1–7.37, Saro 8–9.37, MAEE 9.37, SOC by MAEE 12.4.39. Total flying 584.15 hr.

Mk I

K5257: RAF Calshot 2.4.36, to 201 Sqn 2.11.36, Saro 19.5.38, MAEE 21.11.38, to 204 Sqn 1.3.39, to 240 Sqn 17.7.39, RAF Calshot 4.6.40, to 202 Sqn 26.11.40, RAF Calshot 21.6.41, to 4(C)OTU 4.7.41. Damaged Cat A 7.7.42. SOC: to Saro and reduced to produce 13.11.42; K5258: DTD MAEE 22.6.36, to 228 Sqn 10.2.37, MAEE 7.8.37, Saro 8.38, to 240 Sqn 9.1.39, RAF Calshot 4.6.40, to 202 Sqn 8.7.40, to 4MU Cat B 1.8.40, RAF Calshot 16.10.40. SOC Cat E 8.4.41; K5259: To 201 Sqn 10.7.36, MAEE 20.9.37, to 201 Sqn 16.12 37, Saro 7.6.38, to 201 Sqn 20.6.38, MAEE 9.38, to 202 Sqn 6.4.40, RAF Calshot (storage) 9.4.40, 4MU 30.8.40; to 202 Sqn 7.2.41, 4(C)OTU 11.5.41, FBTS Stranraer 27.3.42. SOC: to Saro and reduced to produce 13.11.42; K5260: To 201 Sqn 29.7.36, Saro 18.11.37, to 201 Sqn 18.5.38, RAF Calshot (storage) 9.4.40, 4MU 4.8.40, to 202 Sqn 5.8.40, crashed in sea and sank on tow 13.8.40. Total flying 1,054 hr; K5261: To 201 Sqn 19.8.36, Saro 8.10.37, to 240 Sqn 26.11.37, to 202 Sqn 8.1.40, RAF Calshot 8.4.41, 4(C)OTU 23.10.41, RAF Felixstowe 30.10.42. SOC: to Saro and reduced to produce 30.10.42; K5262: To 201 Sqn 14.9.36, Saro 22.11.37, to 204 Sqn 29.7.38, to 201 Sqn 12.12.39, RAF Calshot (storage) 9.4.40., to 202 Sqn 22.4.40, RAF Calshot 11.7.40, to 202 Sqn 16.10.40. SOC 28.10.41; K5263: To 204 Sqn 7.10.36, to 201 Sqn 13.8.37, Saro 17.2.38, to 201 Sqn 6.1.39, RAF Calshot (storage) 4.6.40, to 202 Sqn 30.8.40, ditched near convoy and foundered on tow to Gibraltar. SOC 20.2.41. Total flying 1,161 hr.

Mk II

K5908: To 204 Sqn 23.10.36, Saro 23.7.37, to 204 Sqn 9.11.37, to 240 Sqn 28.7.39, RAF Calshot (storage) 26.6.40, to 202 Sqn 14.7.40, RAF Calshot 1.8.40. SOC 7.10.40; K5909: To 201 Sqn 30.11.36, Saro 22.4.38, to 204 Sqn

London Mk II K5263, a converted Mk I (*MOD*)

21.3.39, to 240 Sqn 25.8.39, 4MU 2.1.40, RAF Calshot (storage) 4.6.40, 4MU 6.7.40, RAF Calshot 23.8.40, to 202 Sqn 2.9.40, wrecked off Gibraltar 16.2.41. SOC 31.3.41. Total flying 922.45 hr; K5910: To 204 Sqn 8.1.37, Saro 5.37, to 204 Sqn 26.9.37, RAF Calshot 4.6.40, 4MU 8.8.40, 4(C)OTU 17.12.41, FBTS Stranraer 30.3.42, RAF Felixstowe 6.8.42. SOC Cat E. 29.9.42. 41MU for disposal 26.10.42; K5911: To 204 Sqn 21.4.37, to 240 Sqn 31.7.39, RAF Calshot (storage) 4.6.40, to 202 Sqn 24.10.40, RAF Calshot 11.6.41, 4(C)OTU 10.41. SOC: to Saro and reduced to produce 30.10.42; K5912: To 204 Sqn 1.5.37, to 201 Sqn 9.10.39, ditched and lost after engine failure, North Sea, 14.11.39; K5913: To 204 Sqn 26.5.37, to 240 Sqn 28.7.39, 4MU 26.8.39 for repairs, RAF Calshot 29.4.40, to 202 Sqn 11.5.40, RAF Calshot (storage) 22.7.40, to 202 Sqn 11.10.40, RAF Calshot 8.5.41, 4(C)OTU 20.8.41, caught fire after heavy alighting at Cromarty 12.9.41 damage Cat E, sank; K6927: To 204 Sqn 8.6.37, 4MU 27.2.39, RAF Calshot (storage 6.10.39, to 201 Sqn 11.10.39, to 240 Sqn 11.11.39, hit sea on approach, Holyhead, Anglesey, sank, 5.2.40. Total flying 452.35 hr; K6928: MAEE 8.7.37 for experimental purposes, RAF Calshot 24.1.39 for disposal action. SOC 10.3.39; K6929: To 204 Sqn 14.7.37, to 240 Sqn 17.7.39, RAF Calshot 21.10.39, to 201 Sqn 15.12.39, RAF Calshot (storage) 9.4.40, caught fire, damage Cat E, 27.6.40. Scottish Aviation 7.10.40. SOC 12.40; K6930: To 204 Sqn 29.7.37, to 240 Sqn 1.8.39, to 201 Sqn 21.2.40, RAF Calshot (storage) 9.4.40, to 202 Sqn 8.9.40, capsized in gale, Gibraltar, 11.4.41. SOC 31.5.41. Total flying 1,007.45 hr; K6931: RAF Calshot 8.37, to 202 Sqn 6.10.37, 4MU 5.4.40, RAF Calshot (storage) 12.9.40, to 202 Sqn 17.9.40, RAF Greenock 14.5.41. SOC 9.7.41; K6932: To 240 Sqn 7.9.37, to 202 Sqn 6.10.37, RAF Calshot 1.5.38, 4MU 1.5.40, RAF Calshot 10.11.40, 4(C)OTU 15.4.41. SOC and to 41MU for disposal 29.9.42; K9682: RAF Calshot 1.9.37, to 202 Sqn 8.11.37, missing off Casablanca 14.9.40. SOC 1.10.40. Total flying 673.15 hr; K9683: RAF Calshot 16.10.37, to 202 Sqn 9.11.37, 4MU 5.7.40; SAS 18.11.40, 4(C)OTU 16.4.42, crashed 6 miles NW Portpatrick, Kirkcudbright, 10.5.42. SOC Cat E 1.6.42; K9685: To 201 Sqn 4.11.37, to 202 Sqn 6.12.37, RAF Calshot 5.5.40, 4MU 22.6.40, SAS 24.12.40, 4(C)OTU 13.1.42. SOC: to Saro and reduced to produce 13.11.42; K9684: To 201 Sqn 27.11.37, to 202 Sqn 6.12.37, RAF Calshot 4.4.40, 4MU 6.5.40, RAF Calshot 20.3.41, 4(C)OTU 15.4.41, damaged Cat A 7.42. SOC: to

Saro and reduced to produce 13.11.42; K9686: To 201 Sqn 15.12.37, to 204 Sqn 26.12.37, to 240 Sqn 26.8.39, lost at sea 3.11.39 but not SOC until 2.40; L7038: To 201 Sqn 24.1.38, 49MU 9.1.40, to 202 Sqn 18.1.40, RAF Calshot 7.8.40, 4MU 27.8.40, 4(C)OTU 25.6.42. Saro: reduced to produce 13.11.42 and presumably SOC at that time; L7039: To 201 Sqn 19.2.38, to 240 Sqn 4.1.40, RAF Calshot 4.6.40, to 202 Sqn 5.6.40, RAF Calshot 24.8.40, 4MU 11.9.40. Suspected present at FBTS during 1941, until SOC Cat E 12.41; L7040: To 201 Sqn 14.3.38, to 240 Sqn 18.1.40, burnt out at moorings and sank, Sullom Voe, SOC 22.2.40; L7041: To 201 Sqn 1.4.38, lost at sea, SOC 19.1.40; L7042: To 201 Sqn 23.4.38. Set on fire by bomb, sunk, Lerwick, SOC 22.11.39; L7043: To 201 Sqn 13.5.38, to 240 Sqn 18.1.40, RAF Calshot 4.6.40, to 202 Sqn 15.8.40, RAF Calshot 9.4.41, 4(C)OTU 4.7.41, RAF Felixstowe 9.2.42, 4(C)OTU 21.5.42, RAF Felixstowe 16.9.42. SOC 16.9.42 and to 41 MU 26.10.42 with damage Cat E, though it is not clear when this was inflicted.

Saunders-Roe A.33

An enigma among British flying-boats, the Saro A.33 was conceived in response to Air Ministry Specification R.2/33 for a long-range monoplane patrol flying-boat. This specification was designed to yield a replacement for the biplane flying-boats in service during the early and mid-1930s. The Short Sunderland was initially built to R.2/33, but whereas the Sunderland was broadly a development of the C class Empire Flying-boat, the Saro design was wholly original.

In late 1933 the company began to consider R.2/33. With the A.27 London well advanced, Saro felt confident enough to begin a larger

On tow in the Solent, K4773, its bow turret retracted, before one of its very few flights.

project. However, it had become clear to the firm over the previous few years that their established method of 'corrugated' hull construction might have to be abandoned at last. This technique had never been entirely durable and it appeared that damage could be inflicted fairly easily in some cases if it received rough treatment. On several occasions, the MAEE had criticised the 'corrugated' method as of unduly light construction. In view of these considerations, coupled with the required size and weight of the aircraft laid down in R.2/33, it was decided by the firm to construct more conventional hull.

Knowler's proposals made in early 1934 were in the form of a design employing a parasol Monospar wing and sponsons in lieu of the much more usual wing tip floats. The high wing position was designed to give good water clearance and the parasol configuration dispensed with the need for a very deep hull, which became a feature of most monoplane flying-boats. Knowler's hull, being comparatively shallow, had far less drag and weight than a deep hull and this increased speed and range.

The Air Ministry was impressed with these unusual proposals but it seemed to them that a great deal of research would be necessary before Saro's submission to R.2/33 could be achieved. In fact, Knowler had been considering the Monospar wing for a large monoplane flying-boat as far back as 1931, in an effort to overcome the problem of the deep hull. In 1932, Saro had received a Ministry contract for the modification of Cloud K2681 by equipping it with such a wing.

The Monospar wing (type number ST.7) built for K2681 was similar in principle to that later adopted for the design to R.2/33. Both designs were accomplished in conjunction with General Aircraft Ltd, who held the Steiger Monospar rights, the method of wing arrangement having originally been developed by H.J. Steiger of Beardmore. The Cloud wing

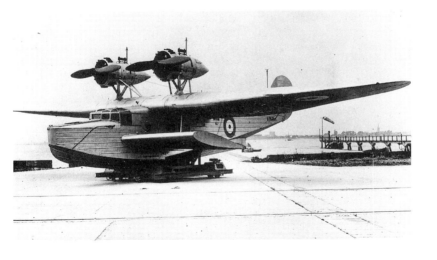

Cloud K2681 as modified to test the sponson and Monospar wing adopted for the A.33. The Townend rings have also been modified. (*RAE, Crown Copyright*)

was built at Cowes under the supervision of General Aircraft personnel. K2681 flew successfully in this form during mid-1934 (probably August) and was tested by Sqn Ldr Ash, Saro test-pilot. The arrangement was by that time included in the R.2/33 proposal and the performance of K2681 was most encouraging. Despite the unorthodox layout, the Air Ministry eventually ordered one prototype to R.2/33 from Saunders-Roe.

By early 1935 the hull form had been designed and in accordance with Air Ministry instructions of October 1934, when the order had been placed, model tests began. A one-twelfth scale model was used in tank tests to examine drag, attitude and pitching moment of the projected hull, the tests taking place at RAE Farnborough and at the Vickers tank at St Albans between February and May 1935. The original hull form was found to be unstable above 48 mph scale speed unless trimmed forward. Though this was eventually rectified through step adjustment, it was then found that water thrown up from the hull seriously interfered with the tailplane when using the modified configuration. Accordingly, several very large scale models of the rear hull, tailplane, and the main spar were produced at Cowes in order to minimise uncertainty over the behaviour of the full-size aircraft. These models were tested aero-and hydrodynamically as well as structurally and as a result the tailplane was raised and the rear hull substantially strengthened. Because of the un-usual nature of the Monospar wing, a full-size spar was tested to destruction.

Construction of the prototype, Saro type number A.33, began at Cowes in October 1936, after substantial research into sponson form. Two main sponson configurations were considered, and tested again with the use of models. The first employed sweptback leading- and trailing-edges, the second featured tapers. Both were tested attached to models of Cloud hulls. It was concluded that though take-off might be impaired if sponsons were adopted rather than wing floats, lateral stability on the water would be adequate. After wind-tunnel testing at the National Physical Laboratory, it was found that in the case of the Cloud models at least, the substitution of sponsons for floats was an aerodynamic improvement.

The Cloud K2681 was duly fitted with sponsons while the arrangement was re-tested in model form. It was found that the tapering sponsons provided the best lateral stability and this layout was adopted for the Cloud. Tests with K2681 were completed by March 1937 and in spite of dirty running at low speeds, no sign of either lateral or longitudinal instability was found. K2681 tended to bore through the water to a certain degree, especially when travelling slowly, but seaworthiness was not altered to any marked extent. Take-off time was significantly longer than with floats but other qualities were consistent with test results. Of course, all tests had been made with the land undercarriage removed, and after a very full life K2681 was finally retired, becoming 1255M in February 1939.

With all the data gleaned from these studies, the design of the A.33 sponsons was finalised with a sharply tapering configuration with an incidence of 3 deg. Development and construction took a long time because of all the novel features involved. The A.33 prototype did not emerge from Columbine until late September 1938.

The Saro A.33 was powered by four 830 hp Bristol Perseus XII nine-cylinder sleeve-valve radial air-cooled engines set equidistant along the leading edge of the wing. The engines drove three-blade variable-pitch air-

The nose area of K4773, showing the unusual four-piece beaching chassis, unarmed turret and relatively shallow hull.

screws. The 95 ft Monospar parasol wing, probably one of the largest ever built, was arranged to take bending loads through the spar itself, and torsion by a pyramidal system of wires from the top and bottom booms ahead and aft of the spar. The wing was fabric covered, though this was becoming an outmoded method of construction by the late 1930s. Two large N-struts connected the wing to the sponsons. Trailing-edge moveable surfaces extended the full width of the parallel-chord centre-section and along the sharply tapering outboard sections. The aerofoil-section sponsons contained the fuel tanks, and extended 20 ft from each side of the hull; they were also given slight anhedral.

The all-metal two-step hull of the A.33 was a beautifully streamlined structure 75 ft in length. The hull bottom aft of the rear step tapered to a small upright knife-edge. The enclosed side-by-side cockpit was glazed all round and high in the hull to provide excellent visibility, a similar arrangement to that adopted for the A.27 London. No water rudder was fitted but two drogues were included for on-water manoeuvring.

The A.33 was intended to employ a powerful (for its time) defensive armament. Power-operated turrets were provided in bow and tail positions, intended to deploy either single or multiple ·303 in Browning machine-guns. Two beam positions under sliding hatches in the large dorsal hump forward of the fin were to be armed with single, pillar-mounted Vickers K guns. In fact it does not appear that any of these

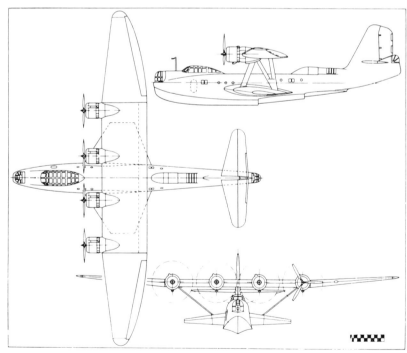

A.33

166

K4773 on the East Cowes apron; its parasol configuration and sponsons were a distinct departure from the British flying-boat tradition. (*BHC*)

weapons were fitted. The tail turret position was blanked off when the A.33 began test-flights and there is no reason to suppose that this was ever altered.

Accommodation was provided for a crew of seven: pilot, co-pilot, engineer, radio operator and three gunners. The area aft of the cockpit under the centre-section comprised sleeping quarters and cooking facilities. As had become standard practice by this time, the bow turret could be cranked back to aid mooring.

The tail comprised a conventional tapered tailplane with divided elevators and large single fin and rudder. The rudder had two trim-tabs, main and auxiliary. The tail arrangement gave slight trouble which in the event was never corrected.

Taxi-ing trials with the prototype A.33, by then K4773, started from Cowes on 10 October, 1938, lasting until 12 October and revealing a tendency to porpoise at high speeds. K4773 would also bore through the water at low speeds, much as the Cloud had done, if allowed to. However, no modifications appear to have been done; the programme had taken a considerable time to reach this stage and it was felt that the A.33 should be flight-tested as swiftly as possible if it were to stand a chance of earning a production contract. The Sunderland had made much more rapid progress.

On 14 October, K4773 made its first flight, the test-pilot being Frank Courtney, who had previously tested the A.3 Valkyrie for the company. The only problem encountered in the air appears to have been a slight tail shudder, but on the water, take-offs were dirty as well as uncomfortable, due to the porpoising tendency. The weight of K4773 for these trials was 31,500 lb, 10,000 lb less than the design maximum. This weight was only once exceeded, when the aircraft flew at a weight of 35,000 lb.

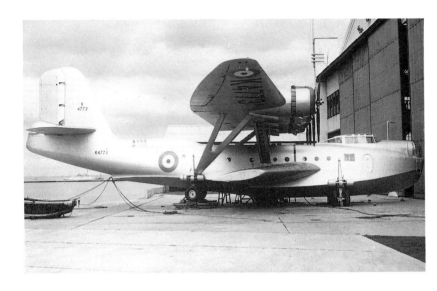

K4773, unarmed, at Cowes. Note sharply tapering sponsons, also rotating beaching chassis.

Immediately after the accident, K4773 moored at the mouth of the Medina, its rear beaching chassis members installed, before the move back onto Columbine apron. (*L.S. Ash*)

The Saro hydrodynamic department was understandably perplexed by the behaviour of K4773. Courtney was instructed to allow the porpoising to develop a little if he could, so that it could be observed and studied. Why another series of model tests was not initiated at that stage remains a mystery. The full-size aircraft was used instead, with catastrophic results.

On 25 October, during its fifth take-off run from the Solent, K4773 was moving at high speed when it hit the wake of a nearby Southampton ferry-boat. The aircraft at once began to porpoise severely and made a huge leap from which it came down in a stalled condition and out of control. On impact, the wing failed in torsion at a position in line with the inner starboard engine. The starboard side of the wing then twisted forward about the single spar while the starboard inner airscrew penetrated the hull (missing Henry Knowler by inches) and also the starboard sponson. The tail was then damaged by flying debris from the wing.

K4773 came to rest but did not sink as all damage was above the water-line. None of the crew was seriously injured and the powerful motor launch *Saro 1* towed the A.33 ignominiously back to East Cowes. After an examination of the beaching chassis points on the hull sides had revealed no damage, K4773 was dragged onto the Columbine apron.

Very reluctantly, it was decided to abandon development of the A.33, and a contract for the production of eleven further (developed) examples to R.21/36, L2147–L2157, was cancelled by the Air Ministry. It was felt at Cowes that a great deal of time and perhaps money would be necessary to

The damage: K4773 suffered a collapse of the starboard side of its Monospar wing, and the design was eventually abandoned. (*BHC*)

169

The damage: close-up. The starboard inner airscrew penetrated the hull and starboard sponson. A crude reinforcing strip has been placed across the resultant gash. (*BHC*)

rectify the faults experienced with the A.33. The MAEE had not tested K4773 before the crash, because it had only just begun manufacturer's trials. Had they done so, more faults might have been found and development retarded further than it was already clearly going to be. On the other hand, progress by Saro on a smaller flying-boat prototype, the S.36, had been very promising. The A.33 and S.36 prototypes had been built side by side in Columbine but the S.36 was by the time of the A.33 crash guaranteed a production run. In view of these considerations, it was decided to concentrate on the smaller flying-boat and scrap the A.33 programme which had already cost more than £80,000 compared with the original development figure of £68,000.

Four 830 hp Bristol Perseus XII.
Span 95 ft; length 75 ft; height 22 ft 8½ in; wing area 1,194 sq ft.
Weight for first flight 31,500 lb; maximum tested weight 35,000 lb; design normal maximum weight 41,500 lb; design maximum overloaded weight 44,650 lb.
Maximum speed 200 mph; maximum cruising speed 174 mph; long-range cruising speed 155 mph; climb to 3,300 ft—8 min 20 sec; service ceiling 14,280 ft; normal endurance 12 hr; maximum overload endurance 13 hr 25 min.
Armament: single or multiple ·303 in Browning machine-guns in bow and tail turrets, two Vickers K machine-guns in beam positions, 2,000 lb bomb load on underwing mountings outboard of sponsons.

One example, K4773

L7248, the first Lerwick of 21 built, Cowes, early 1939. The rear turret location is blanked off and the wingfloats are as yet unstepped. (*BHC*)

Saunders-Roe S.36 Lerwick

During the mid-1930s it became apparent that war was becoming inevitable. Re-equipment and expansion of the RAF were rapidly planned. A swift rearmament programme caused a number of new aircraft designs to be ordered 'off the drawing-board'. Some were successful; others failed and were discarded once superior replacements were available. The S.36 Lerwick was one of the failures, yet remained in service with the RAF until late 1942.

Specification R.1/36 called for a monoplane flying-boat to replace the Saro London and Supermarine Stranraer biplanes which were in service during the mid-1930s. This Specification was issued on 2 March, 1936, to Blackburn, Saro, Short Brothers, and Supermarine. R.1/36 requested a twin-engined flying-boat of 25,000 lb all-up weight with a crew of six. Defensive armament was to be contained in three power-operated turrets and offensive load to total 2,000 lb. Entries from the companies were quickly received and on 22 June an Air Ministry tender conference judged the competitors.

Blackburn's entry, the B.20, was judged separately. The B.20 sought to eliminate the disadvantage of a very deep hull usual in the monoplane flying-boat by the substitution of a horizontally-split 'fuselage', the lower portion of which was extendable to form a single central float when on the water. In this way, the upper fuselage and flight stucture was lifted high above the water. The B.20 design secured an order for one prototype, V8914, powered by the ill-fated Rolls-Royce Vulture, but this order was merely to assess the practicality of such an arrangement. The B.20 was

171

Lerwick L7248. (*Saro/BHC*)

thought too revolutionary to enter service without extensive trials and there was no time to indulge in such long-term tests. The Air Ministry therefore looked at the remaining designs to find the winner of R.1/36.

On 22 June, the Supermarine design, also Vulture-powered, emerged as the favourite, though it was thought rather expensive. The Saro and Short Brothers submissions were placed equal second. Orders for the Supermarine design were to be made 'off the drawing-board', but there was some delay in this, because of Supermarine's commitment to Spitfire production and possible inability to develop their flying-boat as well.

During the delay, Knowler revised his original drawings to R.1/36. These had featured a fairly shallow hull in combination with a gull wing. Knowler deepened the hull and provided high-mounted cantilever wings of increased span and area. The original complex method of mounting the bomb load underwing was discarded in favour of two small bomb bays formed in the underside of the engine nacelles. When it became clear that Supermarine would be unable to start producing their design for at least another two years, the Air Ministry awarded the R.1/36 contract to Saro's revised design. This was agreed in November 1936 and the order placed was again 'off the drawing-board'. A batch of twenty-two serials (L7248–L7269) was allocated for the new Saro flying-boat, though the initial order was for only ten. Unit price was £54,750. This quantity was swiftly revised; a December 1936 Minute records the decision to order 16–20 examples. Eventually, twenty-one were built, but only after grave misgivings, cancellations and reinstatements.

The Saro design thus won R.1/36 through default of a preferred design. Designated the S.36, development proceeded rapidly at Cowes throughout 1937 and into 1938. The chosen powerplant for the new 'boat was the fourteen-cylinder sleeve-valve Bristol Hercules HE.1M. In early 1937 this was the most powerful engine in the world, having been rated at 1,290 hp

172

for take-off and 1,375 hp at 4,000 ft. The earlier Saro choice, the Rolls-Royce Vulture, was abandoned as the more powerful Hercules became available and in hindsight this proved a wise move.

The use of the Hercules allowed a gross weight of 28,500 lb (later reduced to 28,400 lb), with a maximum overload of 33,200 lb, and a range of 1,540 miles. Three-blade 13 ft 6 in diameter de Havilland constant-speed airscrews were chosen and their large diameter necessitated a very deep hull, which provided accommodation for the initial crew complement of nine.

Structure of the S.36 was all-metal with fabric-covered control surfaces. The hull had a single step but the taper aft of the step gave the appearance of a second, vertical knife-edge, step beneath the tailplane. Armament was heavy, comprising a ·303 in Vickers K gun in an FN 7 bow turret, a twin ·303 in Browning-armed retractable FN 8 dorsal turret and a four-Browning installation in the tail turret, an FN 4A. The bow turret could be cranked back to allow mooring operations. Main fuel tanks were arranged in two groups of three in each wing, as well as three overload tanks in the hull. Normal tank capacity was 780 gal and overload 1,440 gal. The cockpit was extensively glazed, and seating was provided for three: pilot and co-pilot in tandem, with the engineer further aft and to starboard.

The high cantilever wing had a parallel-chord centre-section carrying the engines, and the tapering outer wings carried cantilever shock-absorbing V-struts to which stepless (on the first example only) stabilising floats were attached. Later wing floats had a single step. Provision was made for the carriage of four depth-charges in the engine nacelle undersides, as an alternative to the normal 2,000 lb bomb load.

The bomb-aimer's aperture was placed in the extreme bow underside and took the form of an upwards sliding hatch, behind which was a glass screen. The field of vision was found to be rather limited, and it became

Lerwicks under construction in Columbine, mid-1939. L7252 is to the rear.

L7248's flight deck. The letters indicate soundproofing perimeters—with the engines as close to the cockpit as they were, the noise level was considerable. (*RAE, Crown Copyright*)

standard procedure to sight, at least at low level, from the co-pilot's positon. Smoke floats could also be carried, deployed from small hatches one in each side of the hull under the wing roots.

The standard tail unit comprised a cantilever tailplane, single fin and rudder. All control surfaces had trim tabs. Although originally intended to carry a crew of nine: pilot, co-pilot, engineer, observer/air-gunner, three fitter/air-gunners, WEM air-gunner and WT air-gunner, it was considered that, even in the large hull, nine people would be very cramped and the crew was reduced to six or seven.

One remarkable aspect of the S.36 was its very high wing loading of 33·5 lb/sq ft. The Hercules engines were expected to give the S.36 a maximum speed of 230 mph and enough thrust to keep take-offs to a reasonable distance, despite the highly loaded wing, but the S.36 never achieved this speed.

In April 1937, a contract was placed for the production of ten S.36s, the December 1936 decision having been laid aside. In June 1937, this order was expanded to twenty-one, of which the first three (L7248–L7250) would serve as prototypes. The first example was completed at Cowes by October 1938 and launched on the last day of that month. L7248 was airborne for the first time during early November and was tested by Frank Courtney and Ash. Several problems immediately came to light. L7248 suffered from severe hydrodynamic instability and overbalance of the elevators. It was also found to be unstable in roll and yaw under cruising conditions.

174

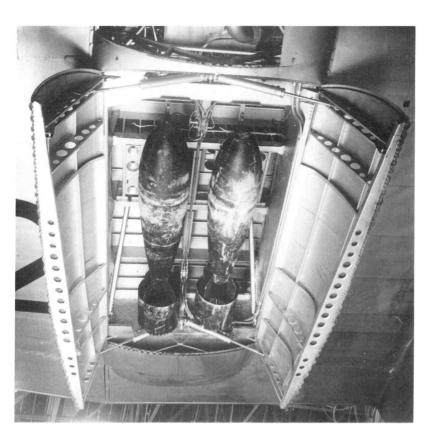

The bomb installation of L7265, mounting two 500 lb bombs in each engine nacelle. (*RAE, Crown Copyright*)

'Hands-off' flight was found impossible in the first S.36, which had by that time received a name—Lerwick. Modifications never succeeded in providing adequate 'hands-off' properties.

The water performance of the Lerwick was not only disappointing but in one sense alarming. In model tests before construction of the first aircraft, porpoising difficulties had been eliminated after RAE Farnborough had been called in to assist. To cure the model, the step had been moved aft and this modification was adopted for the first full-size Lerwick. When tested, L7248 revealed a bouncing type of porpoising which occurred at high speeds and attitudes.

By January 1939, L7248 and the second Lerwick, L7249, were undergoing full company trials at Cowes during which the above faults were confirmed. Testing lasted from 9 January to 11 February before L7248 was delivered to the MAEE for full type trials on 14 March. At that stage it carried a blanked-off rear turret position, as its FN 4A had arrived late and

175

L7248 at MAEE Felixstowe for type trials, March 1939. (*RAE, Crown Copyright*)

it was felt essential to proceed with the testing. L7249, by that time fully-armed, was retained by Saro for further testing.

The MAEE was unimpressed with the properties of the Lerwick. Tests confirmed Saro's fault-finding and L7248 was sent back to Cowes on 22 May for modifications. These consisted of an extended-chord rudder and two auxiliary tailplane fins, and was an attempt to gain some semblance of stability in the air. L7248's place at Felixstowe was taken by L7249, which arrived on 13 June. On 1 September, it was lost while being launched from the Felixstowe swing-launcher. The camera-gun hatch, located in the extreme nose, was not properly secured and the Lerwick filled with water before it could be re-attached to the hoisting slings. Subsequently recovered, it was then used statically by the MAEE.

By the midsummer of 1939, L7248 had again been modified after the auxiliary fins were found ineffective. These were removed and a large rectangular area added to the top of the rudder. The fins were later replaced in conjunction with the (twice) enlarged rudder and by late 1939 a number of other tail configurations had been tested by the MAEE. These were: original fin and rudder (L7248, L7249 and L7252); original fin and rudder plus auxiliary fins (L7248); original fin plus rudder of increased height and chord (L7248); original fin plus enlarged rudder plus auxiliary fins (L7248); enlarged fin plus enlarged rudder (L7252). The last arrangement was that later adopted as standard, both lateral and directional control having been somewhat improved.

By January 1940, L7248 was under conversion at Cowes to have twin oval fins and rudders scaled up from those of the A.37, with a modified tailplane set 15 in higher than the original configuration, on a slightly

Initial Lerwick fin and rudder layout, L7248. (*RAE, Crown Copyright*)

revised upper rear hull. This arrangement was not found to have advantages in improving handling and was later discarded. The standard tail modification introduced to nearly all Lerwicks consisted of building out the leading edge of the fin and fitting the rudder with an auxiliary top-plate. This made flight characteristics reasonably acceptable, providing adequate directional control in most circumstances and reducing the rolling tendency.

As a result of the poor take-off and flight qualities revealed by the test programme, on 26 June, 1940, the disposable load of the Lerwick was officially limited to 8,300 lb. This restriction was placed on all examples (except L7249) up to L7254, which had been authorised for construction up to that time. On 29 July, L7252 arrived at the MAEE and the revised

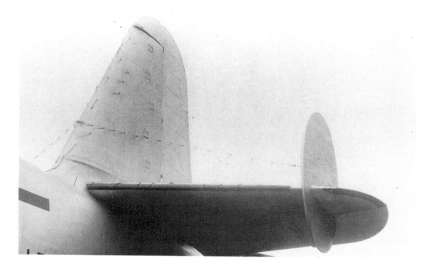

The original fin and rudder layout, combined with auxiliary fins, L7248. (*RAE, Crown Copyright*)

Original fin, enlarged rudder and auxiliary fins, L7248. (*RAE, Crown Copyright*)

tail configuration was finally agreed on shortly after. Hydrodynamic problems persisted, however.

New tanks tests were initiated at RAE Farnborough and by the end of the year Short Brothers had been called in for their advice. At RAE, the models' hull forms were altered extensively: steps were moved aft various

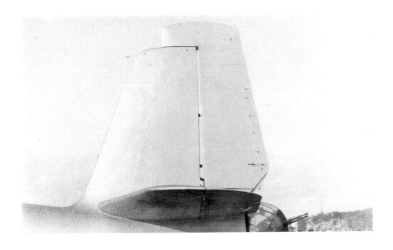

Enlarged fin and rudder, L7252. This became the standard layout. (*RAE, Crown Copyright*)

L7249, with its rudder extension still in primer, off Cowes during the summer of 1939. This and the following 19 examples were built with stepped wingfloats. (*Saro*)

distances and the planing bottoms made deeper. Shorts proposed fitting a Sunderland-type afterbody and raising the tailplane, but initial tests were unsatisfactory. Step depth was altered by both teams and Arthur Gouge suggested tests with a complete (scaled down) Sunderland hull bottom, though this idea was not adopted. The first and third prototype Lerwicks were, during the summer of 1940, sent to Cowes for hydrodynamic experiments. Their hull bottoms, step positions and depths were altered time and again until a marginally acceptable arrangement was found, using a deeper step placed slightly aft of the original position, and a slightly lowered planing bottom. This reduced, but did not eliminate the porpoising tendency at high speeds.

During initial trials at the MAEE with L7248 it had been found that top speed was not the expected 230 mph, but about 16 mph less. Specification R.1/36 had demanded 235 mph. Nor were take-off runs of reasonable length. When L7251 was tested in these respects at Felixstowe during the summer of 1939, it was found that with a normal loaded weight of 28,500 lb, take-off time was 41 seconds. At an overload of 31,500 lb, this rose to 60 seconds. To provide even this mediocre performance, the Hercules had to be worked very hard and thus tended to overheat. Weight-shedding became essential. It was suggested that the rear turret be deleted, but this was wisely vetoed on the grounds that the Lerwick would have to operate in areas were there was likely to be enemy air activity. It was partly due to the weight problem that the crew complement finally became six. Some moveable parts of the dorsal turret were deleted and eventually, on operations, items such as anchor chains were usually left behind. Normal loaded weight dropped 100 lb to 28,400 lb on all Lerwicks except for the first two examples; this did little to increase top speed or decrease take-off runs.

The disappointing performance caused a faltering production programme and it was only because of a chronic shortage of patrol flying-boats during the early part of the war that the type was ordered in quantity. During the summer of 1939, L7250, L7251, L7253 and L7254 were allocated to No. 240 Squadron at Invergordon, L7252 remaining at the MAEE. L7254, at the time only partially complete, was never delivered; the other examples went to the RAF seaplane base at Calshot, pending a decision on the whole future of the Lerwick.

It was at Calshot that the S.36 came under the most severe scrutiny. On 16 December, 1939, Air Vice-Marshal Sholto Douglas wrote to Air Chief Marshal Sir W.R. Freeman on the subject. His views on the Lerwick, formed by hearing of the complaints made by RAF officers who had flown it, was that the S.36 was dangerous at take-off, its range inadequate and flight characteristics difficult and unpleasant. He recommended that the whole programme be scrapped and Saunders-Roe be set to building Sunderlands.

Meanwhile, on 24 October, production of further Lerwicks, including L7254 which was still at Cowes being completed, was cancelled. This order was countermanded on 1 November after it was recognised that even the Lerwick was better than nothing. It was also felt that conversion to the production of Sunderlands at Cowes could take many months. Under the 1 November agreement, L7254 and L7255–L7259 were to be completed, though the last two were intended for storage at Cowes. Also, further hulls

Summer 1939; Lerwicks L7250 and L7249 at East Cowes. The clip-on engine maintenance platform for on-water work can be seen. (*BHC*)

were to be manufactured at a pace that did not interfere with the production of the Supermarine Walrus, a contract for which was then under negotiation. By February 1940, it had been decreed that twenty-one Lerwicks should be built. The first four having received Hercules HE.1Ms, it was intended that the next eight would have Hercules IIs and the last nine Hercules IVs. In May this was revised, and finally L7252–L7260 received the Hercules II while L7261–L7268 had Hercules IVs, a reflection on the shortage of the later model.

During these vacillations L7254 was completed and modified in an attempt to improve take-off performance, with an increase in wing incidence from 3·5 deg to 5·5 deg. In addition, it was provided with 14 ft 6 in diameter airscrews, and spinners. L7254 went to MAEE Helensburgh and by April 1940 had been tested. The modifications shortened take-off time (31 sec at 28,400 lb) and improved flying qualities, controls being more effective with even less roll and yaw problems than from previous modifications. However, the increased diameter of the airscrews made for poor water performance and so a compromise was reached; the 2 deg increase in incidence was retained but the original airscrews reinstated.

In this form the S.36 was cautiously deemed useful and began to enter service. The spate of MAEE and other complaints which criticised the type, both before and after this decision, were not enough to prevent a

L7250, the third 'prototype' Lerwick, showing the great depth of hull, and the beaching chassis. The relationship between the hull and the seemingly undersized flight surfaces is clearly shown.

short service life, mainly in the Hebrides and Shetland areas, until better aircraft could be provided. The Lerwicks with RAF Calshot were eventually transferred to No. 209 Squadron at Oban, which was given the dubious pleasure of operating the new type instead of their elderly Stranraers.

Throughout the Lerwick's Service career, complaints persisted. In early 1940, it became apparent that bomb-doors were liable to open in flight due to hydraulic leakage. A pilot-operated locking device was subsequently fitted. By May 1940, the MAEE had found considerable corrosion around some rear turrets, caused by excessive spray at high take-off speeds being sucked into the discharge chutes and openings between the rotating ring and cupola frame. This problem was never completely cured, though flexible rubber masking plates were added in an attempt to prevent ingress. By September, it had been noted that single-engined flight was almost impossible, the Lerwick being quite unable to maintain height or directional control against the torque of the remaining engine at increased output. There was thereafter a series of rudder trim-tab alterations.

There was also a marked tendency for the centre of gravity to be at the aft of the range, which made weight reductions and redistributions a complex task. The floats on the last batch of Lerwicks, those with Hercules IVs, had to be modified at the bow to increase nose incidence; buoyancy was raised by some 15 per cent, and improved bilging facilities were fitted. Various deflector devices had to be installed in order to prevent a marked pitch-down in attitude when the rear turret was rotated from aft to beam. By July 1941 it had been observed at Helensburgh and elsewhere that excessive pitching vibration of the nacelles was occurring, especially at take-off and on alighting in rough seas. Engine mountings were subsequently reinforced.

A little before this, in March 1941, the MAEE found during routine inspection that the wings of L7248 had in some way failed. Since April 1940, L7248 too had received the wing incidence conversion and now had the new twin fins and rudders. The wing failure was spotted through the discovery of buckling in the upper surface wing skinning along the chord: compression failures apparently caused by an upward deflection of the wing. L7248 had been treated fairly gently in relation to what might have been expected on operations, yet no similar faults were found with Service Lerwicks. It appeared that failure had perhaps occurred on a very heavy alighting, or perhaps during side-slips during recent stalling tests, or more probably during 'falling-leaf' tests.

The stalling tests with L7248 which might have contributed to the wing failure had been undertaken after some debate. It seems that no-one was rash enough to deliberately stall the Lerwick until the MAEE did it in December 1940. The clean power-off stall proved to be vicious, though without a tendency to spin, but with power-on and flaps lowered the Lerwick went out of control. The tests were repeated in March 1941 with the same results and the wing skin failure, previously mentioned, was noted shortly afterwards.

As these new faults became apparent, and though some were partially cured, Lerwick Pilot's Notes (and, later, accident enquiry reports) naturally became increasingly critical. In early 1942, after the crash of L7265 at Invergordon, the enquiry report stressed that the Lerwick 'is unstable in all three planes and pilots must be prepared to re-trim the aircraft at any time, particularly during the approach and landing'. Pilot's Notes indicated that the probable swing to starboard on take-off was due

Left to right, Lerwicks L7250, L7249 and L7248, East Cowes, summer 1939. All have rudder extensions and L7248 has auxiliary fins. The building of Medina hangar is underway. (*BHC*)

183

to torque reaction, to be corrected by rudder and through using the starboard engine in advance of the port. Certain stringent flying-speed guidelines were set down: 117 mph at 500 ft when alighting and touchdown at 93 mph. A 'rumble' approach with full flap was suggested, to be performed only by pilots used to the Lerwick's peculiarities. Despite the many modifications to the Lerwick design it can safely be said that on the water porpoising persisted, while in the air, rolling and yawing was never entirely cured. The Lerwick was understandably unpopular with those who flew it and accidents were frequent.

By early 1940 the first ten Lerwicks had been built. During December 1939, No. 209 Squadron had begun to receive Lerwicks at Oban. First to arrive was L7255, which flew there from Calshot on 2 December, a day late because of bad weather. Training flights began on 4 December, but during the following day, L7255 went unserviceable with a defective magneto on the starboard Hercules. It flew next on 18 December and made its first operational patrol on Christmas Day, though it sighted only two neutral ships. This patrol lasted 6 hr 10 min. On 26 December, L7256 arrived and immediately went unserviceable with leaking hydraulics and fuel tanks. Only on 6 January, 1940, did L7256 become operational. L7251 arrived on 1 January and L7257 on 17 January, but on 5 February all Lerwicks were grounded for modifications after the collapse of a throttle lever on one example, fortunately while it was on the water.

Meanwhile, Lerwicks L7250 and L7253 remained at Calshot; L7250 had been damaged in a collision and L7253 was unserviceable with turret ring and ASI problems. When the grounding of Lerwicks was lifted during the second week of February, movements were resumed. L7253 arrived at Oban on 13 February, but was soon lost. After shake-down tests on 16 February, four days later L7253 went on operational patrol for the first time, but this was soon aborted due to bad weather. On the approach, L7253 stalled and struck the water, collapsing the starboard float. The

Warpaint: an unidentified Lerwick, lacking fin flashes, on Columbine apron, late 1939. The 'seige towers' are *in situ* for engine maintenance.

184

aircraft turned turtle and sank. Though all six crew on board escaped from the wreck, four were drowned before rescue boats arrived.

On 5 February, subject to the grounding restriction being lifted, permission was given to deliver L7258 and L7259, and to construct the remaining batch L7260 to L7268, the fate of which had again come under scrutiny. All but the first of this batch had the improved Hercules IV and all were completed with increased wing incidence. Meanwhile, during March, L7257 engaged in gunnery practice with a drogue-towing Hawker Henley and on 25 March the Lerwick made its first offensive gesture (at the enemy) when L7256 released a bomb at a submerged submarine, though without any positive result. By late April, No. 209 Squadron had received Lerwicks L7251, L7253 (sunk), L7255, L7257, L7258 and L7259, these being joined by L7254 and L7260 during May. The final Stanraer sortie by No. 209 Squadron was flown on 22 April and the unit was thereafter completely Lerwick-equipped.

For a short time after this, various Lerwicks were switched about as those on operations returned to Cowes for the wing modification, those already having the increased incidence arrived at Oban as replacements. During May, troubles seemed to decline and serviceability reached a laudable 81 per cent, but this fell to 40 per cent during June, mainly because of engine failures. On 16 June, L7261 arrived from Pembroke

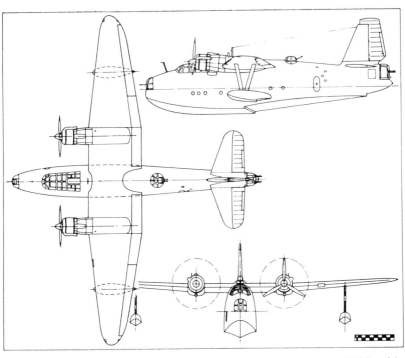

S.36 Lerwick

185

Dock, but this aircraft was lost on 29 June. After returning from shipping escort duties, L7261 was taxi-ing crosswind when a float collapsed. The aircraft turned over and sank, though without loss of life. Nine days earlier the Lerwick had been involved in more offensive action when L7260 bombed the head of a submarine trail. However, success was not confirmed. No. 209 Squadron then began a transfer to Pembroke Dock to participate in the Battle of the Atlantic and patrol the Irish Sea.

A party ready to receive the transferred Lerwicks arrived at Pembroke Dock on 12 July and L7259 arrived four days later. The move was completed by August. During this period, No. 209 Squadron was taken off operations, though L7262 did during 26 July take part in a search for a lost Fokker T.8W of No. 320 Squadron. All Lerwicks were again grounded, on 3 August, for more modifications, by which time the aircraft had become scattered, some with No. 209 Squadron, some at Calshot, some still at Cowes, and one (L7257) remaining at Oban. The modifications involved that time were the unsuccessful rudder trim-tab alterations, and the successful changes to the floats. Also, light alloy extractor pipes were replaced by a copper variety to prevent a recurrence of breakages which had caused some loss of engine control. First to fly after these conversions was L7261 and this ably demonstrated that while the float conversion increased the nose-up attitude on the water and improved handling qualities, the trim tab alteration was not a success. During mid-September, L7257 received new Hercules IIs and was the only Lerwick of No. 209 Squadron to fly that month.

As the Lerwicks returned to operations, most were flown to Stranraer, their new home with the again transferred No. 209 Squadron. However, L7262 left Pembroke Dock to join No. 4 (Coastal) Operational Training Unit, at Stranraer, on a short detachment starting on 21 October, while

Lerwick L7257 WQ-F of No. 209 Squadron, undergoing overhaul at East Cowes. In the background is the A.37 'Shrimp', and in the foreground, Walrus flight surfaces. (*BHC*)

L7250 went to Scottish Aviation at Greenock during November and in January 1941 L7258 arrived at Helensburgh. First to arrive at Stranraer for No. 209 Squadron was L7255 (6 November) followed by L7250, L7264, L7258, L7263, L7266, L7262 and finally L7265 on 3 January, 1941. No. 209 resumed operations but quickly lost three Lerwicks. In fact, L7255 had already been lost; on 6 December she sank while moored on Loch Ryan, when a severe gale blew up. The loss was put down to a collapse of the starboard float caused by poor workmanship. L7262 crashed on 7 January, 1941, after an inordinately long take-off during which flying speed was never reached. The hull was eventually holed by a floating obstacle and the Lerwick sank in two minutes, with the loss of two lives. On 22 February, in fine weather, L7263 was reported missing and was never found.

On top of these misfortunes, L7251 had been lost, though in unusual circumstances. On 21 November, 1940, it sank at its moorings on Loch Ryan during a strong gale. It was found on recovery that the front turret and entrance hatches had not been properly secured and the aircraft had simply filled with water. After recovery, L7251 was transferred to Scottish Aviation where it remained until struck off charge.

No. 209 Squadron should have returned to Oban but eventually went to Lough Erne, County Fermanagh, an advance party arriving on 23 March, 1941. On the following day, another Lerwick was lost. L7252, operating temporarily from Pembroke Dock but still with No. 209 Squadron, was testing an experimental blind-flying apparatus in poor weather conditions. She alighted in an 8 ft sea after failing to reach the safety of Milford Haven. On hitting the water, she was thrown vertically upwards by a large wave. An engine broke off at the bulkhead and the airscrew sliced through the hull. L7252 sank rapidly but without loss of life.

By 22 April, the first Consolidated Catalina (AH542) had arrived for use

L7257 WQ-F of No. 209 Squadron at Oban. Large fin flashes have been applied; so have underwing roundels, though most Lerwicks did not have these. (*RAE, Crown Copyright*)

by No. 209 Squadron and the Lerwicks were gradually transferred elsewhere. The last operational duty by a Lerwick of No. 209 was on 29 April when L7267 escorted the *ss Arden Vohr*. No. 209 gradually became Catalina-equipped and most of its surviving Lerwicks joined No. 4(C)OTU at Stranraer, this transfer being completed by the end of May.

No. 4(C)OTU had moved from Calshot to Stranraer during June 1940 and received nine Lerwicks. L7258 arrived on 29 April, 1941, and was followed by L7257, L7264, L7260, L7267, L7268, L7265, L7250 and L7256. Two more accidents occurred. L7268 was lost on 14 October after the port engine failed in flight and the aircraft dived into the sea; nine were killed and three injured, the extra crew members having been carried without written permission. L7257 sank at its moorings on 11 November. L7259 joined 4(C)OTU during late March 1942, while L7267 was posted to the MAEE betwen February and May. The remainder continued training duties but on 19 May L7266 joined a search for a lost Defiant.

Surprisingly, some surviving Lerwicks later re-entered operational service, as a stop-gap, joining No. 422 (Canadian) Squadron at Lough Erne, from 4(C)OTU, during the summer of 1942. No. 442 was to operate Sunderlands but allotted the Saro 'boat until these became available. Lerwicks L7258, L7259 and L7260 arrived from Stranraer on 23 July and were followed by L7267, L7264, L7266, L7250 and L7256. Three Catalinas also arrived for use by 422 Squadron and all aircraft were assembled by 1 September. By the end of the month, however, both Lerwicks and Catalinas were withdrawn and No. 422's first Sunderland arrived at Lough Erne on 12 October. On 10 September, meanwhile, L7267 had been

L7257 as TA-S while with No. 4 (C)OTU, summer 1941.

Unidentified Lerwick, its bow turret retracted for mooring operations, with Short Sunderlands in the background. Not all Lerwicks had DF loops, but this example does.

destroyed in an accident, though without loss of life. On alighting in a moderate sea and gusting wind, the Lerwick hit the water and bounced. It then skidded violently and the whole tail section was severed. This accident was put down to the inexperience of the pilot combined with certain vagaries experienced with the exactor control system.

The first Lerwick, L7248, was lost shortly afterwards, on 21 October, while making calibration tests near Dumbarton. The starboard wing was seen to drop, the aircraft dived, crashed into the side of a hill, and was totally destroyed. The crew of seven were killed. The subsequent enquiry suggested at least partial failure of the starboard engine before the crash and stressed that 'the handling characteristics have never been satisfactory when flying with one engine'.

The replacement types heralded retirement for the Lerwick. First to leave Lough Erne for Scottish Aviation was L7258 on 14 October. Most remaining Lerwicks finished there, but L7250 appears to have been abandoned at Pembroke Dock after having originally departed for Felixstowe. L7254, after mooring trials with the MAEE, passed to the Maritime Training School, Wig Bay, as 3300M, before transfer on 30 March, 1943, to No. 63 MU, also at Wig Bay.

Two 1,375 hp Bristol Hercules HE.1M (L72481–7251), Hercules II (L7252–7260), Hercules IV (L7261–7268).
Span 80 ft 10 in; length 63 ft 7½ in; height 20 ft; wing area 845 sq ft.
Normal loaded weight 28,400 lb; normal maximum overloaded weight 33,200 lb; maximum tested weight 34,000 lb.
Maximum speed 214 mph; cruising speed 166 mph; initial rate of climb 880 ft/min; service ceiling 14,000 ft; range at 200 mph 1,540 miles.
Armament: one ·303 in Vickers K in bow turret, two ·303 in Browning machine-guns in dorsal turret, four ·303 in Brownings in tail turret; four 500 lb or eight 250 lb bombs or four depth charges.

189

Twenty-one examples, L7248–L7268, c/ns S.36/1–S.36/21, delivered March 1939–March 1941. All withdrawn by December 1942. L7269 allotted but not taken up.

L7248: MAEE 14.3.39, Saro 22.5.39 (mods), AMDP Cowes for experience work, MAEE 9.39, Saro 12.39 (mods), MAEE 5.40, Saro 7.40, MAEE later in 1940, crashed into hill, Faslane, Dumbarton 21.10.41, and SOC during 10.41; L7249: MAEE 13.6.39, sank 1.9.39 at MAEE, subsequently recovered and used statically by this establishment; L7250: To 240 Sqn 9.6.39, to RAF Calshot 9.39, to 209 Sqn 30.11.39, RAF Calshot 14.6.40, Saro 8.7.40, RAF Calshot 25.7.40, to 209 Sqn 8.9.40, Stn Flt Greenock 19.11.40, Scottish Aviation during 11.40, 4(C)OTU 18.8.41, to 422 Sqn 18.8.42. SOC 19.10.42 and dumped for a short time at Pembroke Dock; L7251: To 240 Sqn 11.7.39, MAEE 8.39, RAF Calshot 23.9.39, to 209 Sqn 1.1.40, sank Stranraer 21.11.40, but recovered. Scottish Aviation 10.12.40. SOC 22.7.41; L7252: MAEE 20.8.39, Saro AMDP 29.6.40, MAEE 29.7.40, to Pembroke Dock for trials 21.11.40, to 209 Sqn 10.2.41, Pembroke Dock 15.2.41, crashed and sank off Pembroke Dock. SOC 24.3.41 Cat E.; L7253: To 240 Sqn 22.8.39, RAF Calshot 20.9.39, to 209 Sqn 13.2.40, crashed and sank off the Lismore Islands. SOC 20.2.42; L7254: Saro 22.11.39, MAEE 13.2.40, RAF Calshot 24.4.40, to 209 Sqn 4.5.40, Saro 7.7.40, RAF Calshot 7.10.40, Pembroke Dock 12.10.40, held at Greenock 26.11.40, MAEE DGRD 3.6.41, Scottish Aviation 3.11.41, MAEE 28.5.42, returned to Scottish Aviation 10.7.42, Marine Training School Wig Bay 24.7.42 as 3300M. Scrapped 30.3.43 at 63 MU, Cat E2; L7255: RAF Calshot 20.11.39, to 209 Sqn 2.12.39, RAF Calshot 26.6.40, 4MU 4.7.40, RAF Calshot 16.9.40, Pembroke Dock 18.9.40, to 209 Sqn 6.11.40, sank off Stranraer and SOC, 6.12.40; L7256: To 209 Sqn 26.12.39, 4(C)OTU 4.5.41, RAF Calshot 4.6.41, 4(C)OTU 20.8.41, to 422 Sqn 23.7.42, Scottish Aviation 26.10.42. SOC 3.12.42; L7257: To 209 Sqn 17.1.40, 4(C)OTU 30.4.41, sank 11.11.41 in gale, Invergordon; L7258: To 209 Sqn 20.2.40, MAEE 22.1.41, 4(C)OTU 29.4.41, to 422 Sqn 23.7.42, Scottish Aviation 14.10.42 and later scrapped; L7259: To 209 Sqn 4.40, RAF Calshot 9.5.41, 4(C)OTU 23.3.42, to 422 Sqn 23.7.42. SOC 29.11.42; L7260: RAF Calshot 22.5.40, to 209 Sqn 31.5.40, RAF Calshot 16.5.41, 4(C)OTU 4.6.41, to 422 Sqn 23.7.42, Scottish Aviation 20.10.42. Scrapped 3.12.42; L7261: RAF Calshot 1.6.40, to 209 Sqn 16.6.40, sank off Oban 29.6.40; L7262: RAF Calshot 28.6.40, to 209 Sqn 1.7.40, 4(C)OTU 21–24.10.40, sank off Stranraer after crashing on take-off 7.1.41, Scottish Aviation 27.1.41 for scrap value; L7263: RAF Calshot 19.8.40, to 209 Sqn 8.9.40, missing 22.2.41; L7264: RAF Calshot 29.8.40, to 209 Sqn 8.9.40, 4(C)OTU 16.5.41, to 422 Sqn 1.8.42, Scottish Aviation 22.10.42. SOC 3.12.42; L7265: RAF Calshot 14.10.40, Pembroke Dock 26.11.40 (storage), to 209 Sqn 3.1.41, 4(C)OTU 23.7.41, crashed while alighting Invergordon 21.12.41 due to wing distortion caused during heavy alighting practice. SOC 31.12.41; L7266: To 209 Sqn 4.12.40, Scottish Aviation 19.5.41, to 422 Sqn 16.8.42, Scottish Aviation 20.11.42. SOC 3.12.42; L7267: RAF Calshot 2.3.41, to 209 Sqn 29.3.41, RAF Calshot 16.5.41, 4(C)OTU 4.6.41, MAEE 2–5.42, to 422 Sqn 24.7.42, crashed on alighting Lough Erne 10.9.42; L7268: To 209 Sqn 5.12.40, 4(C)OTU 5.5.41, dived into sea 6 miles ENE Tarbat Ness and sank, 14.10.41, when SOC.

The deceptively small A.37 in hastily applied camouflage but retaining its civil registration G-AFZS, Cowes, early 1940. (*BHC*)

Saunders-Roe A.37

The deceptively small A.37 was designed by Knowler as part of a programme concerned with large flying-boat projects from the inception of the A.33 until the Project P.192, which ended in the middle-1950s. A beautifully streamlined scale model of a design for which metal was never actually cut, the A.37 represented a trend in design research during the late 1930s.

Just one A.37, known colloquially as the 'Shrimp', was built, with its origins in Specification R.5/39 of March 1939. Saro tendered their Project S.38 to R.5/39, which demanded a large, four-engined patrol flying-boat to eventually replace the Sunderland. It was decided to build a model of S.38 in March 1939 to furnish details of aero- and hydrodynamic performance. The A.37 was constructed as a $\frac{1}{2}$-scale model of S.38, on a private-venture basis. Tests on the A.37 proposal were done at RAE Farnborough and detail design followed. Development of the 'Shrimp' was rapid, but by the time it was launched from Cowes, Specification R.5/39 had been cancelled (though it was later half-heartedly re-instated).

The A.37 was used for a variety of tasks for which it had not originally been intended. Registered G-AFZS in August 1939, it emerged from

Cowes in late September and made its first flight during the early part of the following month, in the hands of Ash. Construction of the hull was of metal, with a single step and no water-rudder, on-water movement being aided by drogues, though in fact these were rarely used. The full cantilever mainplane was of wood, with plywood and fabric skinning. The tail was also of wood, with twin endplate fins and tabless rudders. The 'Shrimp' was powered by four 95 hp Pobjoy Niagara III seven-cylinder air-cooled radials of about half the diameter of the contemporary high-performance radials intended for S.38. They were mounted in steel bearers from the leading edge of the wing and were faired with streamlined nacelles. Fixed wing-floats were employed; these were replicas of the full size and retractable floats intended for use on S.38. Other features included a two-seat tandem enclosed cockpit, and a mooring hatch in the extreme bow. The 'boat had a most deceptive appearance: from a distance the illusion was of a very large flying-boat, and only at close range did it become clear just how small the A.37 was. The use of four engines naturally increased the illusion.

By late 1940, the A.37 had moved to Beaumaris, Anglesey. Its activities before this date remain vague and it appears to have been stored for some time, not being tested by the MAEE until early 1941. The suspension of Specification R.5/39 must have slowed the impetus of the programme at Cowes markedly and, indeed, the design team went on to study other projects.

In early 1941, the 'Shrimp' went from Beaumaris to MAEE for testing,

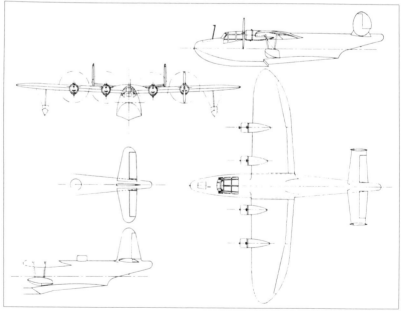

A.37

192

and this was completed by mid-March. The A.37 found immense favour at Helensburgh. It was as yet unaltered to comply with the new Specification, R.14/40, which had superseded R.5/39 in July 1940. When modifications eventually took place, they were made in conjunction with Short Brothers.

It is unusual to find an MAEE report which is more than merely analytical, but that concerning the A.37 was very enthusiastic. Taxi-ing and handling on the water was found excellent, while take-offs were clean and straightforward, with no porpoising and only a slight torque reaction easily cured with rudder. Flying qualities were described as very good, with light and responsive controls over the full flying range. Controls were well harmonised and only the rudder was found slightly at fault, being a little heavy. The only problem encountered was a tendency to drop a wing when stalled without flaps.

Despite this success, the full-size version of the A.37 was never built, partly because the procurement teams could not decide what they wanted, partly because of the emergence of R.14/40 (which went some way to reflecting that uncertainty). Both Short Brothers and Saunders-Roe tendered for R.14/40, and the Ministry of Aircraft Production (MAP) came to the surprising conclusion that development should be in the form of a joint project between the two companies. The result was the Short/Saro S.35 Shetland, nominally a Short design but with certain aspects of design and construction by Saro and employing the 'Shrimp' as

G-AFZS at MAEE Helensburgh, March 1941. Large fin flashes have been added. The original wing floats were of surprisingly narrow chord. (*RAE, Crown Copyright*)

The A.37 at Helensburgh. From this view, it is hard to appreciate how small the 'Shrimp' was; only the size of the cockpit glazing provides an indication. (*RAE, Crown Copyright*)

a research vehicle for the S.35 design. The A.37 was taken over by MAP and the civil registration replaced with the serial TK580.

From the early part of 1944 until the late autumn of the same year, the A.37 was used at Helensburgh to test various scaled-down components for the Shetland. In February the aircraft was test-flown with a scale Shetland hull bottom. The 'Shrimp' was found to be stable at all centres of gravity tested on take-offs, alightings and water movement, though stability with power reduced was slightly less than at full throttle. Tests were useful as, though the aerodynamic differences between the A.37 and the Shetland were too great to justify close comparison, it seemed fairly likely from the results gleaned that stability of the S.35 hull would be good.

Following these hull trials, a scaled-down Shetland fin and rudder were fitted to the A.37, as were Shetland-type floats and elevators. A new series of tests began in April with an adopted speed range of 70–128 mph. By the first week in July, results of the testing of the scaled-down floats were available. It was found that increasing the setting of the floats enhanced the planing characteristics and reduced spray. The starboard float appeared to give less buoyancy than the port, and on the water turns to starboard were made with less power than those in the opposite direction, probably due to torque effect. Crosswinds and choppy conditions tended to submerge the downwind float and cause excessive spray below 12 knots.

G-AFZS in 'Shetland' form, with revised fin and rudder and modified wing floats.

However, overall performance was good and gave grounds for confidence in the full-size configuration to be adopted for the Shetland.

Similarly, no detrimental effect was experienced with the new fin, rudder and elevators. Though stability limits with the new tail were unaltered, the attitude on the hump was lower with the original, at the same tail setting. The Shetland tail was more effective near take-off speeds. Altogether, the high qualities of the A.37 remained intact during this period, though it was indicated that the Shetland hull bottom might give porpoising at the hump if the aircraft were lightly loaded.

The 'Shrimp' remained with the MAEE until the war was over, returning to Felixstowe in the summer of 1945. There, a revised scale Shetland hull bottom was tested and by December 1946 the results were completed. This time, however, the hull bottom was altered by the addition of a 1:15 fairing over the step and the provision for forced ventilation of the afterbody.

It was found that the fairing produced violent skipping characteristics on both take-off and alighting, and caused marked pitching disturbance because of the impossibility of increasing the water resistance beyond the hump at take-off within a certain range of altitudes. With forced ventilation there was no amelioration of the alighting stability, though with natural ventilation the steady run stability remained somewhat better. These experiments were soon discarded and indeed their purpose is rather unclear, for by that time it had become obvious that interest in the Shetland had all but disappeared.

The A.37 continued flying from MAEE Felixstowe until early in 1949, when it was scrapped. Though the full-size S.38 had not been built, the 'Shrimp' had proved useful; the Shetland of course did not, only two examples being built. One burned out at its moorings, the other was eventually broken up. The A.37, however, was one of the finest waterborne aircraft that the Cowes firm ever produced; it was virtually viceless.

Four 95 hp Pobjoy Niagara III.
Span 50 ft; length 42 ft 3¼ in; height 12 ft 8¾ in; wing area 340 sq ft.
Empty weight 4,362 lb; normal maximum weight 5,700 lb; maximum overloaded weight 6,200 lb.
Maximum speed 152 mph; cruising speed 114 mph; initial rate of climb 635 ft/min; greatest altitude reached in trials 8,000 ft; endurance 3 hr.

One example, G-AFZS/TK580 c/n A.37/1.

TG263 in original form, Cowes, summer 1947. (*AQD, Crown Copyright*)

Saunders-Roe SR.A/1

During 1943, Sir Arthur Gouge joined Saunders-Roe after resigning from Short Brothers Ltd over Government nationalisation of his old company. This coincided with the birth of a most progressive idea at Cowes. The new concept involved a jet-propelled flying-boat fighter. There was nothing new in the idea of a water-based fighter itself, and its advantages were obvious, especially in a mobile campaign. Such aircraft needed no prepared bases, merely sheltered stretches of water, which would be impossible to bomb out of use.

The newly developed jet engine captured the imagination of all who were made familiar with it. Saunders-Roe recognised that the Pacific Ocean in particular might provide an area of operation for a waterborne fighter, with island-hopping to consider as well as the possible destruction of existing runways by the Japanese. Jet power would be able to provide the Allies with a waterbased fighter of relatively favourable performance against the Japanese, who relied on piston-engined types. In this way, the traditional advantage of the land-based fighter against its waterborne opponent might disappear.

It was also realised that the absence of an airscrew would be most beneficial to a flying-boat fighter (and flying-boats generally), removing the traditional disadvantage of a high thrust line, and the associated need for a deep hull. This in turn would decrease structure weight and improve aerodynamic properties. Less power and thus less fuel would be needed than in the case of a large-hulled or float fighter. The combination of turbojet and flying-boat might provide a most potent force.

It was with these ideas in mind that the SR.A/1 was born. Knowler had talks in the summer of 1943 with Dr Hugh Francis, chief technical officer of the MAEE, and Dr D.M. Smith, chief engineer with Metropolitan-Vickers' Gas Turbine Department. Following this, in December 1943 Saro submitted to MAP proposals for a turbojet-powered fighter flying-boat able to operate from protected coastal waters.

So impressed was MAP by these proposals that after some amendment a contract was awarded to the company. This was to Specification E.6/44, which was written round the Saro submission and was placed with the firm in May 1944, the Limit of Liability being £305,000 and the order being placed as a Directorate of Technical Development venture.

Though most aspects of the new prototype progressed smoothly, the hull form came under some scrutiny. A very slender planing surface was considered to try to reduce aero- and hydrodynamic drag, but it was rejected because the arrangement offered less longitudinal stability than hulls employing the traditional length-to-beam ratio in the order of 6:1. Knowler proposed that the turbojets be mounted side-by-side within the fuselage, so beam was in any event made subject to that requirement. E.6/44 did not require open-sea capability (largely because Saro did not undertake to supply it) and it was not necessary to employ a deep hull to ensure that the engine intake would clear spray in rough seas. By early 1946 the hulls for three prototype E.6/44s were under construction. A tendency to porpoise at overload shown in model form had been eliminated by moving the position of the step slightly aft.

The new aircraft did not receive an official name. Known colloquially as the 'Squirt', it was designated SR.A./1 following the then new system of SBAC nomenclature of aircraft types, A/1 indicating the first Saro aircraft to appear after the introduction of that system. Design work was initially undertaken at Beaumaris but when at the end of hostilities the Design Department returned to Cowes, the work was completed on the Isle of Wight. Components for three prototypes were manufactured at Beaumaris and Eastleigh as well as at Cowes, but assembly and testing were at Cowes itself. Though an attempt was made to be as conventional as possible under the circumstances, the resulting prototypes were in fact unique, as well as highly successful.

Metropolitan-Vickers F.2/4 Beryl axial-flow turbojet. (*AQD, Crown Copyright*)

The SR.A/1 was designed around two Metropolitan-Vickers F.2/4 Beryl axial-flow turbojets, a promising design which was first run in January 1945, and which was small in diameter when compared with the centrifugal-type compressors then being built in much greater quantities. The F.2/4s could be situated side by side in the hull without an overlarge beam resulting and there was sufficient space between the installations to stand and work in the engine compartment.

Air was fed via a large common intake situated in the nose through a bifurcated duct to the engines. The intake was provided with an extendable snout with a movement of 10 inches, intended to prevent water ingestion. It was proposed that this be linked to the float-retracting mechanism so that when the floats were lowered, the snout was extended in harmony. In fact, this linkage was never connected, except in the case of the third prototype built, for trials proved the snout unnecessary; the SR.A/1 was not intended for operation in choppy seas and at low taxi-ing speeds was designed to sit in a tail-down attitude. At fast surface speeds the aircraft lifted partially out of the water in the normal way. No problems of water ingestion were experienced. While both engines shared the nose intake, each had its own exhaust mid-set behind the wing roots and toed out 5 deg to keep the hull clear of jet efflux.

The hull form adopted was a faired V-form single-step layout trailing to a knife-edge where the water rudder was situated. Construction was all-metal and consisted of strong keel members, closely spaced frames and light stringers, under a riveted and carefully filled skin. Internal structure was shaped round the powerplants. The single-seat cockpit was a small

The hull bow and keelson of the first SR.A/1, TG263, under construction. (*AQD, Crown Copyright*)

and separate pressurised unit let into the hull just forward of the main wing spar. The single-piece Triplex bubble canopy was electrically operated and pressurisation of the unit catered for by means of hot air drawn from the engine compressors and cooled through circulation round the air intake. This system was pre-set to activate at 9,000 ft. Provision was made for a G-suit, and a Martin-Baker ejection seat was fitted, the first to be delivered to an aircraft manufacturer from the Martin-Baker works.

Armament, four Hispano Mk 5 20 mm cannon each with 760 rounds, was designed to be mounted in the nose decking above the air intake, eliminating harmonisation problems. A gyro gunsight was placed under the windscreen with a suitable graticule and attachment for rocket ranging. The cockpit was protected with armour plating supplied by the English Steel Corporation and behind the cockpit unit was an engine-access hatch.

Three aspects of the cockpit are of particular interest. Because the wing floats were designed to be semi-retractable, float position indicator lights were installed in the cockpit in the same manner as undercarriage position lights would be in a landplane. A toggle control was provided for inter-connecting the air rudder with the water rudder while taxi-ing. It was necessary that a water rudder be installed since the differential engines could not be used for steering because of their position. Finally, a semi-automatic mooring hook control was included, operated by the pilot through a push-pull knob. The mooring system incorporated in the SR.A/1 was ingenious; the aircraft was taxied between two marker buoys connected by a cable. The mooring hook itself was located in the nose of the aircraft at a point on the keel just below the waterline. When this hook was engaged on the cable, which was performed by merely taxi-ing over it, the aircraft could be dragged to a suitable pontoon or dock. An auxiliary hook, also controlled from the cockpit, was provided for towing.

The wing was of high-speed Goldstein aerofoil section, built around a central main spar and a subordinate rear spar and fitted with dive-brakes and dive recovery flaps (though only those of the third prototype were

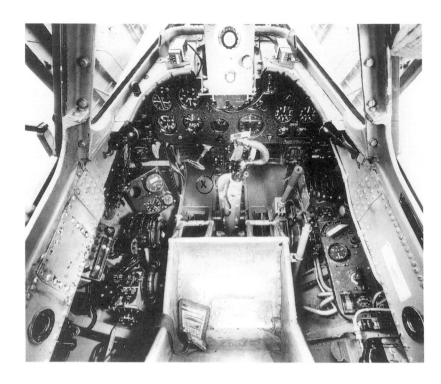

The cockpit of TG263. Throttle and trim controls are on the port side, single-exposure camera gun controls in the centre, fuel controls to the right. The button indicated by X is marked 'PORT IGN'. Just above the X is the water-rudder toggle. (*AQD, Crown Copyright*)

operable), as well as ailerons and split flaps. Fuel tanks were situated two in each wing within the D of the leading-edge torsion box and bounded spanwise by wingroot and float-strut attachments. Total capacity of these tanks was 424 gall. Various underwing loads could be carried on hardpoints close to the wing roots. The partially retractable wing floats rotated through 180 deg when retracted so that the unaerodynamic planing bottoms became positioned in underside wells leaving only the streamlined upper portions exposed.

The tailplane of the 'Squirt' was designed round a light spar near the leading edge and another adjacent to the elevator. The assembly was high-set in order to clear spray and jet efflux. The originality of the flight surfaces lay in the adoption of combined geared trimming and spring tabs mounted on 'boundary bars' which permitted manual control without trailing-edge problems or fine balance.

The all-up-weight of 16,000 lb produced a flying-boat somewhat bigger than its land-based equivalent but performance was still high, especially by waterborne-aircraft standards and the S.R.A/1 was in a class of its own. This performance was not achieved at the expense of general handling characteristics and the wing loading was of a fairly normal value by

TG263 with acorn fairing at the junction of tailplane and fin, off Cowes during late 1947.
(BHC)

contemporary standards. Throughout construction, conventional materials were used and Saro applied a fine Titanine finish over the flush riveted exterior, to help in preserving laminar flow far back over the wing.

When in May 1944 it had been agreed that construction should go ahead, three prototype SR.A/1s were ordered, with serials TG263, TG267 and TG271, and though it was suggested by the Ministry of Supply in January 1946 that one be cancelled, three eventually emerged. TG263 had been completed by the spring of 1947 and Geoffrey Tyson undertook flight testing. Following successful taxi-ing trials, Tyson made the first flight in TG263 on the evening of 16 July, 1947. He announced generally sound water and air handling but one problem was a slight snaking tendency. This was cured during the following month when a small acorn fairing was added at the junction of the tailplane and fin. Also during the initial trials, a tendency to roll was discovered. This resulted in a reduced rudder horn balance and the addition of metal strips to the rudder trailing-edge. Premature tip stall was cured by increasing the nose radii of the wing outer sections, TG267 at least being modified in this way.

The fifth flight of TG263, made at the end of July, was observed by representatives from the RAF, RAE, Naval Aviation, the aircraft industry, and the press. Tyson made low flypasts at nearly 400 mph and demonstrated a short take-off technique he had perfected. This consisted

201

TG271 in Columbine hangar, adjacent to the hull of Princess G-ALUN, early spring 1949.

One of TG263's early take-offs; Geoffrey Tyson's 'sharp-start' technique is well illustrated.
(*BHC*)

The final modification made to TG263 was the replacement of the transparent cockpit hood by a metal one. (*Saro*)

of retracting the wing floats as soon as the flying-boat had attained lateral stability, thus minimising drag.

The only other alteration made to the first prototype was the replacement of the transparent cockpit hood by a metal canopy following the loss of the former during a much later test-flight in May 1948. In fact, testing was so successful that TG263 was exhibited at the 1947 SBAC Show two months after its first flight. After more tests at Cowes, it passed to the MAEE for type trials. It was found that take-offs could be made in 26 sec and that the rate of climb was exceptional.

Meanwhile, construction of TG267 and TG271 had proceeded well at Cowes and both aircraft were airborne by 1948, TG267 first flying on 30 April and TG271 on 17 August; the latter was exhibited at the 1948 SBAC Show in September. Whereas development of the SR.A/1 had begun with Beryls of only 3,230 lb st (TG263), TG267 had Beryls of 3,500 lb st and

The third example, TG271, built with an acorn fairing, off the Columbine slipway, late 1948. The protective inlet snout is extended.

TG271 received fully-rated Beryls of 3,850 lb st. Flying TG271, Tyson gave a fabulous demonstration at Farnborough in September with a superb display of aerobatics and a very low inverted pass, the aircraft being fitted with extra compartments in the fuel tanks, together with a special inverted-flight fuel valve, and sufficient fuel for just one such performance at a time. While TG271 was usually based at Cowes for general aerodynamic and hydrodynamic research and carried extensive engine test equipment. TG267 eventually arrived at the MAEE during the summer of 1949. The first prototype had by that time been put into store while the programme's future was considered.

During 1949, both TG267 and TG271 were lost. In August of that year, the very experienced Service test-pilot, Lieut Cdr Eric M. Brown, was alighting off Cowes in TG271 when a half-submerged obstruction suddenly became visible. Brown was committed to alighting and while still travelling at speed he hit the obstacle. The hull of TG271 was holed, the aircraft lost its starboard float and turned over. Brown managed to get clear and was rescued by Geoffrey Tyson, who dived from a nearby safety launch and dragged him aboard. TG271 sank in the Solent and was never found, despite frantic searches to recover its on-board flight recorders.

Following this unfortunate accident, in September of the same year TG267 was lost off Felixstowe. The pilot, Sqn Ldr K.A. Major, was re-hearsing in poor weather for a Battle of Britain air display and suffered (it is thought) loss of control in roll. TG267 dived into the sea, broke up and sank. It was suggested at the enquiry that the pilot might have blacked out or perhaps had pulled the control column back too swiftly after a bad roll.

TG263 in original form, over southern England, summer 1947. Geoffrey Tyson is at the controls. (*BHC*)

Sqn Ldr Major was at that time out of practice at aerobatics and it was also suggested that he might have made rolls while facing out to sea rather than towards land, and had not realised quickly enough that the nose of TG267 was dropping. The wreckage was later recovered and examined, but the cause of the accident was not found.

The loss of the second and third SR.A/1 prototypes was not the result of a design flaw, but nevertheless the development programme was retarded. One problem was to find suitable engines should there be further orders. Under an agreement with MAP, as part of a general postwar contraction of the aviation industry, Metropolitan-Vickers reverted to its original prewar activities of building electrical generators and allied machinery. The design of the Beryl was passed to Armstrong Siddeley along with other gas turbine projects. Beryl orders remained at eleven only, enough for three SR.A/1s and five spare engines. Armstrong Siddeley did not continue production of the Beryl so even had Saro acquired orders for the SR.A/1, powerplant problems would have been immense. The company mooted the idea of using just one Armstrong Siddeley Saphire 3 turbojet instead of the two Beryls, but this was rejected because of the hull redesign it would have entailed, especially when a production contract was nowhere in sight.

TG263 remained in store until November 1950. No further orders for

TG271 off Cowes, early 1949. This example was the only one to have exhaust fairings, just visible here. (*Saro*)

the SR.A/1 were placed and the possibility of interest from abroad remained unlikely, though the United States had by that time received particulars of the design. British Service interest in waterborne aircraft generally was waning. Though undoubtedly in a class of its own as a flying-boat, by the time the 'Squirt' was flying it was rapidly losing parity with the new generation of land-based fighter types.

The whole project appeared to be dying naturally when in November 1950 hydrodynamic tests were resumed with the remaining aircraft, TG263. The Korean War had suggested an application for a flying-boat fighter able to operate from advanced bases. However, the SR.A/1 was not adopted for this role in Korea; redesign around new engines would have taken far too long, though it was considered briefly at Cowes.

The last public appearance of the SR.A/1 was in June 1951, when Geoffrey Tyson took TG263, by that time wearing 'B' Conditions identity G-12-1, to London for display on the Thames at the Festival of Britain. After exhibition, the aircraft was presented to the College of Aeronautics

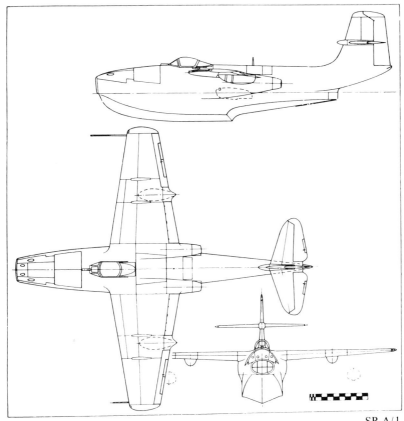

SR.A/1

at Cranfield, where one of the Beryls was removed and used to power Donald Campbell's ill-fated *Bluebird* speedboat. In 1966, G-12-1 passed to the Skyfame Museum at Staverton, Gloucester. During early 1978, the SR.A./1 arrived to join the Duxford collection of the Imperial War Museum. By late 1981, the aircraft was wearing a white primer coat before receiving its original decor once more. It is now restored as TG263, a unique and priceless exhibit.

The SR.A/1 was in a class entirely of its own. Had the war against the Japanese lasted longer than it did, the type might have seen service and would have been most effective on short-range operations. It is interesting to note, however, that surviving records fail to confirm any intention to apply the SR.A/1 to the Pacific theatre. In fact, and perhaps surprisingly, the limited range of the 'Squirt' was remarked on by MAP as precluding use in that theatre.

Two Metropolitan-Vickers Beryl F.2/4: TG263, 3,230 lb st; TG267, 3,500 lb st; TG271, 3,850 lb st.

207

TG263 as G-12-1, at the 1951 Festival of Britain.

G-12-1 at the College of Aeronautics, Cranfield, June 1965.

208

Two views of the remains of SR.A/1 TG263's cockpit at Duxford in 1982; it is remarkably intact. (*A. G. London*)

Engine bay of SR.A/1 TG263 at Duxford in 1982. The starboard Beryl has long since been removed. Note access ladder to hull decking. (*A.G. London*)

Span 46 ft; length 50 ft; height 16 ft 9 in; wing area 415 sq ft.
Empty weight 11,262 lb; maximum weight without slipper tanks 16,000 lb; maximum overloaded weight 19,033 lb.
Maximum speed recorded 512 mph; take-off run 21 sec; initial rate of climb 5,800 ft/min; service ceiling 43,000 ft; endurance without slipper tanks 1 hr 48 min, with slipper tanks 2 hr 24 min.
Theoretical armament: four Hispano Mk 5 20 mm cannon and 760–900 rounds; two 250 lb, 500 lb or 1,000 lb bombs; two 200 lb smoke-floats; eight rocket projectiles, or four rocket projectiles and two semi-filled 141 gal slipper tanks; two 141 gal slipper tanks.
Actual armament: TG263—rocket projectile installation and bomb carriers for aerodynamic tests, not operable; TG267—operable bomb installations; TG271—operable rocket projectile installation and bomb carriers. Cannon ports blanked off.

Three examples, TG263, TG267, TG271.

Saunders-Roe SR.45 Princess

Saunders-Roe, with its very long maritime tradition, believed in the flying-boat even after the war when large numbers of concrete runways had been laid down throughout the world. The development of the gas-turbine powerplant, offering a higher power/weight ratio than had previously been available, encouraged Saunders-Roe in the design of an even bigger flying-boat than those which had gone before, though provision of really

Princess G-ALUN off Cowes during early trials, summer 1952. (*Saro*)

suitable and powerful engines eventually proved a major problem in the development of the definitive type, SR.45. However, almost immediately after a 1944 study for a six-engined 187,000 lb 'boat was complete in broad outline, Knowler and Arthur Gouge made three fundamental changes. Adopting the gas-turbine as a powerplant, size was scaled up; at the same time, a further innovation came when Knowler made provision for a pressurised hull. By mid-1945, the enlarged study, SR.45, was in existence though very far from finalised. The initial proposal was for a flying-boat of 220 ft span, powered by six Armstrong Siddeley Cobra propeller turbines.

The wing-form was of very thick section inboard, but it was decided to place the engines in conventional nacelles ahead of the leadingedge rather than imitate the buried installation adopted in the Bristol Brabazon then under development. The hull, 146 ft long, was arranged as two decks with what Knowler described as a 'figure eight cross-section'. This later became known as a 'double-bubble' section, and in the case of SR.45 was pressurised to 8 psi. Range of the flying-boat was to be 3,300 miles and ideal operating height 39,000 ft. Wing float arrangement was to be similar to that of the SR.A/1 also then under development, the floats retracting into the lower surface of the wing, with their normally outer sides down. An automatic docking facility similar in principle to that employed by the SR.A/1 was adopted.

During the spring of 1945, Saro made proposals for the building of

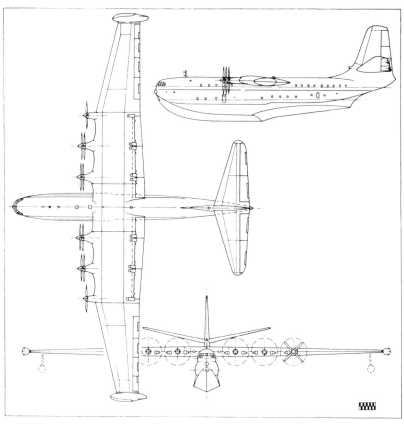

SR.45 Princess

SR.45 to the Ministry of Supply (MoS), and the Minister, George Strauss, was most enthusiastic over the proposals. He regarded SR.45 as an important part of BOAC's future service. BOAC indicated some interest (though at no time firm commitment) to both the MoS and the Ministry of Civil Aviation. An order was placed for three SR.45s in May 1946, after the MoS had issued the Specification for the type, C.10/46. Total contract price was £2.8 million. The Ministry of Civil Aviation was deemed the 'contracting authority' in the May 1946 development but soon afterwards the MoS asserted that *it* was the sole authority for the purchase of new British civil aircraft. Shortly after this, the Director-General of Technical Development (Air), MoS, stated that operators could deal directly with manufacturers if they wished, which was probably the most sensible policy.

It was generally taken for granted by the Government, the MoS, and in particular George Strauss, that BOAC would want SR.45, especially for its trans-Atlantic routes. Only BOAC appeared to query this. Thus develop-

The hull of G-ALUN under construction inside Columbine hangar, showing to effect its double-bubble form. (*AQD, Crown Copyright*)

ment of SR.45 was continued at Cowes though rather slowly because of the numerous innovations incorporated.

By January 1947 the design had been stabilised and detail drawings were well in hand. The originally planned power units had by that time been replaced by Rolls-Royce Tweeds. Wing design was far advanced when it was announced that the Tweed would not go into production. In all, five different powerplants were considered before a final choice was made; Clyde, Cobra, Eagle, Python and Tweed. The underdeveloped Bristol Proteus 2 propeller-turbine was finally selected.

In early 1948 the press was invited to Cowes to see the first SR.45 hull in its jigs. At the same time, more details of the new aircraft emerged. It was here that the decision to adopt the Proteus was announced. These engines were (on paper) rated at 3,200 shp/800 lb thrust, and were to be installed as four coupled pairs and two single outboard units, a total of no less than ten units.

The adoption of the Proteus had necessitated considerable redesign of SR.45's wingform, for it was a reverse-flow engine with air entering near the rear. Large inlets and ducts had to be incorporated in the wings ahead of the front spar to cater for this installation. Other changes from the original study revealed in 1948 included a larger fin and a higher mounted tailplane than had previously been planned. The nose, originally to have been hemispherical, was modified so that the cockpit was extended slightly forward, providing an improved view. The floats were re-positioned and by this time were designed to form the wingtips when retracted.

Perhaps the most advanced aspects of SR.45 were the inclusion of hull pressurisation, air-conditioning and power-operated irreversible flying controls. At that time these systems were by no means fully developed and Saunders-Roe broke a great deal of new ground in incorporating them into SR.45.

Pressurisation and air-conditioning was achieved through a labyrinth of piping and valves, pressure being supplied by a large two-stage centrifugal compressor driven by each inboard power installation via a four-speed gearbox with auto-change. The greatest breakthrough, however, lay in the development of a power-control system for SR.45. Saunders-Roe rightly felt that an aircraft as large as SR.45 could not possibly be flown on muscle-power and so some form of artificial aid became essential. The company had in fact some experience in this field through the S.35 Shetland, but this was of a primitive nature. In conjunction with Boulton Paul, Saro designed a new system. Boulton Paul was made responsible for the manufacture of some components, but Saunders-Roe retained design authority throughout.

The dual controls in the flight deck were coupled to three similar power units, two in the stern dealing with the rudder and elevators and one in the top hull centre-section for the ailerons. Each unit was composed of two torque-converters manufactured by Boulton Paul, driving through a differential gearbox so that failure of either converter merely reduced output speed. The converters were 120 volt DC motors producing 7·5 hp and geared down to hydraulic variable-delivery pump/motor units. These motors ran at all times but mostly the pump action was zero, so the hydraulic aspect remained dormant until a manoeuvre was required.

As soon as a manoeuvre was called for from the controls the pump came

Bristol Proteus 2 series coupled engine. (*Saro*)

Bristol Proteus 2 series single engine. (*AQD, Crown Copyright*)

215

into operation, driving the hydraulic motor at a speed proportional to the handling of the controls. The output shafts powered lengths of rotating shaft via many change-speed gearboxes, right-angle boxes and universal joints, along to the surfaces, all shafting passing through a large number of aligning bearings. The surfaces were split; three parts to the rudder, two to each elevator and four to each aileron. Each split section was separately driven by its own screwjack from the main drive, providing good failsafe redundancy at the surface. An added safeguard should the system fail was the inclusion of handwheels that enabled the surfaces to be placed in the trail position.

The whole system was tested thoroughly, first on a rig, during 1949, and later on a Short Sunderland 5 which was converted for the work at Cowes. The Sunderland also featured a slightly larger fin than normal. Geoffrey Tyson flew the Sunderland during 1949 and 1950 and reported that the system worked well. However, Saunders-Roe already had ideas on improving the system for the SR.45. Another new development, a hydraulic-feel generator, was inserted in the flight deck, and the possibility was considered of developing a q-feel arrangement. Also, it was planned to reduce power unit size and weight through the employment of aero-dynamically-balanced surfaces, and to move the units adjacent to their respective surfaces. Even 'fly-by-wire' was considered. These innovations represented a fundamental step forward in the late 1940s and early 1950s.

G-ALUO under construction, Columbine, 1949.

In January 1948, the first flight date was put at late 1949, and it was in 1948 that the SR.45 finally acquired a name—Princess.

During March 1949, Saro issued a further bulletin claiming that progress was satisfactory and on schedule, and giving a completion date of late 1950. During October 1949, due to a revised delivery date for the engines, it was announced that flight trials would begin in the summer of 1951. In February 1951 the first coupled Proteus was finally installed and yet again the date for the start of flight trials was changed, on this occasion to some unspecified time in 1952.

The major effect on Cowes of building such a large aircraft was naturally one of expansion. Apart from the establishment of a new (power) Control Section, the number of design staff, as well as the rest of the workforce, was increased. New flight-test facilities were established and a half-scale wing (and later hull) specimen was built for evaluation at RAE Farnborough.

Meanwhile, the complete mechanical, electrical and hydraulic systems were constructed and tested at Cowes. Full sections of the hull were built in mock-up form. The construction of the three Princess examples took an immense amount of planning. All were partially assembled in Columbine hanger, with little room to spare. At the same time, Columbine apron and slipway was reinforced and extended to cater for the heavy load and to

G-ALUN's hull under construction, its large gunwale member *in situ*. (*Saro*)

G-ALUN is moved onto the reinforced Columbine apron, minus outer wings, engines and fin tip, autumn 1951. The beaching chassis route from hangar to apron has been marked on the concrete.

allow launching within a reasonable time either side of high tide.

By autumn 1951, the first Princess, minus engines, outer wings and fin tip, had been moved from Columbine hangar on to the adjacent apron because of the limited space within, and it had been necessary to pivot the aircraft backwards about 10 deg on the main beaching chassis, lowering the tail and raising the bow high in the air. Although by that time a coupled Proteus and two single units had been delivered, they were not fitted until after the move out of the hangar, and the single units could not be fitted until the outer wings were in place. Some 3,000 gal of water were pumped into the flight test ballast tanks before the move took place.

When the fin was completed the aircraft was swung round until the tail pointed toward the slipway. It was here that the outer wings and floats were added and the engines installed. The second aircraft, still inside Columbine, was receiving most of its tail assembly and the inner wings, and the moving procedure was repeated for the second and third, though these had to be parked further away from the slipway.

The Princess was a great technical success. At the time, the SR.45 was the heaviest all-metal passenger transport ever built and the biggest ever metal flying-boat, as well as the largest aircraft powered by gas-turbines.

Completion of G-ALUN's fin, late 1951. (*Saro*)

The newly-completed G-ALUN, dwarfing Columbine slipway. In the background, G-ALUO.

This view of the Princess shows the graceful lines of the hull and almost imperceptible step.
(*BEA*)

220

The hull was 148 ft long, with a beam of 16 ft 7 in and a draught of 8 ft. A 'double-bubble' cross-section provided a rigid structure for cabin pressurisation and the waist of the 'double-bubble' formed the division between upper and lower decks. To this structure an orthodox chined planing-bottom was attached. This was unpressurised and had a large

G-ALUN's flight deck, surprisingly spartan. The engineer's large panels are aft and to starboard. (*AQD, Crown Copyright*)

221

number of watertight compartments formed round every third frame. The upper portion of the hull was cut out to receive the high-mounted wing and was edged with an extruded-channel gunwale member to which the wing was bolted at various chordal stations to take out drag loads. Lift and side loads were taken through the main attachment points. At the upper and lower deck levels, Y-section longitudinals united the skin panelling of the deck structures and distributed pressurisation loads into the decks and underbody walls. A single vestigial step of $\frac{5}{16}$ in was incorporated in the planing bottom, which tapered to an angled knife-edge under the leading-edge of the fin.

On the flight deck, at the forward end of the upper deck, were the Captain and First Officer positions in the extreme bow, while behind and to starboard were seats and instruments for the two flight engineers. Navigator and radio operator positions were to port. Aft of the flight deck were a crew rest-room and forward galley, while below were manual mooring facilities in a separate, unpressurised compartment; of course, the automatic option was also available. Two cargo holds were provided in the lower deck with a total capacity of 18,000 lb. Various plans for passenger accommodation were suggested. The most popular of these was that evolved in conjunction with a cautious BOAC, which did not want to

The complex leading-edge of the Princess wing, showing the multi-purpose inlets, contra-rotating airscrews and engine cowlings which doubled as maintenance platforms. (*AQD, Crown Copyright*)

create the impression that involvement in interior design implied agreement to buy the Princess, but nonetheless helped to design such a layout. It consisted of accommodation for 105 passengers in tourist and first-class cabins, and also included a cocktail bar, powder rooms and toilets, bunks, and two spiral staircases connecting the decks. A passenger galley was planned, adjacent to a spacious dining-room. Port-holes were made fail-safe in the event of a cracked pane or even a blow-out, but were large enough to provide a good view. In fact, none of the passenger cabins were ever installed and the three Princesses remained unfurnished.

The wing, a two-spar structure built in five sections had an aspect ratio of 9.5 and was basically a Saro-developed Goldstein section designed to give low cruising drag, but with a transition to a modified NACA 4415 series section at the tips, this transition being associated with a wash-out of 2 deg. The wing comprised the centre section bridging the hull and extending to the inboard nacelle, inner wings extending to just beyond the outboard nacelle, and outer wings extending to the tip floats. Centre-section and inner wing spars ran parallel, at a chord-wise spacing of 12 ft, but in the outer panels they converged to 5 ft 4 in at the float support rib. The centre section was of parallel chord but the inner wings were slightly tapered and the leading edges of the outer wings swept back. The wing span was 209 ft 6 in, but with the floats retracted this was increased to 219 ft 6 in. Four integral fuel tanks were contained in the inner wing with a total capacity of 14,000 gal. Construction of the wing leading edges was made particularly complex because of the intake and nacelle fairing structures. The single-slotted flaps were divided into three on each side, and all eight aileron sections were fitted with servo-tabs. The wing de-icing mechanism was powered by hot air drawn from the tail-pipe cooling shrouds. The air used for cabin heating was also taken from here. The wingtip floats were actuated by a Dowty hydraulic system with power-packs mounted in the wingtips, and were flat-topped to align with the end-ribs.

The tail was of conventional arrangement. At the dorsal fin fillet was situated a ram orifice feeding the tail de-icing, a pair of paraffin combustion heaters which circulated hot air to the three leading-edges. In the top of the fin and on the inner edges of the elevators were housed three plate aerials. The rudder was split into three with the bottom section incorporating a servo-tab while the elevators, also fitted with tabs, were split in a similar way, this time into two. The tailplane had 12 deg dihedral.

Power was supplied by ten Bristol Proteus 2 propeller-turbines arranged as four coupled and two single units. All were fitted with specially-developed de Havilland four-blade airscrews of 16 ft 6 in diameter fitted with solid duralumin blades. The single outboard units drove single airscrews but the coupled units drove contra-rotating airscrews and all incorporated electric de-icing. The outer coupled units had a 12 deg pitch range for manoeuvring on the water. An Airspeed Ambassador was used as a convenient test-bed for flight trials of the single airscrews before the type was installed on the Princess.

The lower parts of the engine nacelles were hinged at the front spar and could be lowered to provide maintenance platforms. There were also facilities for collapsible engine hoists to be placed on the upper mainplane surface, allowing engine changes without external assistance.

Certainly a unique and beautiful aircraft, Saunders-Roe Princess G-ALUN.

While drive from the single turbines was conventionally arranged, that from the coupled units was via unifying and reduction gearboxes situated ahead of the engines and powering the contra-rotating propellers on co-axial shafts. These were arranged so that in the event of a failure of one unit within a coupled pair, the live unit would continue to drive its propeller. Engine tailpipes protruded near the trailing edge and the flaps were tailored around them. The ten intakes were more complex than they appeared from the outside, and were split vertically, for four purposes; the three largest vents ducted air to the engines and could be turned to blank off in case of fire. The middle vent was itself split and led to jet-pipe heat-exchangers and to the generators, providing cooling air. The vent formed in the point of the vee-shape served engine and gearbox oil coolers.

Air-conditioning of the hull was by way of the compound units housed in the wing-root leading edges. Air serving the heater was ducted from the tailpipe shrouds and air serving the cooler was obtained from the main intakes. Cabin conditions were selected and maintained by a Normalair pressure system and a Teddington Controls humidity and temperature system. The required air was delivered via the wing centre section and into a mixing chamber to enter the decks just above floor level.

Total generating capacity of the electrical system was 4×39 kW at 120 V and 2×6 kW at 24 V. The 39 kW generators were driven by accessory gearboxes on the sides of the coupled units, the outboard of which also drove the 6 kW generators. From both generator busbars, feed was given to a pair of distributor busbars from which services were taken. The 6 kW system was similar.

Nearly ready for its first flight; G-ALUN, to the left, is almost complete. G-ALUO, in the foreground, was never finished. On the extreme left is SR.A/1 G-12-1.

The developed engine for the Princess, the Proteus 3, was light and much improved in terms of output, but was not available in 1952. Thus when the Princess finally emerged, it was disastrously underpowered.

By March 1951 the original contract price of £2.8 million had risen to £10.8 million. Engine costing had climbed from an optimistic £407,000 in 1946 to £4,920,000, also by March 1951. When Bristol was approached about the soaring costs, and it was pointed out that the Proteus and coupled Proteus were already being funded as part of the Bristol Brabazon programme, the company was unable to give a satisfactory reply to why engine development had become so expensive.

The three Princesses were registered to the MoS as G-ALUN, G-ALUO and G-ALUP. By August 1952, G-ALUN was finally completed. On 19 August it was cleared for flight but the intention to launch it was thwarted by a powerful northeast wind. Two days later, shortly after midnight, G-ALUN was finally lowered into the water from Columbine slipway and moored at the mouth of the Medina. After being fuelled it was moved outside the harbour breakwater. The first flight was a momentous occasion, and crowds gathered to watch.

On 22 August, G-ALUN flew for the first time. Following engine runs and brief taxi-ing trials, a two-mile stretch of water was cleared in the Solent off Cowes, though the take-off run was expected to be less than 1,000 yards. On board was a crew of eleven including Geoffrey Tyson in

The night of 21–22 August, 1952. At last, G-ALUN is launched for the first time. (*Saro*)

command, and John Booth as co-pilot. After the homeward-bound *Mauretania* had passed, at 12.13 pm G-ALUN took off on its maiden flight, a leisurely circuit of the Isle of Wight. Half an hour later she was again on the water having recorded a fastest speed of 280 mph. Tyson was quite satisfied with air and water handling and had wanted to stay airborne longer. However, the two airscrew translation bearing temperature gauges had started to give false readings and so the flight was curtailed. All else had been trouble-free.

G-ALUN made three further flights, totalling 6 hr 10 min, before making a public debut at the 1952 SBAC Show at Farnborough on 2 September, where it is fair to say the aircraft dominated the proceedings. Part of its demonstration included a very steep and sustained bank past the stands; what the guests did not know was that the Princess had reached such a high airspeed that the feel units in the power controls caused Tyson great difficulty in rolling back to level flight and an accident was only narrowly averted. Upon return to Cowes, one further flight was made and G-ALUN was then beached for inspection and resonance tests which lasted until October.

Although the Princess had been successfully flown, its future was uncertain. In October 1950, BOAC had created a Princess Unit under Capt H.W.C. Alger, an experienced flying-boat pilot and formerly manager of

Early days; G-ALUN under test over southern England, summer 1952. (*Saro*)

BOAC No. 4 (Flying-Boat) Line at Hythe, to study the preparations needed for the introduction of flying-boats in the 105-seater class, the airline was evasive when asked if the SR.45 would actually be employed. However, it was unofficially announced in February 1951 that the third Princess would be scrapped in order to save money, some £1 million being mentioned. There were suggestions that British South American Airways might use the Princess, but in March 1951 it was suggested that all three examples be used by the RAF, a fairly strong indication that BOAC were no longer interested in the type. The possibility of RAF use was reinforced in October, with accommodation for 200 troops rather than 105 civilians. In December, a new company named Princess Air Transport Co Ltd was formed by Saro, with Airwork Ltd holding a 25 per cent interest, to 'study the factors affecting the operation of the Princess flying-boats and to be in a position to tender for their operation should the opportunity arise'. BOAC's interest appeared to resurface, meanwhile; Alger was seconded to Princess Air Transport as general manager. In August 1952, BOAC again expressed a tentative interest in the Princess, though in what sense this might manifest itself was left unclear.

In the following month, the interest crystallised into an offer of establishing a marine development flight. However, this gesture was hastily withdrawn after it became clear that there was no immediate prospect of

G-ALUN taxi-ing toward the mouth of the Medina. The split flight control surfaces are visible. (*Saro*)

the aircraft entering service because of the unsuitability of the Proteus 2 for commercial operations and the failure of an alternative powerplant to emerge.

Later in 1952, Sir Miles Thomas, chairman of BOAC, stated that in his opinion the Princess was out of date technically, although having watched G-ALUN's maiden flight he had claimed BOAC was 'tremendously interested' in the aircraft. He went on too point out the existence of the new Bristol BE.25 propeller-turbine, it later named the Orion, and indicated that this might be the engine to revitalise the future of the Princess, providing the long-range and passenger-carrying facility necessary to make it competitive on the major air routes. This observation came in October 1952. However, by that time it had been decided at Cowes to install the Proteus 3, which involved only minor modifications.

Installation of the Orion would not be possible for some time as development was far from complete; also, it would be necessary to make major modifications to the Princess airframe. It was felt at the time by Saunders-Roe that perhaps only six Proteus 3s would be required, but tis would have reduced range to just over 2,000 miles and in any case, the Princess would not have begun commercial operations before late 1956 at the earliest because the flight and water tests were likely to take some time.

228

G-ALUN moored off East Cowes during the summer of 1952, with one of its main beaching chassis members to the left—these had buoyancy capability.

In view of the uncertainties surrounding the programme, a decision had been made by the MoS in March 1952 to halt work on G-ALUO and G-ALUP, and cocoon them. Both aircraft were eventually towed across the Solent to Calshot Spit where they were beached, G-ALUO on 13 February 1952, and G-ALUP following shortly afterwards. Meanwhile, Duncan Sandys, the new Minister of Supply, remained evasive over the fate of the aircraft but did indicate that the development of new engines necessary for the Princess was being given only low priority.

In September 1953, G-ALUN appeared once more at the SBAC Show, finished in a new livery of blue, yellow and white, and this was the last public appearance of the Princess. In October 1953, the MoS invited independent operators to submit bids for. Eoin C. Mekie, chairman of Aquila Airways, made a firm bid to buy all three aircraft at a price of well over £1 million each, but the offer was not accepted.

The entire Princess programme had ceased by June 1954. Only the first example, G-ALUN, had flown, having completed a total of 96 hr 50 min in 47 flights between August 1952 and June 1954. The MAEE was enthusiastic about the Princess. Basic aero- and hydro-dynamic performance of G-ALUN was described as satisfactory. On the water, the Princess was adequately stable on take off and alighting, while spray

229

Ominous signs; Princess G-ALUO during cocooning, Cowes, late 1952. The black area is a bituminous layer applied between coats of polyvinyl plastic. (*AQD, Crown Copyright*)

characteristics were considered good overall. In the air, the only mildly adverse point made concerned the simulated feel characteristics and control to surface ratios, which it was felt needed modification to improve the feel of positive stability. Even under asymmetric power, the aircraft was adequately controllable, right down to the stall. Stall behaviour itself was good with good stall warning. Despite the satisfactory findings of the MAEE, however, there were no orders and finally G-ALUN was cocooned too, minus its engines, but remained at Cowes.

However, that was not the end of the affair. More schemes, most of them vague, emerged during the 1950s and into the 1960s concerning the operation of the aircraft. Providing a backdrop to these discrete ideas throughout the period were the detailed examinations made jointly by the Government, Saunders-Roe and even BOAC, into operational requirements associated with the aircraft. Searches were made for suitable sites from which to operate, methods of conveyance to and from the Princess were assessed, as were docking procedures and maintenance facilities. Route planning was examined; such destinations as Cape Town, Hong Kong, Sydney, Wellington, Vancouver, San Francisco, New York and Jamaica were considered. It was felt by the Government at least that a London base might be made on the Staines reservoir.

During 1955, rumours started over the possible purchase of the Princess by the United States Navy for use as flying test-beds for atomic reactors.

1953; G-ALUN in its new livery of blue, yellow and white. (*BHC*)

These rumours persisted until 1958 and finally crystallised in July of that year when a Saro team visited America to discuss purchase. However, nothing came of the talks and in late 1958 a new potential buyer emerged. Air Vice Marshal D.C.T. Bennett, together with B.G. Halpin, a Southampton businessman, made a bid for all three aircraft, planning to install six Rolls-Royce Tyne 11 engines, which would have provided the Princess with much of the power it so desperately needed. Bennett and Halpin were kept waiting over a year for a Ministry decision on their offer and in March 1960 the idea was abandoned.

Earlier, during the latter stages of 1957, Saro had mooted a plan to make the Princess more attractive to the market, by converting SR.45 to a landplane. Saro also favoured Tyne engines, and thought the idea might be of use to the military, for the Princess might have made a first-class troop transport. However, this plan was only really a suggestion and because no enthusiasm was forthcoming it was never implemented.

231

G-ALUN moored off East Cowes during 1953.

In November 1960 a new company was registered; British Princess Flying-Boats Ltd, the founder being B.G. Halpin. Despite his previous disappointment in alliance with Air Vice Marshal Bennett, Halpin was still interested in operating the Princess and the new company was eager to buy all three aircraft if the Government would guarantee operating rights on at least one high-density route. Halpin was particularly interested in linking Southampton with Baltimore, Chicago and Detroit. Again, Tynes were to be adopted and Halpin hoped to begin services in late 1962. No route guarantee was given, however, and Halpin's interest understandably waned.

By May 1962 the Ministry of Aviation had announced a definite sale of Princess G-ALUN for an undisclosed five-figure sum to the Winder Corporation based in Florida. This in fact was far from definite and eventually evaporated. During 1963 the War Office, acting on behalf of the MoA, asked for tenders from any (remaining) interested parties to be submitted by 12 December; this request was made during November 1963 and so gave little time for parties to decide on any commitment. However, Aero Spacelines showed enthusiam and made a study for NASA on the possibility of the Princess being employed for the carriage of Saturn V components. This study even considered a twinned 'boat with a new wing centre-section. Like the other plans, this one came to nothing.

Princess G-ALUN, in its protective coat, on the west bank of the Medina in 1963.

G-ALUN at the breaker's yard, Southampton, mid-1967.

233

In January 1964, the War Office announced that one of the bidders had purchased all three Princesses. This proved to be Eoin Mekie, who had wanted the aircraft some years before for Aquila. However, the price by this time had dropped considerably; Mekie paid £30,000. It was intended that he supply Aero Spacelines with the components necessary for their Saturn V transport and in July 1965, G-ALUO and G-ALUP were de-cocooned and partially dismantled for shipment to the United States. In September, this work stopped.

Cocooning had worked. Corrosion during most of the storage time was minimal and the Princesses remained in good condition. However, the contract between Westland and the MoA covering inspection and maintenance was not renewed after expiry in the summer of 1964 and consequently, by the time Mekie began to examine the second and third aircraft, they had begun to deteriorate. Neither left Calshot, where they had lain for over 12 years, except on a last journey to a Southampton scrapyard later in 1965.

In May 1966, G-ALUN was towed across the Medina to the yard of J. Samuel White and was de-cocooned ready for Aero Spacelines, but this arrangement fell through, also because of deterioration problems. Finally, on 12 April, 1967, G-ALUN, the remaining example and the only Princess to fly, was towed to the yard of a Southampton breaker. The wings and tailplane were removed, but part of the hull was used as an extension to the breaker's premises, the upper deck serving as an office and the lower as a workshop. Finally, when the breaker expanded his premises further, the Princess's berth was filled in and the hull was broken up. Parts of the aircraft survive; a yacht based at Cowes incorporates six of the portholes.

G-ALUN, the sole Princess to fly, as it was in summer 1967.

234

Ten Bristol Proteus 2. (later designated Proteus 600, single units, and Proteus 610, coupled units). Various powers have been quoted for these engines. The following are from Saunders-Roe *Report FT/15/0/24 Part 1* of January 1955 covering trials at the MAEE—Nominal rating, sea level, static: Maximum 10,000 crpm, 2,500 shp and 820 lb jet thrust, maximum continuous 9,500 crpm, 2,050 shp and 700 lb jet thrust. Airscrew diameter 16 ft 6 in.

Span 209 ft 6 in floats down, 219 ft 6 in floats raised; dihedral 0 deg; root chord 30 ft; tip chord (at wing/float juntion) 12 ft 6 in; gross wing area 5,019 sq ft; root thickness/chord ratio 18 per cent; tip (at wing/float junction) thickness/chord ratio 15 per cent; float track (floats lowered) 199 ft.

Length 148 ft; beam 16 ft 7 in; maximum hull depth 24 ft 3 in; draught 8 ft; length to beam ratio 7.24.

Tailplane span 77 ft 2 in; tailplane dihedral 12 deg; height of fin 31 ft 6 in; overall height 55 ft 9 in.

Pressure differential 8 psi; maximum during trials 4.25 psi.

Empty weight 190,000 lb; normal maximum disposable load 137,000 lb; normal maximum weight 330,000 lb; design overload weight 345,000 lb; normal wing loading 65 lb/sq ft.

Maximum cruising speed at 37,000 ft—380 mph; maximum cruising speed at 32,500 ft—360 mph; take-off run about 2,880 ft; rate of climb at 184 mph at sea level 1,900 ft/min; stalling speed 127 mph flaps up, 113 mph flaps down; absolute ceiling 39,000 ft; range with maximum payload 5,720 miles; maximum endurance 15 hr.

Design limitations in force while testing of G-ALUN took place at MAEE Felixstowe.

1. Weight range tested 220,000 lb–315,000 lb; normal alighting weight 250,000 lb; emergency alighting weight up to 315,000 lb; handling, stability and control tests were usually undertaken within the range of 250,000 lb–270,000 lb.

2. Level flight and diving speed limitations:

Altitude	Level	Dive
0–10,000 ft	301 mph	335 mph
15,000 ft	289 mph	not listed
20,000 ft	279 mph	309 mph
25,000 ft	262 mph	not listed
30,000 ft	247 mph	274 mph

Maximum speed undertaken with floats down 198 mph.
Maximum speed undertaken while operating floats 169 mph.
For tests, astro-hatch fitted in place of dorsal escape hatch.

3. Engine operating limitations:

RPM	Compressor	Propeller-turbine	
		Single	Coupled
Maximum for take-off (5 minute limit)	10,000	10,300	10,700
Maximum continuous	9,500	9,250	9,650
Ground idling	3,000/3,250	—	—
Minimum approach idling	6,500	—	—
Maximum for reverse pitch (5 minute limit)	10,000	10,300	n/a
Maximum for reverse pitch (10 minute limit)	9,500	9,250	n/a

Normal operating limits of G-ALUN

All figures apply to a 250,000 lb all-up weight.

Max speed

Altitude (ft)	Max speed (mph), IAS	Max speed (mph), IAS, auto-pilot
0–10,000	307	271
15,000	295	257
20,000	285	245
25,000	269	234

Max flap deflection (degrees)	Max speed (mph), IAS
45	168
30	185
15	198

Three examples, G-ALUN, G-ALUO, G-ALUP, c/ns SR.901–903.

Cierva W.14/Saunders-Roe P.501 Skeeter

The first involvement of Saunders/Saro in rotorcraft occurred when, in 1929, Saunders-Roe constructed Vittorio Isacco's Helicogyre (*see* Appendix Four). The Helicogyre was of distinctive configuration but was not successful as a flying machine, and after its departure to Farnborough for tests, Cowes' connections with rotorcraft ceased until after the Second World War.

In 1925 Don Juan de la Cierva arrived in Britain, bringing with him his autogiro for demonstration. Cierva autogiros flew, and in 1926 the Cierva Autogiro Company was formed, to hold the patents taken out by Cierva and to grant licences for the manufacture of autogiros, which went to firms in Britain and elsewhere. One firm in Britain which acquired such licences was G. and J. Weir Ltd of Glasgow. Cierva was killed in the crash of a Douglas DC-2 at Croydon in December 1936, but in 1943 the firm was revived when C. G. Pullen of G. and J. Weir became managing director. Cierva then took over the helicopter interests of Weir and all drawings were taken to Hanworth and finally Eastleigh, where in the immediate postwar years the Cierva company was established, based in part of the Cunliffe-Owen site. Alan Marsh became Cierva's chief test-pilot, and the design team was led by Pullen.

One of Cierva's postwar projects was the large triple-rotor W.11 Air Horse which was evolved to meet civil Specification CAOR 3/46. The MoS sponsored the development of the W.11 with the issue of Specification E.19/46, which indicates how unusual the proposals were. The Air Horse was powered by a single Rolls-Royce Merlin 24 twelve-cylinder liquid-

Skeeter 6 XK773 in full camouflage during 1957, over Southampton Water.

cooled engine which drove three separate rotors on outriggers. The W.11 also featured primitive powered controls and the design all-up weight was 17,500 lb.

The Air Horse met with several setbacks. Cunliffe-Owen, who had been sub-contracted to build major parts of the airframe, went into liquidation soon after starting this work, and progress was slow because of lack of money. For these reasons Kenneth Watson, Cierva's chief mechanical engineer, had an office full of staff with little to work on. Pullen suggested that they might begin work on a project for a very small helicopter and this became the W.14 Skeeter.

Design work was begun on the W.14, during 1947, as a light helicopter suitable for the civil market or a military observation role. Main criteria were good all-round visibility, generous cabin size, and cheapness and simplicity of construction. It was estimated that, when in production, the civil variant would cost £3,000 and that running costs would not exceed those of a large car. An orthodox rotor configuration was adopted, with a single three-blade main rotor and an anti-torque rotor at the rear of the fuselage. The extensively glazed cabin had two seats and aft of the cabin was a single 110 hp Jameson FF-1 four-cylinder air-cooled engine fed by a 10 gal tank also situated amidships. Behind the front fuselage was a triangular-section tailboom provided with a fixed skid in case of accidental

Cierva Skeeter 1 G-AJCJ, showing its unusual triangular-section tailboom and spindly undercarriage, autumn 1948.

Cierva Skeeter 2 G-ALUF on the Eastleigh apron, autumn 1949.

nose-high landings. The undercarriage was a non-retractable tricycle type. In this form the helicopter was designated Cierva W.14 Skeeter 1.

Both the airframe of the Skeeter 1 and its engine were prototypes, and this Skeeter was the only example to receive the Jameson, whose performance later proved disappointing. The W.14 Mk 1 made its public debut at the SBAC Show of 1948, though as a static exhibit only, as G-AJCJ. On its return to Eastleigh, G-AJCJ was cleared for its first flight and this took place on 10 October, 1948, the pilot being Alan Marsh. Early tests were quite promising though the Jameson proved insufficiently powerful; also, the cylinder heads tended to overheat after about 20 min flying. In late 1948, studies started on a Mk 2 Skeeter, G-AJCJ meantime being used for various development trials until it was scrapped in late 1952.

The Skeeter 2 differed in a number of ways from the first example. The Jameson FF-1 was replaced by the proven 145 hp de Havilland Gipsy Major 10. Cockpit glazing was revised to end forward of the rotor spindle rather than enclosing it, as had previously been the case, while the shape of the cockpit was also somewhat reworked. The undercarriage legs were shortened and the tailskid strengthened and repositioned further aft. Most noticeable change was the replacement of the triangular-section tailboom with one of circular section set at an angle closer to the horizontal, with consequently greater angle on the arm bearing the tail rotor.

The Skeeter 2, registered G-ALUF, appeared for the first time at the 1949 SBAC Show (as a static exhibit) and first flew on 15 November, 1949, again with Alan Marsh at the controls. Early trials were in most ways satisfactory but a problem emerged in the form of ground resonance at certain rotor and power settings. Though a great deal of time was devoted to finding a cure, none was forthcoming under Cierva and on 26 June, 1950, G-ALUF was destroyed on the ground as a result of this resonance.

Also during this summer, Air Horse G-ALCV/VZ724 (c/n W.11/1) crashed after a rotor-hub failure, killing Alan Marsh and Fred 'Jeep' Cable. By that time, the company had received only an order for three further (developed) MoS-financed Skeeters. These were to be the Mks 3 and 4, to Specification A.13/49.

In January 1951, Cierva closed as an independent company. Its facilities, designs and most of the technical staff, as well as the very small labour force, were all acquired by Saunders-Roe. Saro bought Cierva as a diversification from its waterborne projects, and needed additional space at Eastleigh for its sub-contracted Vickers Viscount wing-building programme. Saro took over Cierva on an understanding with the MoS that it would complete the Skeeter programme contract together with outstanding work on the surviving Air Horse, although not much appears to have been done on the Air Horse, G-ALCW/WA555. After tethered testing by Basil Arkell, it was eventually put into store at the MoS sub-depot at Byley and later broken up.

The Eastleigh factory site became the Saunders-Roe Helicopter Division. Development of the Skeeter continued, the type having received the new designation Saro P.501. At the time of take-over, the three MoS-financed examples (WF112—WF114) were under construction. The first two, Skeeter 3s, were powered by the Gipsy Major 8, and WF114, the sole example of the Mk 4, by the 180 hp Cirrus Bombardier 702. The Mk 4 was designed for possible use by the Navy and the Mk 3 with Army or Navy in

Skeeter 3 WF113 undergoing test-flying at Eastleigh, late 1951. (*Saro*)

Close-up of the Gipsy Major 8 installation of Skeeter 3 WF113. *AQD, Crown Copyright*)

mind. In fact the Skeeter programme was far from straightforward and a great deal of development was necessary before the it could be considered for military service.

WF112 and WF113 both had detail improvements to the rotor-head design and undercarriage, while all-up weight rose from the 1,800 lb of the Mk 2 to 2,000 lb. Service trials were undertaken at A&AEE Boscombe Down and with the Royal Navy at Gosport during 1951–52, but results were disappointing, especially hot and high trials at all-up weight. Thus in early 1952, these examples were re-engined with the 180 hp Bombardier 702 and re-designated Skeeter 3b. WF112 was displayed in this form at the 1952 SBAC Show. All-up weight rose 100 lb, while range became 260 miles at a cruising speed of 93 mph.

WF114, designed for the Royal Navy as a light observation utility helicopter, had certain items of naval equipment as well as the other improvements common to all three examples. Saro considered that the Skeeter could be used for a variety of tasks; installation of cameras, armour plating, and stretcher facilities were all considered and duties might include observation, casualty evacuation, communications, or cable-laying. These

Skeeter 3 WF112 in hovering flight, Eastleigh, late 1951.

241

The sole Skeeter 4, WF114, Eastleigh, early 1953.

were rather optimistic ideas in view of the mediocre payload. The Mks 3 and 4 were tested by Ken Reed.

During March 1953, WF113 and WF114 went to the A&AEE for trials which confirmed that ground resonance problems were still present. At the end of April, WF112 had been badly damaged at Eastleigh, causing Ken Reed's back to be broken and preventing him from flying again until the following December. On his recommendation, however, Skeeters WF113 and WF114 continued to fly, but in early May WF113 disintegrated while attempting to ground-run at 40 mph—the aircraft started to break up at only 28 mph—and Government aid was withdrawn. All research leading to the solution of the resonance problem from then on was funded by Saunders-Roe. Only after the military had intensively tested the later and much-modified Skeeter Mk 6, found it free of ground resonance and expressed an interest in operating it, did Government support revive.

After the early setbacks with the Mks 3 and 4, Saro began a long programme to eliminate the resonance problem. Much of the work on Skeeter development was the responsibility of T. L. Ciastula although design work was initially done by Maurice Brennan. Impedance tests were conducted, to determine those natural frequencies where resonance between the rotor blades and the airframe would occur, by means of a specially-constructed 'shaking test-rig', as well as tests to establish a satisfactory fatigue life for the transmission, rotor-hub and blades, a programme completed by mid-1954 and involving extensive endurance running using the sole Skeeter 4. Simulated fluctuating stress conditions similar to those obtained in flight were created, and a comprehensive strain-gauging programme was run using a Saro-built gauge. Subsequent inspection of WF114's transmission showed that the mechanical design of the components was basically sound. A number of modifications were made, however, and were incorporated in the next version of the Skeeter, the Mk 5: improved rotor-hub torsion bearings, new intermediate shaft universal joints and a change of rotor shaft from light alloy to steel.

The undercarriage damping units and the main rotor blade friction dampers were redesigned to prevent the resonance, after a theoretical study had been made to determine the instability range. Finally, using the Skeeter Mk 4, full-scale ground-resonance tests were made in the Eastleigh helicopter ground-running compound, with a suitable snubbing facility to damp out vibration when it occurred. During these final tests, the minima of undercarriage and blade damping required to do the job were determined and actual ground resonance was reproduced. Behaviour of the new damping was analysed under various oscillating conditions. After this, the modified example (Skeeter 5), with the redesigned undercarriage and blade dampers incorporated from the onset, was subjected to final resonance tests in the compound and then flown in varying conditions. It was landed on various surfaces before being pronounced free of ground resonance problems. In March 1954, the Skeeter 5, G-AMTZ, went to the A&AEE for evaluation trials and it was confirmed that resonance had disappeared. During 1952 and 1953, over 230 hr of ground running had been done by the Skeeter 3b alone; WF114 was also used. The whole range of motor rpm, with collective pitch settings corresponding to rotor thrust of up to 85 per cent of all-up weight, were covered during the course of the tests. Motion of the Skeeters was recorded throughout on a Hughes pen-recorder and by continuous cine-camera records.

The tests undertaken with the Skeeter 5 G-AMTZ had been equally intensive: engine running, vertical take-offs and landings in calm and windy conditions using concrete and grass areas, taxi-ing in various wind

G-AMTZ in Skeeter 5 form, over the Eastleigh works, summer 1953. (*BHC*)

243

directions, running take-offs, hovering for long periods with the under-carriage just in contact with the ground.

The Skeeter 5 led a varied existence. Virtually a commercial variant of the Mk 4, it was powered by a similar engine, but some new aspects were introduced. It had featured the new steel rotor shaft, improved main rotor hub bearings and improved universal joints in the intermediate tail-rotor drive-shaft, the same as those experimentally incorporated in WF114. G-AMTZ was the first Skeeter to be built with a Saro construction number and was originally registered G-AMDC but changed in August 1952. The first flight was made in the early summer of 1953 before G-AMTZ appeared at Farnborough in September, in the hands of John Jeffrey, Saro helicopter test-pilot. In March 1954, G-AMTZ went to the A&AEE wearing camouflage and serialled XG303, where it underwent the successful testing of resonance cures.

Reverting after the trials to G-AMTZ, in 1955 the airframe received a 200 hp Gipsy Major 200 engine to bring it up to the later Skeeter 6 standard with a slightly improved performance. By 1957, G-AMTZ had assumed a new guise and was demonstrated at that year's SBAC Show in overall white and carrying two external stretcher panniers, one each side of the cabin.

When G-AMTZ had received its new engine, it had been redesignated the Skeeter 6. After gaining its C of A with the Gipsy Major, it was modified yet again in May 1957 by the addition of a Napier NRE.19 High Test Peroxide rocket booster system to the main rotor. Propulsive nozzles were fitted at the tips of the three blades, fed by an HTP tank mounted

G-ANMI in Skeeter 6 (mod) form, with NRE.19 rocket booster system.

244

Skeeter 6 G-ANMG as XK773 on loan to CFS South Cerney during 1955.

above the rotor hub, providing 67 eshp and increasing vertical climb rate considerably. Endurance was a little under 15 min, and the system was designed to give the Skeeter tropical performance as an alternative to the de Havilland turbo-supercharger also being considered. Only G-AMTZ and Skeeter 6 G-ANMI were modified in this way despite the obvious advantages; the HTP-boosted Skeeter was deemed unsuitable for military use because of logistic considerations. The eventual fate of G-AMTZ remains unclear, though it was reported sold to the Army Air Corps in April 1960 and was seen in the summer of 1962 at Middle Wallop, still painted white overall but with no markings. It is reasonable to assume that it ended its days as an instructional airframe. There are reports of an all-white Skeeter discovered abandoned at Thruxton during 1978, and this may well have been G-AMTZ. With the HTP system, it was designated Skeeter 6 (mod).

Three Skeeter 6 examples were built. The Mk 6 was intended as a trainer version of the Mks 4 and 5 but powered with the Gipsy Major 200. Full dual control was fitted and the Skeeter 6 was in other respects similar to the Skeeter 5. The first example, G-ANMG, gained its C of A on 8 June, 1955, and transferred as XK773 to the Central Flying School (CFS) at South Cerney for trials in the late summer of that year, also appearing at the 1955 SBAC Show in its new markings, overall natural finish with a yellow trainer band around the boom. It reappeared at Farnborough two years later in full camouflage and was used for various tests, including autostabiliser trials, until 1960.

The second example, G-ANMH, appeared at the 1954 SBAC Show; this was the first Mk 6 to fly. G-ANMH was also transferred to the military for tests, becoming XJ355 for its trials at the A&AEE. It appeared at the 1957 Farnborough Show with Saro interchangeable rotor blades, still as XJ355.

The final Mk 6, G-ANMI, passed to the military for trials in March 1956 as XK964, being returned to Eastleigh in the summer of the same year and then reverting to civil markings. Over the summer, a Napier rocket booster similar to that employed on G-AMTZ was installed, and it first flew in this

G-ANMH, second of the three Skeeter 6 examples. (*BHC*)

form on 5 August, appearing at Farnborough in the following month. With this booster the aircraft was also known as Skeeter 6 (mod).

When the Skeeter Mk 7 appeared it was but a modification of the Skeeter 6 (mod) G-ANMI, in which a Gipsy Major 215 of 215 hp was installed. Power output was by that time virtually double that of the original Skeeter Mk 1, and the Skeeter 7 was tested by the company extensively. Minus the rocket booster system, this format became the basis for the subsequent Mks AOP.12 and the 50 and 51 export models. G-ANMI was finally retired in August 1960.

Last of the civil Marks, the Skeeter 8 was represented by only one example. Three were laid down, as G-APOI, G-APOJ and G-APOK, but only the first was completed, this in September 1958. G-APOI underwent manufacturer's trials until March 1961 when it was put into store at Eastleigh. The registration was finally cancelled in April 1964. G-APOI too was powered by the Gipsy Major 215 and was similar in most respects to the Skeeter 7. This example was subsequently used as a rotor test rig under BHC at Cowes.

Intensive testing of the Skeeter 6 by the military, and the eventual successful results, led to an MoS evaluation order for four examples to the Mk 6 standard. These were serialled XK479—XK482, powered by the

246

Skeeter 6 G-ANMI as XK964 for Army photographs, spring 1956. (*Saro*)

Gipsy Major 200 and designated AOP.10 and T.11. All had provision for a rearward-swinging seat for the observer and a Plessey A.62 Army HF R/T set, and dual control was optional. The only difference between the two variants was confined to the control columns; the T.11 was fitted with a cyclic bias trim switch on the port side, while the AOP.10 was not. All four examples were ordered under contract 12206. XK479, the first example and the only T.11, went to the RAF Handling Squadron on 18 December, 1956, transferring to South Cerney during March 1957, where it stayed for some time, this visit interrupted only for two short trips back to Saro for overhaul and repair, and a temporary move to Little Rissington. Finally, it was flown to 15 MU at Wroughton, for disposal, during October 1961.

XK480 and XK481 were both completed as AOP.10 variants and arrived with 1906 Flight, Middle Wallop, on 18 January and 16 February, 1957, respectively, but both went unserviceable after colliding on 26 March. After repair XK480 was on charge to the CFS for some time and in January 1961 was sent to the AATDC at Old Sarum for dropping trials, before being written off in October 1963. XK481 also had a varied career before suffering a Category 5 accident and then became an instructional airframe.

The final AOP.10, XK482, arrived at Eastleigh from Cowes on 26 March, 1957. It went to 1906 Flight in April but was subsequently returned to Saunders-Roe where it was converted to Mk 12 standard, apart from some parts of the structure which were not used in the mass-produced

Sole example of the Skeeter 8, G-APOI, late 1958. (*Westland*)

Skeeter 6 G-ANMI as XK964 for trials with the Army Air Corps in March 1956.

variant. Like XK481, the final AOP.10 eventually became an instructional airframe.

Having successfully completed military trials some eight years after its inception as a civil type, the Skeeter finally entered series-production for the British Army Air Corps in the AOP.12 form, which was similar to that of the Mk 7. Production was in three batches; contract 13919 of May 1956 (from XL734), contract 15410 of November 1957 (from XM524), and contract KF/C/021 of January 1959 (from XN339). Deliveries to the Army Air Corps began with that of XL734 on 17 June, 1958, and ended when XN353 arrived at 15 MU for holding on 28 November, 1960. The Specification around which the Skeeter was ordered was H.163/P2 and a total of sixty-four AOP.12s was built. The Skeeter was the first helicopter to enter Army Air Corps service.

XL734 arrived at Middle Wallop on 17 June, 1958, for use by the Helicopter Training Flight, followed by three more examples during August. XL734 remained for a mere two weeks before transfer to de Havilland and only in October 1961 did it finally return to the Army. Further aircraft continued to arrive at Middle Wallop, meanwhile, and on 6 October, 1958, No.654 Squadron received XL763, this marking the introduction of the AAC Skeeter to West Germany, though the Germans had by that time received some Skeeters of their own. During 1959, XL739 was freighted to Edmonton, Canada, for cold-weather trials, which were

Skeeter AOP.12 XL811, of the first production batch for the AAC. (*Westland*)

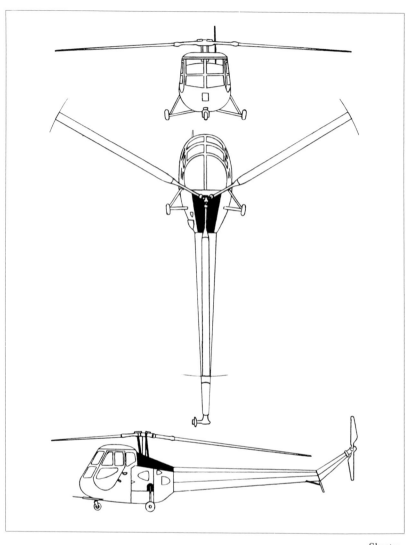

Skeeter

very successful indeed. This example did not return to AAC use until January 1962.

No.652 Squadron's Skeeters started arriving in late 1958 with deliveries continuing into 1959. During March 1959, XL807 undertook further cold-weather trials, this time in Norway. Again, the trials were successful, the only difficulty being in finding low enough temperatures against which to test the aircraft. The Skeeter was always successful operating in the cold, but hot weather tests were rather disappointing, even with the late production model. Why the AAC did not accept the bolt-on HTP booster system remains a mystery, for surely logistic problems could have been overcome.

The second batch of Skeeters started leaving Eastleigh in April 1959, XM524 departing for Middle Wallop on 1 April. Also, as an experiment, XM528 was fitted with a (non-standard) de Havilland exhaust-driven turbo-supercharger for hot and high trials, first at the A&AEE and later in Aden, being handed over in this form on 18 June. The Aden trials were made at temperatures of ICAO +20 deg C (35 deg C) and were in two parts, first in the normally-aspirated condition and then with the supercharger. The first condition gave satisfactory handling but poor vertical climb, but the second improved the rate of climb, though tests were restricted to a maximum height of 5,000 ft because of inadequate engine and oil cooling. However, after the trials, the cooling system was modified and this improvement was standardised on the third batch, giving slightly more satisfactory performance. In August 1960, XM528 undertook further tests, this time involving a skid undercarriage, under the designation Saro P.534. Presumably this arrangement held no real advantages, because no other Skeeters were similarly converted. XM528 was returned to standard and arrived with the AAC in January 1962.

The last batch of Skeeter AOP.12s was delivered between December 1959 and November 1960, when XN353, retained by Saro for eight weeks, finally arrived at 15 MU. Most of the last batch went to 15 MU for holding, many staying for as long as six months, before release to Nos. 651, 652, 654 and 655 Squadrons.

The first Skeeter MK 50 for the Federal German Heeresflieger, PC-117.

West Germany also received the Skeeter, in Mks 50 and 51 form. These were export versions of the AOP.12. The German Army and Navy operated the Mk 50 (six examples) and the Mk 51 (four examples) respectively, in the liaison and communications role. The sole contract, covering all ten examples, was signed at Koblenz in July 1957, by the Germans, the MoD and Saro. These Skeeters served from 1958 until mid 1961, when they were declared surplus to requirements. The first three examples for Germany were produced between XK482 and XL734, and the last before XL808 in January 1959. The six Heeresflieger Mk 50s were coded PC-117 to PC-122 and were used initially by HFB 3 at Rotenburg, three arriving on 22 May, 1958, followed by two in October and the last in December. The four Mk 51s joined the communications section of Marinefliegergruppe 3 at Nordholz, coded SC-501 to SC-504, and arrived mostly in the late autumn of 1958. The German Army Skeeters were subsequently transferred to HFB 6 at Hungriger Wolf and were re-coded PF-155 to PF-160, but in June 1961 all ten were withdrawn and sold to the Portuguese, being replaced in Germany by Sud-Aviation Alouettes. The intentions of the Portuguese in buying these aircraft are uncertain, as Portugal is hardly the ideal operating area for the Skeeter. In any event, after arriving at Alverca, near Lisbon, none of the Skeeters received any Portuguese coding and it is presumed they did not see military service, though they were inspected by Westland engineers during the summer of 1961.

Saunders-Roe was taken over by Westland in August 1959, but continued working on the Skeeter and also on the P.531, in connection with which Skeeter XM563 was re-engined with a Blackburn Turmo 603 gas-turbine, being re-designated P.537. This aircraft was allotted to the MoA on 23 December, 1959, and first flew in its new form during March 1960. The purpose of this conversion was to allow tests not only of the engine itself, but also the Elliot autostabiliser system intended for the P.531 and then being developed. After extensive trials, XM563 reverted to standard and joined No. 652 Squadron in 1963.

After the Westland Scout (developed from the P.531) entered production, it began to replace the Skeeter as the AAC light helicopter mainstay, and the Skeeters began transfers to individual units on a regimental basis out of the direct control of the AAC. No. 3 Wing in Aden and No. 4 Wing in the Far East were unable to use the Skeeter in any event because of its poor hot and high performance; in fact even during some European summers the rate of climb became mediocre. During 1967 and 1968 several batches of Skeeters returned to Britain for use as training airframes or for storage; many eventually arrived at 15 MU.

There were some varied asides in the career of the Skeeter AOP.12. The CFS used it on a very small scale, employing XM556/V, XM564/X and XN339/Z, which carried the School's insignia on the boom. While these examples were used by the CFS they were referred to as the T.13, though they were identical to the AOP.12. They operated from both Little Rissington and Tern Hill, XM564 between 1961 and 1964, and XN339 between July and November 1964.

XL735 and XL807 were delivered to the Empire Test Pilot's School, Farnborough, in October 1964 but were never actually used there, reverting eventually to Army operations. Various AOP.12s were used

Skeeter AOP.12s on parade; left to right, XL814, XM527, XL737 and XL811. (*Westland*)

briefly by the RAF for training and checking Army Pilot Instructors, but these machines were loaned from and serviced by the AAC.

So the career of the Skeeter finally drew to an end. Several of those arriving at 15 MU were dispersed to various airfields for fire practice. Some were used instructionally, some were preserved. A number were auctioned off in The Netherlands. A few have even been flown again after restoration. The last Skeeter to leave military service was XL763, struck off on 16 October, 1969.

The Skeeter was the only Saunders/Saro type to achieve a quantity foreign order, and the AOP.12 enjoyed the biggest production run ever achieved by the company with one of its own designs, albeit an inherited one.

One 110 hp Jameson FF-1 (Skeeter Mk 1), 145 hp de Havilland Gipsy Major 10 (Mk 2), 180 hp Blackburn Bombardier 702 (Mk 3b), 180 hp Blackburn Bombardier 702/4 (Mk 5), 200 hp de Havilland Gipsy Major 200 (Mk 6), 200 hp de Havilland Gipsy Major 200 and Napier NRE.19 HTP booster (Mk 6 (mod)), 215 hp de Havilland Gipsy Major 215 (AOP.12, Mk 50 and 51), supercharged de Havilland Gipsy Major 215 (AOP.12 supercharged), 425 shp Blackburn Turmo 603 de-rated to 250 shp (Skeeter 12 (mod)).

The supercharged Gipsy Major 215 maintained rated power in all climates and at heights up to 4,000 ft. A methanol injection system was available to maintain rated power at sea level in tropical conditions.

Skeeter dimensions, weights and performance

	Mk 1	Mk 2	Mk 3	Mk 5	Mk 6
Length, ft, in	26 8	28 5	28 5	28 5	28 5
Height, ft, in	8 0	10 0	9 10	9 11½	10 2
Rotor diameter, ft, in	29 0	32 0	32 0	32 0	32 0
Empty weight, lb	810	1,200	1,450	1,500	1,607
Loaded weight, lb	1,210	1,800	2,100	2,100	2,202
Maximum speed, mph	79	95	97	99	107
Maximum cruising speed, mph	75	90	93	94	105
Max. inclined climb, ft/min	520	600	940	1,010	1,120
Vertical climb, ft/min	175	—	—	—	365
Hover ceiling, ft	990	1,110	1,420	1,440	1,700
Hover ceiling in ground effect, ft	c 2,700	c 3,400	c 3,750	c 3,790	4,800
Service ceiling, ft	—	(1)	(2)	(3)	12,300
Absolute ceiling, ft	9,600	c 11,000	c 12,100	c 12,145	13,500
Cruising range, miles	155	185	260	260	240x
Endurance, hr, min	—	—	—	—	3 20

Note: Mk 4 as Mk 3b except empty weight 1,476 lb

(1) Vertical climb ceiling 7,200 ft
(2) Vertical climb ceiling 9,200 ft
(3) Vertical climb ceiling 9,220 ft
x Maximum

Skeeter dimensions, weights and performance

	Mk 6 (HTP boosted)	AOP.12*	AOP.12 Supercharged	Skeeter 12 mod. P.537
Length, ft, in	28 5	26 8	26 8	26 8
Height, ft, in	10 2	9 6	9 6	9 6
Rotor diameter, ft, in	32 0	32 0	32 0	32 0
Empty weight, lb	—	1,656		1,572
Loaded weight, lb	2,272	2,200(1)	2,250	2,350
Maximum speed, mph	117	109	109	111
Maximum cruising speed, mph	—	106	106	104
Max. inclined climb, ft/min	1,850	1,150	—	1,420
Vertical climb, ft/min	1,470	425	—	—
Hover ceiling, ft	8,800	2,500	7,800(3)	—
Hover ceiling in ground effect, ft	—	5,500	—	15,000
Service ceiling, ft	—	12,800	—	18,000
Absolute ceiling, ft	—	14,000	17,800(3)	—
Cruising range, miles	—	260(2)	—	130
Endurance, hr, min	—	3 0	—	—

Minimum rate of descent engine off
Skeeter Mk 6 1,350 ft/min,
Skeeter Mk 6 (HTP-boosted) 650 ft/min
*Includes Mks 50 and 51

(1) Normal, maximum 2,300 lb
(2) 86 mph with 23 gal
(3) At ISA plus 20 deg C

Skeeter 1

G-AJCJ c/n W.14/1. Sole example. Reg Cierva 26.8.48, SBAC Show 1948 (static). Ff 10.10.48 Eastleigh by Cierva CTP Alan Marsh. Reg cancelled 31.1.51 but development trials until 11.52 when scrapped.

Skeeter 2
G-ALUF c/n W.14/2. Sole example. Reg Cierva 18.7.49, SBAC Show 1949 (static). Ff 15.11.49 Eastleigh. Development trials until 6.50. Destroyed 26.6.50 due to ground resonance.

Skeeter 3/3b
WF112 c/n W.14/3. Ff 3.10.51, trials 10.51 at A&AEE, later with 705 Sqn until 2.52, re-engined for 1952 SBAC Show becoming Mk 3b, ground resonance tests 1952–53, crashed and seriously damaged 28.4.53 while at Eastleigh, scrapped 1956; WF113 c/n W.14/4. Ff late 1951, straight to trials at A&AEE 10.51, later with 705 Sqn until 2.52, re-engined 3.52 becoming Mk 3b, ground resonance tests 1952–53, to A&AEE 3.53 where destroyed due to ground resonance 5.53.

Skeeter 4
C/n W.14/5. Built with RN in mind and some items of naval equipment on board. Sole example. Ff 15.4.52 Eastleigh, company trials until to A&AEE 3.53, ground resonance tests until at least 6.53 — during this period believed to have suffered an accident due to the resonance problem. However, used for ground running tests in Eastleigh compound until 6.54.

Skeeter 5/6
G-AMTZ/XG303 c/n SR.907. Sole example of Mk 5. Commercial variant of Mk 4. Markings taken up by Cierva 31.7.50 were G-AMDC. This cancelled 31.1.52, but reg Saro 20.8.52 as G-AMTZ. To SBAC Show 1952 (static). Ff 5.53 by John Jeffrey, Saro Helicopter Test Pilot. SBAC Show 1953. As XG303 to A&AEE 2.3.54 for evaluation, no ground resonance encountered. To Eastleigh 6.54, reverting to G-AMTZ. To Wahn, Germany, 7.54, for demonstration. 8.54 flown by CFS from Eastleigh. SBAC Show 1954. Re-engined 1955 to Skeeter 6 standard. First Skeeter to visit Middle Wallop, 14.7.55. Spring 1957, NRE.19 booster installed. To Paris Air Show 22.5.57. SBAC Show 1957 as 'flying ambulance'. Civil reg cancelled 7.12.59, reverted to XG303. Sold to AAC 4.60, used unmarked as instructional airframe to at least 7.62. Late 1978, found u/s at Thruxton.

Skeeter 6
G-ANMG/XK773 c/n SR.904 — first example with Saro c/n. Reg Saro 1.5.54. Ff 26.5.55, C of A 8.6.55. Paris Air Show 10.6.55. CFS South Cerney 18.8.55 as XK773. SBAC Show 1955. 1956 spent two weeks with 1906 Flt Middle Wallop on user trials. 11.56 to 4.57 at A&AEE for handling trials. SBAC Show 1957. Development trials by Saro to 1960. Last known use engaged in autostabilisation trials; G-ANMH/XJ335 c/n SR.905. Reg Saro 1.5.54. Ff 29.8.54. SBAC Show 1954. XJ335 adopted, trials at A&AEE 24.2.55 to 15.4.55 and 2.5.55 to 23.5.55. To 1906 Flt Middle Wallop 11.55 for user trials. SBAC Show 1957. Boom and rotor assemblies last recorded at the Royal Military College of Science, 8.74.

Skeeter 6/7
G-ANMI/XK964 c/n SR.906. Reg Saro 1.5.54. Ff 23.6.54. 2.56, allotted XK964 for Service trials with A&AEE beginning 3.56. To Saro 6.56.

NRE.19 booster system installed, ff with new installation 5.8.56 Eastleigh as Skeeter 6 (mod). To Luton for full testing of installation, 3–12.9.56 and also to SBAC Show 1956. Re-engined 3.57 becoming sole Skeeter 7 as pre-production basis for AOP.12, Mks 50 and 51. Ff as Mk 7 13.4.57. Not used after 8.60 but reg not cancelled until 7.7.64.

Skeeter 8
G-APOI c/n S2/5081. Reg Saro 29.7.58. Del Eastleigh 9.58. C of A 31.3.60. Manufacturer's trials to 3.61. Stored Eastleigh. Reported transferred to RN but this unconfirmed. Seen Eastleigh 11.61. Reg wdn 3.61 when stored but restored 4.63 after transferring to Westland ownership 4.62. Reg cancelled 4.64. To Cowes as rotor test-rig until at least 1970. 7.74 to B G Heron, Squire's Gate. By 12.83 in use for spares for G-SARO, Inverness. Mid-84 to Shobdon for rebuild for owner Major F. F. Chamberlain. By 12.84 under rebuild at Inverness; G-APOJ and G-APOK c/ns S2/5091 and S2/5111 respectively. Both reg Saro 29.7.58 but abandoned before completion, 10.58. Reg's cancelled 21.11.58. Both airframes thought to have been used for military production.

NB: C/n system changed with the Skeeter 8. Numbers in S2/ series were applied to all major components—drive-shaft, gearbox, rotor-blades, etc—and included all components produced as spares. This accounts for the apparent gaps in the aircraft c/ns.

Skeeter T.11
XK479 c/n S2/3012. Sole T.11, designation of which conflicted with contemporary practice which would usually have resulted in HT.11. Basically Mk 6 with some military equipment. Ff 2.7.56, Cowes, where erected. SBAC Show 1956. To RAF Handling Sqn 18.12.56, to CFS South Cerney 22.3.57 punctuated with two short trips to Saro for repair and temporary visit to CFS Little Rissington 7.57. SBAC Show 1957. Returned to South Cerney 13.1.58, Saro 4.58 to 1.59, returned to South Cerney, to 15 MU 9.10.61 for disposal. SOC 5.7.62.

Skeeter AOP.10
XK480 c/n S2/3036. Del 1906 Flt Middle Wallop 18.1.57, damaged on ground 26.3.57, u/s to 5.57, to Saro 6.57, to No.6 Flt AAC 1.9.57, Saro 19.12.57 following damage, HTF 5.3.58, Saro 17.7.58 to 17.10.58, o/c CFS 3.12.59, returned Middle Wallop 5.2.60, to AATDC 10.1.61 dropping trials, returned Middle Wallop 1.8.62. Cat 5 accident 16.10.63, probably while with 651 Sqn. Fate uncertain but front fuselage and cockpit seen at Middle Wallop 11.63; XK481 c/n S2/3051. This and subsequent aircraft built at East Cowes, usually being transferred to Eastleigh for dispersal. This will be indicated by an asterisk followed by the date of arrival at Eastleigh. XK481*10.1.57. Ff c.1.2.57. To 1906 Flt 16.2.57, to Saro 27.3.57 following heavy landing, to 1906 Flt 24.6.57 becoming 6 Flt 1.9.57, to Saro 4.2.58 to 6.3.58, to 6 Flt, to Heathrow on a lorry 9.8.58, reason unclear. Damaged 22.8.58. To Saro until at least 22.10.58. 1959/60, to Middle Wallop with HTF. Cat 5 15.12.62, becoming instructional, but never allocated an M number; XK482 c/n S2/3070. *26.3.57. To 1906 Flt 1.4.57, loaned to Saro 3.4.57 for mods to Mk 12 standard, o/c Handling Sqn 2.5.58, to Saro 12.1.59, to 15 MU 16.1.61, to AAC Centre 6.6.62 then to

HTF, to 7840M 5.3.64, Middle Wallop, SOC 11.64, though airframe used by AETW to 1969. 2.69 to Ottershaw School, Fairoaks, for CCF. By 6.83, under restoration by J. E. Wilkie at Carnforth, reg'd as G-BJWC 30.11.82.

Skeeter AOP.12

XL734 c/n S2/5064. *2.5.58, AW/CN. To HTF 17.6.58, to de Havilland on loan 2.7.58 to 1.9.61, to A&AEE 4.11.60 to 23.11.60, to AAC Centre 20.10.61, used by 651 Sqn from 7.63, to 1 Wing BAOR and used by 5 Flt from 7.65, to 15 MU 4.67 ex 71 Workshops, NEA 27.5.68, to Wyton 11.10.68 as fire practice aircraft.

XL735 c/n S2/5066. *30.5.58, AW/CN. To HTF 31.8.58, Cat 4 (FA) 27.1.59, to Saro 9.3.59, to HTF 6.7.59, Saro 9.3.59, Cat 4 (FA) 12.60, to Saro repairs and company trials to 9.61, to 651 Sqn 7.63, allocated ETPS 10.64 but not used by them, to 15 MU 4.12.64, to 1 Wing Detmold 2.9.65, served with 4 Flt Munster, to 15 MU 13.4.67, NEA 27.5.68, to Manston Fire School but not used, to 2433 ATC Sqn Manston. Last seen intact 4.76.
XL736 c/n S2/5067. *13.6.58. To HTF 22.8.58, to Saro 2.6.59 to 26.6.59, returned to HTF, flight trials 7–10.61 Middle Wallop, to 655 Sqn 1 Wing, to 23 Flt Detmold by 10.63, allocated ETPS 10.64 but not used by them, to 5 Fld Regt/RA by 7.65, badly damaged in traffic accident en route to Larzac in Southern France 8.68. SOC 9.68. Auctioned at Moordrecht, Holland, 20.10.69.
XL737 c/n S2/5068. *20.6.58. To HTF 22.8.58, to Saro 16.6.59 to 24.7.59, Cat 4 (FA) 5.62, SOC 24.5.62. Seen 71 MU dump 8.64.
XL738 c/n S2/5069. *27.6.58. To HTF 30.9.58 and loaned to C(A), o/c AAC 18.11.58, to Saro 9.9.59 to 30.3.60, to 651 Sqn, flight trials 7–10.61 Middle Wallop, allocated 7860M at Middle Wallop. Fuselage used for Middle Wallop gate guardian, the bogus 'XL769', which is currently in storage there.
XL739 c/n S2/5071. *14.7.58. Loaned to C(A) 9.9.58 to 31.10.61, to A&AEE 31.12.58 to 20.4.59, to Canada 23.10.59 for cold weather trials at Edmonton and Fort Churchill, returned Eastleigh 11.3.60, to A&AEE 5.1.61 to 3.5.61, to Saro, to 651 Sqn 22.1.62, to 1 Wing HQ by 7.65, to 'Reserve Theatre' 6.3.67, to 1 Wing 8.5.67, to Air Troop 15/19 Hussars 5.67. SOC 11.10.68 Cat 5(C). At Detmold, stored, 4.85.
XL740 c/n S2/5072. *18.7.58. To 654 Sqn 22.10.58, to Saro 27.8.59 to 10.12.59, to 654 Sqn 29.12.59, to 652 Sqn 9.11.60, to 654 Sqn 22.1.62, to 652 Sqn by 5.64 when Cat 3 22.5.64, with 19 Fld Regt RA during 8.67. Cat 3 20.11.67. Re-cat 5(C) 7.12.67. SOC 14.12.67.
XL762 c/n S2/5074. *18.8.58. Retained by Saro for SBAC Show 1958. To 651 Sqn 16.9.58. Cat 4; returned to Saro 9.3.59. Flight trials Middle wallop 7–10.61, to Saro for mods 7.3.60, to 651 Sqn 20.3.60, to 654 Sqn 7.4.62 but with 9 Flt 10–12.65, to 2 RTR Air Troop 1966–67, to 15 MU 23.11.67, NEA 27.5.68, To 8017M for use by AETW Middle Wallop, 11.75 to Museum of Flight at East Fortune.
XL763 c/n S2/5075. *25.8.58. To Middle Wallop 9.58 and to 654 Sqn 6.10.58, to Saro (mods) 8.7.59 to 18.9.59, Cat 4 14.10.59, later to 654 Sqn, to Air Troop 15/19 Hussars 1965, to 15 MU 5.12.67 arriving via Middle wallop 7.12.67, to Southall Technical College 16.10.69 where pieces still survive.

XL764 c/n S2/5076. *c12.9.58. To Middle Wallop 9.10.58, to Saro 11.8.59 to 19.10.59, Cat 3 9.1.62 in flying accident, to Westland 4.4.62 to 17.1.64, free loan to MoA 20.1.64 to 31.12.64, A&AEE 3.2.64 to 26.3.64, SBAC Show 9.64 exhibited on Stalwart, to A&AEE 3.11.65 to 3.12.65, to Westland, to A&AEE 7.2.66 to 5.8.66, to Westland 8.8.66, noted at Hayes 10.66, to Arborfield 10.3.67, allocated 7940M 13.3.67, next seen Middle Wallop AETW 7.75, bought 11.75 by Mr J. McArdle of Rotherham, loaned to Nostell Aviation Museum Wakefield 1976. Currently displayed at Newark Air Museum Winthorpe.

XL765 c/n S2/5078. *19.9.58. To 651 Sqn 2.2.59, to Saro 25.6.59, to 651 Sqn 25.8.59, flight trials Middle Wallop 7–10.61, to 654 Sqn by 7.63, next seen at Minden with 17 Flt, 4.65, 15 MU 16.6.67, NEA 5.68, sold to Plaistow Ltd 2.8.68, to Leeds University 1969 and painted in University colours. Intended for Midland Air Museum, Coventry.

XL766 c/n S2/5079. *2.10.58. To Middle Wallop for 651 Sqn 17.10.58 but returned to Saro 17.9.59, to 651 Sqn 17.12.59, during 2.60 used by 13 Flt Aldergrove, with whom declared Cat 4R 24.7.63, repaired and later to 655 Sqn 23 Flt, Cat 5(C) 19.12.63, SOC 10.3.64. Noted on 71 MU dump 3.67.

XL767 c/n S2/5080. *20.10.58. To Middle Wallop 21.11.58, to 652 Sqn/1 Flt via Southend with XL768 and XL769 11.12.58, o/c 1 Flt 20.12.58, later Cat 4R (GA) c9.3.64, to 9 Flt by 10.64, 1965–66 with 9 Flt, 17 Flt and 26 Fld Regt RA. With 19 Fld Regt RA 8.67. Last operational flight 10.68. Cat 5(C) 21.11.68. Auctioned Moordrecht, Holland, 20.10.69.

XL768 c/n S2/5084. *27.10.58. To 652 Sqn/1 Flt with XL767 and XL769, O/c 20.12.58. To Saro 4.8.59 to 22.9.59. Cat 5(FA) Germany 21.6.62, SOC. Wreck with 71 MU 5.65.

XL769 c/n S2/5085. 531.10.58. To 652 Sqn/1 Flt with XL767 and XL768, to Saro 16.7.59 to 17.8.59, to 652 Sqn with 17 Flt 1963–66, to 15 MU 15.2.67, to Arborfield by 8.67 allocated 7981M. Noted at Kelsterton College of Technology, Connah's Quay, 1973 and 1974. Serial 'XL769' used for middle Wallop gate guardian.

XL770 c/n S2/5086. *10.11.58. To Middle Wallop 12.12.58, to 654 Sqn 13.1.59, to Saro 21.8.59, to 654 Sqn 21.9.59, with 652 Sqn and Air Troop 15/19 Hussars between 1963–66, arrived 15 MU by road 29.11.67, NEA 18.1.68. SOC 15.4.69. Later to Royal Military College of Science, Shrivenham, as MC/8046M. Continued to wear 15/19 Hussars insignia, but did not carry M number.

XL771 c/n S2/5087. *21.11.58. To Middle Wallop 18.12.58, to 654 Sqn 31.1.59, to Saro 9.9.59 to 1.6.60, to 654 Sqn 1.2.60, Cat 5(C) 30.9.64 after heavy landing with 5 Flt 31.7.64.

XL772 c/n S2/5088. *10.12.58. To Middle Wallop 15.1.59, to 652 Sqn 23.3.59, to Saro (mods) 30.10.59 to 22.1.60, Cat 4P (FA) 16.6.60 in Germany later re-cat 5. Returned Middle Wallop where seen dismantled 7.63.

XL806 c/n S2/5089. *17.12.58. To Middle Wallop 23.1.59, to 654 Sqn 20.3.59, to Saro (mods) 2.7.59 to 23.9.59, to 12 Independent Flt 1.11.60, later returned to 654 Sqn, to 652 Sqn 7.7.61. Cat 5S (FA) during 10.63.

XL807 c/n S2/5090. *22.12.58. Loaned to C(A) until 1.8.60, 3.59 to Norway for cold weather trials, to Middle Wallop 1.9.60, to 71 MU 1.12.60, loaned to C(A) 19.1.61, 20.10.61 again o/c AAC, allotted ETPS

10.64 but not used by them, to 15 MU 4.12.64, to Queen's Dragoon Guards 11.1.65, to 15/19 Hussars by 5.65, 652 Sqn by 11.65, to 19 Fld Regt RA 8.67, Cat 3R 10.11.67. Re-cat 5C 7.12.67. SOC 14.12.67.

XL808 c/n S2/5093. *7.1.59. To Middle Wallop 2.2.59, to 651 Sqn 18.3.59, with Saro for a short period beginning 23.2.60, returned to 651 Sqn, to 652 Sqn 29.9.63, damaged when rolled over 28.4.64. Noted at Hayes 2.67. Returned Germany, 1 Wing AAC ?652 Sqn. Cat 5 17.6.67 after rolling onto its side following forced landing with engine failure. SOC 22.6.67.

XL809 c/n S2/5094. *15.1.59. To Middle Wallop 16.2.59, to 654 Sqn 28.4.59, to Saro 15.1.60, to 654 Sqn 14.4.60, to 652 Sqn 16.3.61, to 654 Sqn 1.4.62, with 22 Flt by 4.64, to 26 Fld Regt RA 7.65. SOC 12.12.68. Auctioned at Moordrecht, Holland, 26.6.69 reg to P. H. Hofman and later wore PH-HOF. Thought to have been airworthy until at least 1978, then stored W. Germany. Reg'd 3.5.84 as G-BLIX to G.C.L. James, The Old Training Plane Co, Shobdon, and under restoration there.

XL810 c/n S2/5095. *30.1.59. To Middle Wallop 13.3.59, to 652 Sqn/9 Flt, to 651 Sqn 7.63, to 15 MU 26.11.64, to 9 Flt 2.6.65. Cat 5 (FA) 18.8.66 and SOC 30.9.66.

XL811 c/n S2/5096. *6.2.59. To Middle Wallop 27.2.59, to 651 Sqn 1960–63, Cat 4R 7.4.60 but repaired on site after re-cat 3 19.4.60, to 651 Sqn 7.7.60, to 652 Sqn 3.65, to 17 Flt 5.65, to Air Troop 9/12 Lancers 7.65, to 5 Flt 1–7.66, to 15 MU 6.12.67, NEA 27.5.68, sold to Mr P. Scholefield for NAPS 2.12.68. 1972, on loan to Historic Aircraft Museum Southend. To Warmingham, Cheshire, by 9.83 for the Aeroplane Collection.

XL812 c/n S2/5097. *12.2.59. To Middle Wallop 13.3.59, to 652 Sqn 23.4.59, with 9 Flt by 4.64, to 15 MU 15.6.67, short visit to Odiham 16.6.67, NEA 27.5.68, to Leeds University 28.5.69, left Leeds mid-1971. Reg to Maj F. F. Chamberlain as G-SARO 1978. Noted at Inverness 4.6.79, wearing camouflage, XL812 and G-SARO. Current, based Inverness Airport.

XL813 c/n S2/5098. *3.3.59. On loan to C(A) to 31.12.61, SBAC Show 1959 with weapons pack, to AAEE 12.6.61 to 4.8.61 radio trials, to 15 MU 31.5.62, to ARWF 20.7.62, to 15 MU 23.10.64, to HQ 1 Wing Detmold 11.6.65, o/c 9 Flt by 9.65, to 4 Fld Regt RA 29.11.66, to 15 MU 26.11.67, to HQ Army Aviation Middle Wallop 1.68, to Museum of Army Flying 25.3.68.

XL814 c/n S2/5099. *20.2.59. To Middle Wallop 6.3.59, to Saro 27.7.59 to 1960 when reported with 651 Sqn, flight trials with AAC Middle Wallop 7–10.61, to 2 Wing 20.10.64, to Westland for mods at White Waltham 4.3.65, then to Hayes and later Yeovil test-flown 11.5.65, to AAC 25.5.65, to 1 Wing 12.7.65, to Henlow as 8021M, o/c AAC Middle Wallop 15.12.68. Maintained in airworthy condition as part of Historic Aircraft Flight, Middle Wallop.

XM524 c/n S2/5100. *13.3.59. To Middle Wallop 1.4.59, to 651 Sqn 1960–63 but Cat 3 in flying accident 5.6.63, repaired on site by 71 MU, later, to 1 Wing 7.65, subsequently to 4 Flt AAC, to 15 MU 13.4.67, NEA 27.5.68, to Leuchers for fire practice 10.9.68.

XM525 c/n S2/5101. *24.3.59. To Middle Wallop 9.4.59, to 654 Sqn 28.4.59, to Saro (mods) 23.3.60, to 654 Sqn 20.6.60. Noted with 2 Division marks 10.64. Cat 5 11.5.65 after accident 30.4.65 and SOC.

XM526 c/n S2/5102. *10.4.59. To Middle Wallop 24.4.59, Cat 4R 13.5.59, to Saro for repairs 5.6.59 to 27.11.59, to 12 Liaison Flt 21.12.59, to Saro 26.4.60, to 12 Flt 16.6.60, to 652 Sqn 7.11.60, to 654 Sqn 21.3.62, with 5 Flt by 7.65, to 15 MU 13.4.67, NEA 27.5.68, to Waddington for fire practice 10.9.68.

XM527 c/n S2/5103. *4.4.59. To Middle Wallop 18.6.59, to 651 Sqn shortly afterward but held by 49 MU 5.11.59, Cat 5 17.9.63, allocated 7820M 10.63 at Middle Wallop, to Arborfield 3.10.63 but seen at Middle Wallop 5.68 and 7.75 still as 7820M. Presently at Middle Wallop.

XM528 c/n S2/5104. *15.4.59. On loan to C(A) 5.59, 18.6.59 started turbosupercharger trials, ff with this mod 6.8.59 all trials at A&AEE until 3.12.59 when to Eastleigh. Later to Aden for hot-weather trials. Flown with skids for first time 12.8.60. To A&AEE 12.1.61 to 13.2.61, to Saro 3.61, to 15 MU 8.11.61, to 651 Sqn 30.1.62, to 15 MU 20.11.64, to 5 Fld Regt RA 23.8.65. Cat 5 and SOC 27.5.68.

XM529 c/n S2/5105. *12.5.59. To Middle Wallop 18.6.59, to 651 Sqn but returned to Saro (mods) 22.3.60 to 20.4.60, then to 651 Sqn, to C(A) charge 12.9.60, to 651 Sqn 27.9.60, to 654 Sqn 12.6.63, with 5 Flt 7.65–3.67, to 15 MU 11.4.67, to Arborfield allocated 7979M. Next seen Flint Technical College 2.74. Later, nose mated with tail of XM556 and composite reg'd as G-BDNS 2.1.76 to Stockport APS Handforth.

XM530 c/n S2/5106. *20.5.59. To Middle Wallop 26.6.59, to 651 Sqn, Cat 5 14.6.60 but re-cat 4R 20.6.60 and to Saro for repair, to 15 MU 8.3.61, to 655 Sqn/23 Flt 4.7.62, with 17/21 Lancers by 7.65, with 71 Workshops Detmold 10.66, with 5 Fld Regt RA 5.67. Involved in road accident, Larzac, Southern France 25.8.68. Auctioned at Moordrecht, Holland, 20.10.69.

XM553 c/n S2/5107. *27.5.59. To Middle Wallop 26.6.59, to 651 Sqn 1960–63, to 15 MU 26.10.64, appeared at Middle Wallop 7.65, to 5 Fld Regt RA 23.8.65, to 15 MU 5.12.67. SOC 25.11.68. Reg 31.10.68 G-AWSV *Edward* to Maj M. Somerton Rayner. Based Middle Wallop. C of A expired 11.5.78.

XM554 c/n S2/5108. *10.6.59. To Middle Wallop 17.7.59, to 651 Sqn 1960–63, Cat 3R 20.3.63 repaired on site by 71 MU by 27.3.63, with 17 Flt 7.64 to 7.65, to 15 MU 16.6.67, NEA 27.5.68, to Chivenor for fire practice 10.8.68.

XM555 c/n S2/5109. Probably to Eastleigh by road 6.59, to Middle Wallop 14.7.59, to 654 Sqn 8.8.59, with 652 Sqn 6.64 to 11.65, with 5 Flt during 1965, to 15 MU 13.4.67, NEA 27.5.68, to Upwood 15.8.68 for 'familiarisation'. Allocated 8027M. Displayed Odiham 9.5.70 for a Royal visit. By 4.74, gate guardian at Ternhill. Still present 1.76 in scheme of red and white, but became gate guardian at Shawbury 9.76. 6.81, moved indoors for refurbishment in camouflage colours, this completed 1.83. To Cosford Aerospace Museum 29.9.83.

XM556 c/n S2/5110. *30.6.59. Ff 7.59. To Middle Wallop 28.8.59, to 654 Sqn 7.9.59, to CFS Little Rissington 4.7.61 coded 'V', designated T.13 and received full CFS scheme and insignia, allocated 7870M 13.12.64, to Army Apprentice College Chepstow, to Arborfield 10.65–11.69, to Flint Technical College 11.72 where nose mated with tail of XM529/7979M. Composite later sold to British Rotorcraft Museum, 4.76. G-HELI allotted but marks not painted on, reg 6.78 to Elfan Ap Rees. In storage at Weston-super-Mare.

XM557 c/n S2/5112. *14.7.59. To Middle Wallop 30.7.59, to 652 Sqn 15.8.59, to 654 Sqn 18.1.61, to 4 Fld Reg RA, to 652 Sqn/17 Flt 6.64–5.65, with 5 Flt 7–11.65, Wdn 3.10.68 and used instructionally in Germany. Auctioned Moordrecht 20.10.69.

XM558 c/n S2/5113. *17.7.59. To 654 Sqn 2.9.59, to 652 Sqn 7.12.59. Cat 5 1.64, SOC.

XM559 c/n S2/5114. *14.8.59. To Middle Wallop 26.8.59, to 654 Sqn 10.9.59, used by 12 Flt 9.11.59, to 652 Sqn 11.4.61, to 654 Sqn 1.4.62, with 9 Flt 9.65–2.66, to Air Troop 2 RTR to 1.67. Cat 5 27.5.68 and SOC.

XM560 c/n S2/5115. *31.8.59. To Middle Wallop 28.9.59, to 651 Sqn by 7.60, to 13 Flt 1.61, to 652 Sqn 19.4.63, to 5 Flt but crashed during excercises in Denmark 8.5.65. Cat 5 31.10.65, SOC.

XM561 c/n S2/5116. *29.5.59. To Middle Wallop 5.10.59, to 651 Sqn 7.60–8.61 and then 13 Flt, to 2 RTR, o/c 1 Wing 17.8.66, to 15 MU 2.10.67, allocated 7980M, to Arborfield 4.10.67. Appeared at Middle Wallop 7.75. To Moston College Manchester 10.75. To Lincolnshire Aircraft Museum, Tattershall, 28.1.83.

XM562 c/n S2/5117. *25.9.59. To 651 Sqn, flight trials Middle Wallop 7–10.61, to 13 Flt 1963–65, to 1st Queen's Dragoon Guards 6.65, to 2 RTR 10.5.66, to 9/12 Lancers 1.67, declared unfit by QHI due to 'vertical bounce at 40 kts and stick-stir'—the last Skeeter to be used operationally. Reported as Cat 5 scrap 1.11.68 but auctioned at Gouda 20.10.69.

XM563 c/n S2/5118. *8.10.59. Loaned to MoA 23.12.59 until 30.10.61, ff with Turmo 18.3.60, to SBAC Show 1960. After trials reverted to standard AOP.12; to 652 Sqn 1963–64, to 654 Sqn 28.2.64, to 3 RTR and later 9/12 Lancers by 8.67. SOC 29.4.68 and auctioned at Moordrecht 10.69.

XM564 c/n S2/5119. *23.10.59. To 652 Sqn 30.12.59, to 12 Flt 17.5.60, then repainted silver overall, coded 'X' and used by CFS Little Rissington 1961–64, to 15 MU 13.12.64, to 5 Fld Regt RA 23.8.65, also reported in use by 652 Sqn 6.64–2.66, left 5 Fld Regt RA late 1968, to 73 Aircraft Workshops 20.1.69, to Royal Armoured Corps Museum, c2.69, refurbished by Bovington Junior Leader's Regt and then used as gate guardian there.

XM565 c/n S2/5120. *5.11.59. To Middle Wallop 18.11.59, to 651 Sqn, Cat 3 13.2.61 in flying accident and repaired by 71 MU, further Cat 3 3.12.62 and repaired by 71 MU by 14.12.62, declared Cat 5 (inst) and allocated 7861M at Middle Wallop 17.9.64. Tail boom later used for bogus 'XL769' gate guardian at Middle Wallop.

XN339 c/n S2/7145. *19.11.59. To 651 Sqn 8.12.59, with 13 Flt 1960–62, Cat 4R after hitting power cables 7.2.63, to CFS 6.7.64 and seen at Little Rissington 8.64 camouflaged with 'Z' of CFS and ARMY titles, to 15 MU 30.11.64, to HQ 1 Wing 17.6.65, later to 4 Fld Regt RA. Cat 5 1.11.68. Auctioned at Moordrecht 20.10.69.

XN340 c/n S2/7146. *3.12.59. To 15 MU 2.3.60, to 651 Sqn 28.9.60, Cat 3R 24.6.64, after repair to Queen's Dragoon Guards by 12.64, to 1 Wing 17.8.66, to 26 Fld Regt RA. Cat 5(C) and SOC 27.5.68.

XN341 c/n S2/7147. *c25.1.60. To 15 MU 5.2.60, to 651 Sqn 28.9.60, next seen with 3 RTR 7.65, to 15 MU 30.6.67, NEA 27.5.68, to 4 SoTT St Athan 31.7.68, allocated 8022M for engine/airframe fitter training. Seen at Chivenor 22.8.70. Preserved at St Athan for RAF Museum.

XN342 c/n S2/7148. Arrived Eastleigh, probably by road, c14.1.60. To 15 MU 4.2.60, to 651 Sqn 25.9.60, to 652 Sqn 20.4.63, to 17/21 Lancers 28.11.67 but shortly afterwards returned to 15 MU, NEA 27.5.68, to Finningley for fire section to practice rescue training 28.8.68.

XN343 c/n S2/7149. Arrived Eastleigh, probably by road, c15.1.60. To 15 MU 7.3.60, to 12 Flt 19.10.60, to 654 Sqn 7.11.60 but served with 651 Sqn c5.63, Cat 3R 23.5.63, with 1 Wing/17 Flt by 6.65, to 9 Flt 9.65 until 4.66 at least, with 2 RTR by 8.67, Cat 5S. SOC 12.12.68. Auctioned at Gouda 20.10.69.

XN344 c/n S2/7150. *26.1.60. To 15 MU 8.3.60, Middle Wallop 11.10.60, to 652 Sqn 18.10.60, to 654 Sqn 1.4.62, served with 26 Fld Regt RA for some time, to 15 MU 23.11.67, NEA 27.5.68 but allocated 8018M at Middle Wallop (though number not carried on aircraft), remained at AETW Middle Wallop until at least 7.75, to Science Museum South Kensington via MoD 1975.

XN345 c/n S2/7151. *16.2.60. To 15 MU 28.3.60, Middle Wallop 11.10.60, to 652 Sqn 18.10.60, to 654 Sqn 9.11.60, later with 9/12 Lancers, possibly with 5 Flt 7.65–3.67 but Cat 5S 1.11.68. Auctioned at Gouda 10.69.

XN346 c/n S2/7152. *29.2.60. To 15 MU 22.4.60, to 651 Sqn 4.10.60, Cat 3R 26.7.63 and on 5.11.64, to 15 MU 16.11.64 but to 1 Wing Detmold 17.6.65; 9 Flt and then to 19 Fld Regt RA, Cat 5S, SOC 1.11.68. Auctioned Gouda 20.10.69.

XN347 c/n S2/7153. *31.3.60. To 15 MU 26.4.60, to Detmold 11.10.60, to 652 Sqn 18.10.60, to 654 Sqn 18.8.61, to Middle Wallop 21.5.62 for AAC Centre. Re-issued to 655 Sqn/23 Flt 6.62. Destroyed in accident 11.12.65. Cat 5(C) SOC 18.1.66.

XN348 c/n S2/7154. *20.4.60. To 15 MU 22.6.60, to 655 Sqn/23 Flt 7.62, with 5 Flt 7.65–7.66, to 15 MU 11.4.67, NEA 27.5.68 but to Binbrook 6.8.68 for trade training as 8024M. To AAC Museum 7.70. To Bückeburg Helicopter Museum 4.74.

XN349 c/n S2/7155. *5.5.60. To 15 MU 2.8.60 (storage), to 1 Wing 6.62, Cat 3 27.7.63 and returned to 15 MU, to 652 Sqn 1963–64, to 9 Flt 17.6.65, to 19 Fld Regt RA 8.67. SOC Cat 5S 22.12.68. Auctioned at Gouda 20.10.69.

XN350 c/n S2/7156. *23.5.60. To 15 MU 30.8.60, to 651 Sqn 30.8.61, loaned to 2 RTR 28.7.62, to 651 Sqn/13 Flt 1963–66, to 17/21 Lancers 8.66. SOC Cat 5S 12.12.68. Auctioned at Gouda 20.10.69.

XN351 c/n S2/7157. *7.6.60. To 15 MU 30.8.60, to 651 Sqn 8.61, to 652 Sqn 10.63, with 3 RTR by 7.65, to 15 MU 30.6.67, NEA 27.5.68, to Shuttleworth Collection 12.8.68. On long-term loan to Torbay Air Museum from 5.71. By 1983, under restoration by Wales Aircraft Museum. To flying condition by late 1983. Allotted G-BKSC 23.5.83 and based at Shobdon by J. Powell and K. Abbott.

XN352 c/n S2/7158. *21.6.60. To 15 MU 31.8.60 (storage), to 652 Sqn 5.7.62, Cat 3R after hitting power cable while with 9 Flt 17.6.64, with 9/12 Lancers by 7.65, with 5 Fld Regt RA when SOC Cat 5S 22.12.68. Auctioned at Gouda 20.10.69.

XN353 c/n S2/7159. At Eastleigh by 28.9.60, to 15 MU 28.11.60, to 655 Sqn/23 Flt 10.7.62, movements unknown until return to 15 MU 31.1.67, NEA 27.5.68, to Manston for rescue training 2.10.68.

262

XN354 c/n S2/7160. *18.8.60. To 15 MU 16.9.60, to AAC 1 Wing 30.4.62, to 654 Sqn/17 Flt 3.8.62 probably served here until mid-1965. Next noted with 26 Fld Regt RA 8.67. Cat 5S 20.6.68. Auctioned at Moordrecht 20.10.69.

XN355 c/n S2/7161. *30.8.60. To 15 MU 20.9.60, to BAOR 10.7.62, then to 655 Sqn/23 Flt. Cat 3P 5.8.63 but with 655 Sqn to summer 1965. To 15 MU 31.1.67. NEA 27.5.68. To Manston for rescue training 2.10.68.

Skeeter 50

PC-117 c/n S2/5061. *7.3.58. Ff as G-12-2. To HFB 3 Rotenburg 22.5.58, later to HFB 6 Hungriger Wolf as PF-156, to Alverca Portugal 6.61. All Skeeters arriving in Portugal thought to have had no national or other marks applied and there is no confirmation of any of them flying after 6.61.

PC-118 c/n S2/5062. *31.3.58. To HFB 3 Rotenburg 22.5.58, later to HFB 6 Hungriger Wolf as PF-157. To Alverca 6.61.

PC-119 c/n S2/5063. *21.4.58. To HFB 3 Rotenburg 22.5.58 (with PC-117 and PC-118). Later to HFB 6 Hungriger Wolf as PF-158. To Alverca 6.61.

PC-120 c/n S2/5073. *30.7.58. To HFB 3 Rotenburg 14.10.58. Later to HFB 6 Hungriger Wolf as PF-159. To Alverca 6.61.

PC-121 c/n S2/5077. *7.9.58. To HFB 3 Rotenburg 14.10.58, with PC-120. Later to HFB 6 Hungriger Wolf as PF-160. To Alverca 6.61.

PC-122 c/n S2/5082 *6.10.58. To HFB 3 Rotenburg 10.12.58. Later to HFB 6 Hungriger Wolf as PF-155. To Alverca 6.61.

Skeeter 51

SC-501 c/n S2/5065. *16.5.58. To MFG 3 Nordholz 14.10.58, to Alverca 6.61.

SC-502 c/n S2/5070. *4.7.58. To SBAC Show 1958 in German Navy markings, to MFG 3 Nordholz 14.10.58, to Alverca 6.61.

SC-503 c/n S2/5083. *13.10.58. To MFG 3 Nordholz 12.58, to Alverca 6.61.

SC-504 c/n S2/5092. *10.12.58. To MFG 3 Nordholz 18.3.59, to Alverca 6.61.

Saunders-Roe P.531, Scout and Wasp

1958 was the year in which turbine-powered helicopters began to appear in Britain, and the Saro P.531 was the smallest of these newcomers. By that time, Skeeter production was well underway and provided adequate current business for Saunders-Roe but the company foresaw an eventual need for a turbine-powered replacement. Thus the P.531 was created, although until mid-1957 no practical moves could be made because there was no suitable turbine powerplant.

During the summer of 1957, the Blackburn Turmo free-turbine of 425 shp was given a special category type-test certificate and Saro planned the P.531 around it. It was felt that the simplest approach might have been to install a Turmo in the Skeeter and minimise any engineering changes. In

P.531 G-APNU over the south of England, late summer 1958. The cockpit area is strongly reminiscent of the Skeeter. (*Saro*)

fact this was done, but only for experimental purposes; the firm decided that any major production of a Turmo-powered helicopter should involve a new airframe.

In November 1957 serious design work began on the P.531 at Eastleigh and, under the direction of T. L. Ciastula, the first P.531 appeared during July 1958. The new helicopter was of simple construction and had a multi-role capability. Almost the entire airframe was riveted from light-gauge aluminium alloy sheet, except for a thin stainless steel box under the Turmo, steel tubes to suspend the airframe from the main rotor, and the use of honeycomb construction in the ventral fin.

The fuselage of the P.531 was divided into a forward cabin and a rear boom of near-circular section carrying the tailplane and tail rotor. Two vertical webs were placed side by side to form a spinal girder which was extended aft and upwards to meet the four tubes suspending the P.531 from the main rotor. There were two light bulkheads, a floor-pan and a fire-resisting metal tray above which the Turmo was situated. Between the full cross-section transverse bulkheads were three flexible fuel tanks sharing a common sump beneath the centre cell, and the three portions were sub-divided to minimise surging during violent manoeuvres.

The Blackburn-Turboméca Turmo 600 free-turbine was mounted externally on the centre fuselage decking, providing excellent accessibility. The engine was secured by a small pressed-plate trunnion on either side with two light straps on the underside to prevent rotary displacement. Two

The first P.531, G-APNU, Eastleigh, summer 1958. (*Saro*)

lateral meshed intake ducts fed air to the Turmo and, as the free-turbine was located to the rear, the drive was taken through a primary gearbox and then forward underneath the powerplant to the rotor. A freewheel was incorporated in the primary gearbox, though the free-turbine unit dispensed with the need for a clutch, and a rotor parking brake was included in the shaft leading from the secondary gearbox to the oil pump, though in the case of the first P.531, this had insufficient power to lock the rotor with the Turmo at idle rpm. To the port of the Turmo was mounted a large oil cooler with a forward-facing intake. This served the primary and secondary gearboxes while the engine oil was contained in an integral tank around the intake passages and was thus self-cooling.

The canopy structure was of welded aluminium tube, and windscreen panels were made from flat glass where possible to minimise optical problems and allow good use of the wipers. Down the centre of the cabin roof was a switch and control console and, on either side of this, the roof was of bulged perspex to provide additional headroom. All four cabin doors were non-stress-bearing and the P.531 could fly with any or all of them removed.

External ribs strengthened the rear part of the forward fuselage and left the interior clear for the installation of loads or equipment. This space forward of the tailboom attachment face was served by a ventral hatch. The tailboom itself was similar to that of the Skeeter (except for the

265

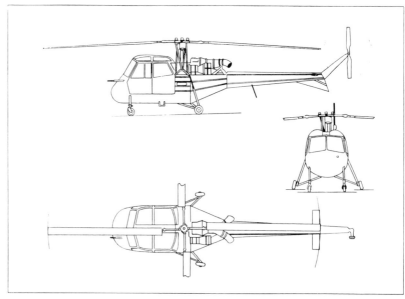

Skeeter 1) but somewhat shorter due to the greater forward fuselage length and rotor axis of the P.531, making the length of the new helicopter between the axis of the main and tail rotors similar to that of the Skeeter.

In the case of the Skeeter, the steel tubes around the powerplant led to a five-point attachment at the tailboom; however, the P.531 relied on four points to anchor the boom, with correspondingly repositioned stiffeners along the boom itself. At the rear of the boom, an angled gearbox transmitted drive to the tail rotor, which was of similar arrangement to those of the later Skeeters except for a small increase in blade chord at the tips. A small tailplane was provided to increase permissible travel of the centre of gravity but the first P.531, G-APNU, undertook a major part of its testing without this surface. Beneath the tailplane was installed a honeycomb sandwich ventral fin to counteract the effect of the greater side area forward of the centre of gravity.

Main rotor blades were of similar construction to those of the Skeeter but the hub, identical in principle to those of the earlier series, had provision for a four-blade rotor configuration. Though the first P.531 was fitted with a three-axis stabiliser and had provision for an autopilot, power controls were not fitted. Control forces were so low that the cyclic pitch control was centred by rubber bushes in torsion.

The cabin seated five and the cockpit was equipped for dual-control. Access to the rear of the instrument panel could be gained through the fibre-glass nose access plates. Each cyclic pitch stick was equipped with a 'press to transmit' trigger and a four-way trimming button under the pilot's thumb.

The Turmo compressor ran at a governed rpm in the case of the first two P.531s, having no mechanical interconnection with shaft output, thus making possible a choice of any governed rotor rpm irrespective of engine output and making output itself something of an automatic process. While later P.531s had a powerful rotor-brake capable of locking the rotor against engine idling torque, on the first two prototypes the rotor-brake was taken off before starting up and the collective pitch twist-grips locked in the idling position corresponding to a rotor speed of some 200 rpm. For training the P.531 could be flown as an ungoverned aircraft, with the governor locked in the fully-open position, by selecting maximum rotor rpm and then flying on twist-grip in the traditional manner. Response of the Turmo was found to be good, with little lag in the event of sudden loads.

Provision was made for the attachment of a 440 lb air-driven hoist mounted on the starboard side, and for the carriage of two stretchers placed transversely at the rear of the cabin, with their ends covered by canvas flaps and the rear doors removed for added space. The second pilot's seat was made reversible for use by a medical attendant. The P.531 had four wheels, the front members castoring and the main oleos similar to those of the Skeeter but of longer stroke.

The design of the P.531 was stabilised at the end of December 1957 and a mock-up was completed by late February 1958. Construction of two prototypes, G-APNU and G-APNV, proceeded side by side and a Turmo was delivered on 16 July. G-APNU began ground-running trials on 19 July and no indication of ground resonance was traced. On the following day, it made its first flight in the hands of Ken Reed. By the end of the month, five hours had been flown, while G-APNV neared completion. Both aircraft

G-APNV, the first of three P.531-0 examples. (*Bob Wealthy*)

The cabin of P.531-0 G-APNV showing the four doors and four-point early undercarriage layout. (*Bob Wealthy*)

were a completely private venture that promised very well for the future. On 30 September, G-APNV made its first flight, Ken Reed again being the pilot.

Both G-APNU and G-APNV were powered by 400 hp turmo 600s de-rated to 325 shp as the transmission was limited to this figure. It was expected that, after testing, the transmission and rotor system would be stressed for 650 shp and that a fully-rated Turmo would be used. Indeed, these areas were stressed, but not, in the event, for the Turmo. The development of the Blackburn A.129 (Nimbus) 960 shp free-turbine was so rapid that this powerplant was selected for subsequent models.

The first P.531, G-APNU, was a basic prototype. After this came three P.531-0s: G-APNV, a developed prototype, together with XN333 and XN334. The refined version was P.531-2. This was a heavier and more powerful helicopter than the initial examples. All-up weight rose to 5,000 lb from the 3,800 lb of the P.531-0s. The fuselage shape was revised somewhat for aerodynamic reasons and was given increased carrying capacity. The cabin floor area was extended to provide seating for six. Perspex panels were let into the doors to improve the view, and the windscreen shape was altered. Ease of servicing was improved by the external installation of the tail-shaft, which was situated on top of the boom and protected by spine covers. Fuel tankage was increased from 126 to 158 gal, and all-metal rotor-blades were fitted, a development of the contemporary standard Hiller blade. Transmission was redesigned and strengthened for installation of the more powerful A.129 Mk 3, and auto-governing was fitted so that selective rotor speed was maintained regardless of the collective pitch setting.

Much effort was made to give the P.531-2 all-weather capability; though a weight penalty naturally arose, it was felt this could be absorbed by the more powerful engine. All-weather ability was seen as essential to secure military orders. There were no plans to capture the civil market with the P.531, though the first four examples did in fact appear on the civil register.

For the military role, the P.531-2 included a three-axis autostabilisation system with cruising autopilot, cabin heating, glass de-misting, cargo sling, lightweight air-driven hoist as before (this was optional), a comprehensive range of radio, night-flying and navigational equipment, windscreen de-icing, and detachable weapons carrier. It was also made possible to carry homing torpedoes, dunking radar, and day/night photographic equipment. The helicopter was aimed at the Navy as well as the Army and the range of possible equipment gave the P.531-2 a great versatility.

P.531-0 XN333, with wheel/skid undercarriage, Eastleigh, autumn 1959. (*BHC*)

P.531-0 XN334 undergoing deck handling trials using suction pads and skids, early 1960.
(*Westland*)

The first P.531-2, G-APVL, with a de-rated 650 shp Blackburn A.129 Nimbus Mk 3, first flew from Eastleigh on 9 August, 1959. In the same month, Westland Aircraft Ltd took over a major portion of Saunders-Roe, including the Helicopter Division; thereafter development of the P.531 series was taken on by Westland, the result being the Westland Wasp and Scout. Though the histories of these aircraft undoubtedly belong to Westland, this successful programme was initiated by Saunders-Roe and it is worth looking at the Saro-built P.531s in the context of the overall programme.

P.531 G-APNU was a purely aerodynamic prototype. After this came P.531-0 G-APNV, a developed prototype with a full-scale tailplane but employing the same powerplant, a Turmo de-rated to 325 shp. During October 1959, this example went to the Royal Navy as XN332, where it was exhaustively evaluated until June 1961, the results being used by Westland for the eventual development of the Wasp. After retirement, G-APNV/XN332 was used as a ground instructional trainer and later went to the Fleet Air Arm Museum where it is preserved.

Two other almost identical P.531-0s were built. These were XN333 and XN334. All three were used by the Navy, making hundreds of take-offs

270

and landings aboard frigates, by day and night, to help solve the problems of deck operations. Altogether, nineteen different landing-gear/deck securing arrangements were tested, including the use of suction pads. Finally, it was decided to adopt a system of four castoring but lockable wheeled undercarriage members and this was subsequently used for the Wasp.

P.531-2 G-APVL, the first Mk 2 prototype, with a 650 shp Nimbus de-rated to 635 shp and a skid undercarriage, became XP116 for trials with the Army Air Corps, being used for the development of the Scout. The second Mk 2, G-APVM, was powered by a de Havilland Gnome H.1000 de-rated to 635 shp and joined the Army Air Corps for similar purposes during 1961 as XR493. This example, too, had a skid undercarriage, but the Gnome installation was not adopted on later models.

An initial pre-series order for a small batch of eight P.531-2s similar to G-APVL was secured by Saunders-Roe before the Westland take-over. This order was placed for the Army Air Corps, and these later examples were evaluated by it for general-purpose duties. The type was originally named the Saro Sprite but, when the Westland take-over occurred, the name was replaced by Scout. XP165 was the first of this batch and flew for the first time on 29 August, 1960.

A short while later, a substantial Army order was placed, to Specification H.201D. Known as the Scout AH.1, forty examples were built at Hayes, and XP846, first of the batch, made its maiden flight on 20 October, 1961. Deliveries began from spring 1963. The Scout was a five-seater with Nimbus 102 engine and skid landing gear, and was used for

The second P.531–2, G-APVM, the sole Gnome-powered example, spring 1960.

271

The first P.531–2, G-APVL, late summer 1959, Eastleigh. The fuselage shape has been somewhat revised and the glazing has been modified. (*BHC*)

passenger/freight transport, liaison and related duties. XP165 eventually joined the collection of historic aircraft at the Southend Museum, and on 10 May, 1983, was bought by the British Rotorcraft Museum.

The first Wasp HAS.1, XS463, which flew on 28 October, 1962, at White Waltham, was much more sophisticated than the earlier P.531s and substantially heavier. By 1965 the Scout and Wasp were both in service in quantity, both powered by different marks of the Nimbus. The Scout/Wasp programme was a great success, and as instigators of the programme, Saunders-Roe must be given much of the credit.

P.531 prototype (G-APNU)

One 400 shp Blackburn-Turboméca Turmo de-rated to 325 shp.

Length (rotors folded) 29 ft; height 9 ft 6 in; rotor diameter 32 ft 6 in.

Empty weight 2,092 lb; normal loaded weight 3,400 lb; maximum overloaded weight 3,800 lb.

Maximum speed 121 mph; typical cruising speed 109 mph; initial vertical rate of climb 540 ft/min; hover ceiling (free air) 2,300 ft; normal range 242 miles; range with long-range tanks 322 miles.

P.531-2 (G-APVL)

One 650 shp Blackburn A.129 (Nimbus) Mk 3 free-turbine de-rated to 635 shp.

Length 39 ft 8 in, length (rotors folded) 30 ft 4in; width 32 ft 3in, width (rotors folded) 8 ft

272

P.531-2 G-APVL with Army markings but without its military serial XP116, late 1959.
(BHC)

$5\frac{1}{2}$ in; height 10 ft $5\frac{1}{2}$ in; main rotor disc area 817 sq ft.
  Empty weight (fully equipped less radio) 2,836 lb; loaded weight 5,000 lb.
  Maximum speed 134 mph; typical cruising speed 122.5 mph; maximum inclined climb 1,700 ft/min; vertical rate of climb 600 ft/min; hover ceiling 10,000 ft; hover ceiling in ground effect 14,900 ft; maximum range 310 miles; maximum endurance (normal tanks) $3\frac{1}{2}$ hr.

Westland Scout AH.1

One 685 shp Bristol Siddeley Nimbus 102.
Rotor diameter 32 ft 3 in; length (rotors folded) 30 ft $7\frac{1}{2}$ in; height 8 ft 11 in.
Empty weight 3,084 lb; loaded weight 5,300 lb.
Maximum speed 132 mph; maximum cruising speed 122 mph; maximum inclined climb 1,660 ft/min; hover ceiling (free air) 10,200 ft; hover ceiling in ground effect 15,600 ft; service ceiling 17,700 ft; maximum range 317 miles.

Westland Wasp AS.1

One 710 shp Bristol Siddeley Nimbus 103.
Rotor diameter 32 ft 3in; length (rotors folded) 30 ft $5\frac{3}{4}$ in; height 9 ft 9 in.
Empty weight 3,384 lb; loaded weight 5,500 lb.
Maximum speed 121 mph; maximum cruising speed 110 mph; maximum inclined climb 1,440 ft/min; hover ceiling (free air) 8,800 ft; hover ceiling in ground effect 12,500 ft; service ceiling 12,500 ft; maximum range 303 miles.

Pre-production P.531–2 XP191, named by Saro the Sprite, and re-named the Scout by Westland. (*Westland*)

The first Wasp HAS.1, XS463, developed under Westland. (*Westland*)

P.531 Prototype

G-APNU c/n S2/5267. Aerodynamic prototype. Reg 6.58 Saro Eastleigh. Ff 20.7.58, Eastleigh, K. M. Reed, Saro Chief Helicopter Test Pilot. Wdn 1960. Reg cancelled 9.64. Stored at Hayes until scrapped at Coley's Yard, Hounslow, early 1972.

P531-0

G-APNV c/n S2/5268. Development prototype with full-span tailplane and external hoist. Ff 30.9.58 Eastleigh, K. M. Reed. To RN 2.10.59 for evaluation, as XN332, under Contract KF/2Q/01/CB25(a). Evaluated by No. 771 Sqn at Yeovil to 6.61, gathering information for development of Wasp. Retired to RNEC Manadon as GI trainer wearing A2579. Preserved at Yeovilton FAAM wearing '759' and A2579; XN333 and XN334, also to KF/2Q/01/CB25(a). For RN evaluation with No. 771 Sqn. XN333 to RN 20.10.59, later became A2519. XN334 to RN 6.11.59, later became A2525. Preserved at Yeovilton Fleet Air Arm Museum, in store.

P.531-2

G-APVL c/n S2/5311. Reg 7.59 Saro Eastleigh. Ff Eastleigh 9.8.59, K. M. Reed. To AAC for trials 1960 as XP166. Skid undercarriage and A.129 Mk 3; G-APVM c/n S2/5312. Ff Eastleigh 3.5.60, K. M. Reed. Reworked Hayes 1960 as Scout AH.1 forerunner. As XR493 1961 for AAC trials and o/c AAC until to 8040M, Fleetlands.

Pre-production batch of 8 P531-2s ordered by MoA for AAC evaluation and trials, named Sprite by Saro. During batch construction, Saro absorbed by Westland and type became known as the Scout AH.1.

XP165, first of the eight pre-production P.531–2s, showing its ability to land on small spaces.
(Van Hallen)

275

P.531-2/Scout AH.1
XP165 c/n S2/8437. Ff 29.8.60. Used for trials with Turmo by Blackburn. Given red and white colour scheme, joined ETPS Farnborough coded '5'. Retired 1972 and on Farnborough dump by 1.73. To Historic Aircraft Museum Southend, 7.75. To British Rotorcraft Museum 10.5.83; XP166 ex G-APVL. Later equipped with Wasp tail. MoD(PE) RAE Farnborough, in store; XP167 c/n S2/8438; XP188 c/n S2/8440; XP189 c/n S2/8441. Later Lynx rotor test rig. MoD(PE) RAE Farnborough. G-ARGI originally allotted, but not taken up. XP190 c/n S2/8443. To GI trainer, Army Apprentice College, Arborfield; XP191 c/n S2/8446. RNAY Wroughton store; XP192 c/n S2/8447. Ff 23.2.62.

Also constructed (with company funds):
C/n S2/8442—pre-demonstrator; c/n S2/8444—to India; c/n S2/8445—structural test specimen.

Scout AH.1
XP846—XP910 (40) c/ns F9472—F9511. First production batch for Scout AH.1 by AAC to Spec H.201D. Built at Hayes under KF/2Q/06/CB25(a). Flight testing at White Waltham. XP846 ff 20.10.61.

Development Wasp HAS.1.
XS463 (c/n F9541) and XS476 (c/n F9542) for RN, built at Hayes under KK/N/014/CB25(a). XS463 ff White Waltham 28.10.62, ex G-17-1, Westland Experimental and Trials Flight. To A2647. Preserved British Rotorcraft Museum, acquired 6.81; XS476 ex G-17-2. Used by Observer Training School Culdrose. To A2656.

Saunders-Roe SR.53 and SR.177

After the war, Britain was able to examine the rocket-powered Messerschmitt Me 163 interceptor and a number of other German wartime projects. Several Walter HWK 509 series bi-fuel motors were captured, and dismantled by the Allies with immense interest. Subsequently, a RATO (Rocket Assisted Take Off) project was initiated and two British rocket motors emerged. These were the de Havilland Sprite of 5,000 lb thrust and the Armstrong Siddeley Snarler of 2,000 lb thrust. The Sprite was a 'cold' rocket motor powered by High Test Peroxide (HTP) as a monopropellant with silver catalyst, while the Snarler ran on methyl alcohol, water and liquid oxygen (lox). The first Snarler flight took place on 20 November, 1950, in Hawker P.1072 VP401. Although the P.1072 with the Snarler had an astonishing rate of climb, the Avon with afterburner, or reheat, was preferred as the method of obtaining improved climb and high-altitude performance.

Interestingly, the RAE Project Office had looked, during the late 1940s, at the possibility of rocket-powered target-defence aircraft, and these investigations inclined toward the 'manned missile' concept. The design of RATO motors, meanwhile, was expanded into a requirement for a rocket-based aircraft and on 2 February, 1952, the Ministry of Supply issued Specifi-cation F.124T. This was derived from RAF OR.301.

SR.53 XD145, Boscombe Down, spring 1957. (A&AEE)

The requirements of F.124T have been described as making the Me 163 'look almost cissy'. Some of the worst aspects of the Me 163 concept were, however, certainly incorporated. The aircraft was to be a supersonic single-seat single-engined type. Though take-off was to be from a short ramp rather than from the detachable trolley used with the Me 163, an extendable skid was to be provided on which to land. It seems fair to say, in view of the dire experiences of the Germans with the Me 163, that the undercarriage arrangements called for in F.124T would have been very dangerous and would certainly have caused a protracted turn-around time. Part of F.124T demanded a huge recovery vehicle, to be used in dragging the aircraft back to base from wherever it landed. A serious problem was that, as a pure rocket aircraft, F.124T would have had a very short range. Thus, it could not have guaranteed a safe post-sortie return to the take-off site. In fact, the Specification stated that landings were to be made with dry tanks after the limited endurance was exhausted. Consideration was given to the employment of ATO (Assisted Take Off) through the use of two Mayfly cordite rockets. RAF/MoS procurement thinking was clouded by uncertainty over what they actually wanted and what was actually practical. Only two criteria were firmly fixed at that time; cheapness and simplicity.

There were several responses to F.124T by those firms to which it was issued; Saunders-Roe was not invited to tender, although the Cowes firm

277

was very much to the forefront of rocket propulsion studies by 1952. Since the previous year, Maurice Brennan (then assistant chief designer but after October 1952 chief designer) had been examining on a theoretical basis the possibility of a small rocket-powered interceptor. Brennan's work was initially confined to a small paper study, to which the Saro Board assented in December 1951. By early 1952, the investigation had yielded the idea for a small rocket aircraft able to fly at altitudes of up to 100,000 ft.

Brennan had also settled on his choice of fuel for such an aircraft, finally choosing HTP as opposed to the two other fuels then on offer, nitric acid and lox. W. G. A. Perring, then Director, RAE, advocated lox because it was cheap. However, the drawbacks associated with this fuel were numerous. A lox-filled fighter could not be kept at readiness without its fuel tanks incorporating some form of topping-up system connected to a bowser. Also, a lox fire is very violent and difficult to contain. Finally, the mechanical systems in a lox-powered aircraft would have to be kept constantly warm to prevent them freezing solid, with consequent increased loss of fuel. Brennan and A.V. Cleaver of de Havilland Engines both preferred HTP in view of the problems with lox, though Sid Allen of Armstrong Siddeley Motors was impressed with the latter fuel because of its cheapness. At the time, HTP was incredibly expensive, in part because it was possible to manufacture only small quantities at a time; as the 1950s progressed, however, the process was developed and the price fell. Brennan and Cleaver both decided to put safety first, and adopted HTP; Brennan at least seems to have given little thought to the possibility of nitric acid. Fortunately, within a few years concerns such as Laporte Chemicals were manufacturing HTP in bulk.

At the same time as Specification F.124T was issued, Saro issued a report, *Investigation of Problems of Pure Rocket Fighter Aircraft*. Brennan's

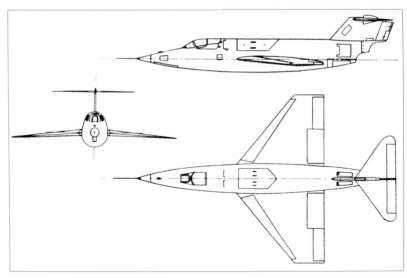

SR.53

278

chance to put theory into practice materialised with the release of F.124T, but this was delayed by the reluctance of the MoS to send Saro a copy.

After lobbying, Saro finally succeeded in extracting a copy of F.124T from the MoS in March 1952, by which time it had changed somewhat. An optional undercarriage of conventional arrangement was included. Because of pressure from a number of the interested designers, it was reluctantly agreed that a very small 'get-you-home' turbojet might be included, which was unpopular with the MoS because it added complication to their originally very stark concept. Small indeed; the suggested turbojet was the Turboméca Palas of just 330 lb st.

Saro submitted a detailed design study to F.124T in April. This was for a single-seater of 12,780 lb all-up weight, powered by an 8,000 lb thrust Saro-designed rocket and fuelled by HTP and kerosene. Maximum speed was to be Mach 2·44. Take-off was to be either from a jettisonable trolley main undercarriage or from a conventional nosewheel type. A landing skid was provided, to be used with the trolley option. Emergency escape facilities consisted of a detachable M. L. Aviation cabin section rather than an ejector seat. This first submission by Brennan to F.124T, Project P.154, is described in Appendix Five.

Brennan suggested at the end of his submission that a turbojet should definitely be included, preferably with more power than the Palas, to ensure safe returns, together with a conventional undercarriage of the nose-wheel variety.

Brennan had his suggestions agreed to by the Ministry in May 1952, when the interested companies were asked to examine the possibility of adding a substantial turbojet in conjunction with a rocket motor. The revised Saro design retained the firm's own rocket motor but incorporated also an Armstrong Siddeley Viper turbojet of 1,640 lb st for increased endurance. Proposed all-up weight was 15,000 lb. A conventional tricycle undercarriage replaced the ramp, trolley and skid. In August, a substitute rocket motor was confirmed; the de Havilland Spectre. The jettisonable cabin concept was abandoned and replaced by a conventional (and cheaper) ejector seat. These ideas were passed to the MoS later in August.

On 30 October, Saro received an Instruction to Proceed on three prototypes to this submission, which eventually crystalised as SR.53. The design underwent further revision before stabilisation was thought to be complete. The Viper was placed above the Spectre rather than below, as had previously been the case. Ear intakes behind the cockpit were employed, with a single jet exhaust pipe rather than the former bifurcated type. Slotted flaps and ailerons replaced the combined flap and aileron arrangement of previous designs, and the wing also featured a large drooping leading-edge. The delta tailplane was moved from its original low-set position to the top of the fin. The tailplane itself featured a small elevator flanked by fences, and a drag or anti-spin parachute in a container at the tip. The original armament of 50 rocket projectiles was replaced by wingtip-mounted de Havilland Blue Jay infra-red homing missiles. This was intended as the finalised form and SR.53 was born. In the meantime, Air Staff Requirement OR.301, Issue 2, had prompted the creation of an amended Specification to replace F.124T. This was F.138D, and it was written essentially around the Saro proposals, except for the armament change which stemmed from OR.301–2 itself.

SR.53 XD145. (*BHC*)

In fact, though it was thought that the SR.53 design would be frozen fairly early in 1953, by April another series of modifications, initiated by RAE, was complete. These involved increasing the mainplane anhedral, with the consequent alterations to the mainplanes themselves, parts of the fuselage and the wind-track Dowty undercarriage. Considering the possible complications that could have been involved in SR.53, it really was a simple design, perhaps kept so by the very inexperience of Saro in designing such an aircraft. It is worth noting that at high altitudes the performance of SR.53 was hard to match even by most aircraft of the 1970s.

On 8 May, 1953, after the Advisory Design Conference held by the MoS, a formal contract was placed for three SR.53 prototypes, XD145, XD151 and XD153. At the same time however, the MoS was interested in the progress made by the Avro 720. This was designed to Specification F.137D, initiated by the MoS as the 'complementary' prototype to SR.53 and powered by a Viper and a lox rocket. This competition encouraged Saro to try to accelerate development of SR.53 and July 1954 was set as the date for the first flight.

Part of the Cowes design team continued working on SR.53, but studies were also made on a phase two aircraft, beginning in early 1954. This was necessary for a number of reasons. SR.53 had no provision for radar except for the gun-laying variety (though it carried no guns), yet it was

280

SR.53 XD151 with its very unusual engine exhaust configuration, autumn 1957.

underlined by Central Fighter Establishment that powerful radar was needed when intercepting high-altitude aircraft at great speed. However, SR.53 was not capable of lifting Ferranti AI (the most suitable choice) as well as the offensive load of missiles.

F.138D had specified the inclusion of 'radar'. CFE knew what it wanted but evidently the MoS did not share its conviction. It seems that the MoS was not thinking further than gunlaying radar. Already, however, curve of pursuit tactics were becoming outmoded by the collision course interception method then being adopted by the Americans. This method allowed an attack from any direction rather than merely from behind, and modern AI was essential for it.

Visual target acquisition was of course impossible in an aircraft travelling at the speeds the SR.53 was designed for. Air Cdre Geoffrey Stephenson of CFE visited Cowes late in 1953 and emphasised the need for modern AI radar. Brennan contacted Royal Radar Establishment, which suggested the AI-23 as the best choice. Though a combination of infra-red homing missiles and gunlaying radar was useless, AI-23 would go perfectly with such weapons and provide the desired collision-course interception. SR.53 was not designed to lift all this equipment but that was not Brennan's fault, because F.138D had been so vague and, at the time he started work on SR.53, collision-course tactics were very new indeed. De Havilland Propellers were concentrating at that time on a new missile which eventually was to become Red Top; this would be quite suitable for a Saro phase-two aircraft containing AI.

In addition to the problem of radar, Brennan was never content with the role of the Viper turbojet in SR.53. This was installed almost purely as a device for returning home after each flight, and SR.53 could not take-off on its Viper alone. In the air, for most of the time the role of the turbojet was rather limited except for short periods of loiter. Brennan sought the installation of a much more powerful turbojet in order to increase the flexibility of the combination. While the jet engine and the aerodynamic design could provide loiter and subsonic cruise, the rocket would provide very high-speed chase, interception and combat. Brennan also knew that endurance could be much improved by cruising on turbojet alone.

It was felt at Cowes that to try to marry at some future date the refined avionics and offensive load which would become available to SR.53 might have produced an out-of-date product, even had the aircraft been made capable of lifting the loads, by combining up-to-date equipment with a revamped machine. To compromise the effectiveness of the aircraft by providing an inadequate radar system would have been unforgivable. SR.53 as an operational interceptor would have worked well only in conjunction with a first-class ground controller. In early 1954 the design of a fully-operational development of SR.53 was begun at Cowes, with funds provided by the company for the paper study.

Plans were made for the inclusion of a turbojet of 7,000 to 8,000 lb thrust in the new study. The powerplants under consideration were the Bristol BE.22 Saturn and the de Havilland PS.50 Gyron Junior. After talks with the MoS, a request was made in November 1953 for more detailed information on a suitably re-engined aircraft. Finalised proposals were made at Cowes for the adoption of a Spectre rocket and the Gyron Junior, and in February 1954 a separate High Speed section was formed by Saro for work exclusively on the new design, Project P.177.

The operational variant was based initially very much on SR.53, with the Gyron Junior mounted above the Spectre and retaining ear intakes. However, provision was made for the installation of AI-23 radar, autopilot, fire-control and collision-course avionics, all carried in the much bigger fuselage. As well as this, a far greater quantity of fuel was provided for; gross weight of SR.53 was eventually 18,400 lb (of which rocket fuel weight was nearly half as much again as tare weight), while gross weight of the eventual SR.177 was in the order of 25,000 lb. First flight date for the operational variant was put at mid-1957.

By May 1955, a contract for detailed design examination had been secured from the MoS and this was followed by an ITP (Instruction to Proceed) for the initial development of P.177 that September. In fact, from the previous winter, the P.177 study had been revised. The ear intakes were replaced with a chin intake, surmounted by the AI cone, with the consequent relocation of the Gyron Junior to the lower half of the fuselage. Enlarged wings and blown flaps were also included, but the P.177 in its finalised form was aerodynamically fairly similar to the SR.53 apart from an approximately 10 per cent increase in linear size. The cropped-delta mid-mounted mainplane layout of SR.53 was retained, as was the high-mounted slab tailplane; increased fuselage diameter made P.177 appear rather tubbier than the SR.53. Both aircraft had a deep but stream-lined fuselage and a very-low-aspect-ratio fin.

Delays hampered the construction of SR.53, meanwhile. A mock-up was built which could be moved into various flight attitudes. The construction of a prototype, however, was not as straightforward. The first prototype, XD145, was in the jigs during 1954 and was structurally complete by the end of the year. Three more years went by before this example was airborne. The SR.53 was of course small and very densely packed, which made it difficult to work on, and de Havilland was slow to supply a Spectre. Projected first flight date was postponed, first to March 1955 and later to some unspecified time in 1957. Problems arose with the Spectre and its fuel. By the end of 1955, a complete rear fuselage section of SR.53 had been built and sent to de Havilland, where a Spectre was finally fitted. When engine tests began with this specimen, the trailing edge of the elevator became damaged and broke off in several places. Damage was also caused to the turbojet pipe fairing. As well as this, there were problems associated with the design of the new bag fuel tanks and of the HTP fuel-flow proportioners. These difficulties were somewhat offset, however, by the cancellation of the enlarged and modified Avro 720 during January 1956 as part of an economy drive.

XD145, first of the two SR.53s built, minus missile load, Boscombe Down, spring 1957.
(A&AEE)

Engine ground-run with the Spectre of XD145, Boscombe Down, early 1957. (*A&AEE*)

SR.53 XD145 takes off for its first flight, Boscome Down, 16 May, 1957. The characteristic diamond pattern of the Spectre efflux can be seen. (*A&AEE*)

284

The maiden flight of XD145 ends successfully. (*A&AEE*)

Also as an economy, in January 1956, XD153, the third SR.53, was cancelled but the others were constructed in one corner of Columbine hangar. XD145 was finally completed by early June 1956. In the interim, two developments had arisen. The first was a rather premature press leak, starting in late 1954, that Saro had already built 'something' of extremely advanced and unusual design. It is probable that the leak referred to SR.53. When in November 1955 the MoS eased its grasp on the secret nature of SR.53, there was considerable publicity.

Also during late 1955, and well into the following year, the runway at Hurn Airport, Bournemouth, was examined for possible future use by SR.53, there being no suitable runway available on the Isle of Wight. A supply depot was erected for the storage of HTP and the Hurn runway tested by a modified Gloster Meteor F.8, supplied by the MoS, and specially equipped to test certain aspects of the SR.53, featuring a centralised flight instrument system and master reference gyro to OR.946, in connection with the Cowes programme. The undercarriage was altered and high-pressure tyres similar to those of SR.53 were fitted so that the Hurn surfaces might be assessed for suitability. However, SR.53 never used Hurn.

XD145, the first SR.53, finally arrived at A&AEE Boscombe Down on 28 June, 1956, where assembly of the main components began. This continued until the new year. Engine ground-runs with the Spectre began on 16 January, 1957. In April, the Viper was tested, and during the second week of May XD145 began taxi-ing trials. On 16 May the SR.53 finally flew for the first time, with the new Saro chief test pilot, Sqn Ldr John Booth DFC, at the controls. Booth recorded Mach 1·33 in early tests, as well as a very fast rate of climb. This might have been the first step towards something very big at Cowes, despite the fact that by the early summer of 1957 the future of the programme had come under the most severe scrutiny.

While development of the fully-operational variant continued on paper and component mock-ups were being constructed, flight-testing of SR.53

285

The SR.53 XD145 on its second flight. Missiles were not carried on early tests. (*BHC*)

continued at Boscombe Down. Both examples appeared at the 1957 SBAC Show, XD145 in the air and XD151 statically. The second example first flew on 8 December, 1957, at Boscombe, again with Booth, and featured increased HTP tankage, being used to continue testing while XD145 was modified in a similar way. In all, 42 flights were made, 31 with XD145 and 11 with XD151. During these trials, the concept of the mixed-unit aircraft seemed fully justified. Flight development was rapid and trouble-free in view of the novelty involved. Great advances were made in the handling of HTP. Protective clothing was developed and a hydrant fuelling system introduced. Both aircraft were used for readiness trials with HTP on board for long periods, frequently two or three days.

However, on 15 June, 1958, a disaster occurred. On the take-off run prior to its twelfth flight, XD151 failed to leave the runway at the A&AEE, overshot and hit a concrete approach lighting pole, exploding on impact. John Booth was killed in the crash. One theory was advanced over the cause, prior to an examination of the aircraft by the Aeronautical Inspection Directorate. This was that the Spectre had cut out just before take-off—the SR.53 could not of course leave the ground on jet power alone—and this was why only the nosewheel of XD151 had left the runway. In fact the examination revealed that the rocket had been deliberately cut by Booth, who had also decided not to apply the wheel brakes or air brakes, or retract the undercarriage. He had deployed the landing para-

XD145 comes in to land at Boscombe Down after its second flight, shepherded by a Meteor chase-plane. (*A&AEE*)

chute, but only as XD151 had crossed the end of the runway. No reason was ever established for the cause of the crash. The investigation indicated that the aircraft had been completely serviceable before the take-off was attempted. The remaining SR.53, XD145, was promptly grounded and never flew again.

By the spring of 1957, good progress had been made with the P.177, which was by that time known as the SR.177. In May 1955, a £25,000 study contract had been awarded from the Royal Navy. It finally became clear that both the RAF and the Royal Navy were interested, but in fact the Admiralty procurement team seems to have been far more positive in its approach than the RAF/MoS team. Led by Lewis Boddington, Director RN Aircraft R and D, the naval team visited Cowes early in 1955 wanting a carrier-based mixed-unit interceptor equipped with AI-23 and Blue Jay IVs. However, at the time they wanted a lox/kerosene rocket; Maurice Brennan pointed out the danger of a lox fire but produced a brochure on a P.177 complete with a lox/kerosene Screamer. When the Admiralty team returned it became clear that they had accepted Brennan's advice and now wanted a navalised HTP P.177. Thus the May 1955 RN study contract was born and it was only after the Admiralty had shown the way that a similar contract was forthcoming from the RAF, also for £25,000. The only

SR.53 XD145 being fuelled with HTP from the Saro/MoS-designed bowser. Water hoses are in evidence. (*A&AEE*)

essential differences between the RAF and RN variants would be extra fuel for the naval type, together with local strengthening round the catapult spools and arrester gear. The requirement bringing the study contract from the RAF was not put out to tender but went straight to Saunders-Roe, and called for a pure land-based version of P.177.

As well as this, in the summer of 1955, the United States had provided a $1.5 million grant for the development of SR.53, under the Maris Agreement. The Americans showed great interest in SR.53 as well as SR.177 and had received full briefings on both soon after they were finalised. There was no comparable programme in the United States and the American evaluation teams visited Cowes with keen curiosity.

Specification F.177D was written round the Saro 'phase two' project, as well as the RAF and RN requirements OR.337 and NA.47. The Project P.177, which might have become the Saunders-Roe SR.54, received instead the designation SR.177. In September 1955, the MoS instructed Saro to proceed with a series of SR.177 mock-ups, wind-tunnel tests and tooling-up for a pre-production batch of aircraft. Sub-contracting arrangements were made. F. G. Miles Ltd was made responsible for the detail design of the canopy, while Marshalls of Cambridge was asked to undertake some design work on the wing. Armstrong Whitworth was later selected for the sub-contracting of the construction of major components.

The first batch of SR.177s were to be pre-production aeroplanes. It was some time before the exact number of aircraft in this batch was decided on, but eventually it was agreed to built twenty-seven. This large number was designed to aid transition to long production runs. During April 1956 it was tentatively agreed that the first five SR.177s be completed by the new year of 1958. These would not be fitted with radar or weaponry, in order to allow accelerated development of the aeroplane itself. All examples would, however, feature a 3 ft 6 in extension to the rear fuselage and tailpipe, designed to eliminate the possibility of acoustic fatigue around these areas. On 4 September 1956, an order was placed for the twenty-seven examples, though the last eighteen of these were for planning purposes alone. The first nine aircraft were to be completed as three basic non-Service prototypes, three RAF and three RN versions, but all without the radar or missile systems. In the same month de Havilland purchased a 33.3 per cent shareholding in Saunders-Roe. The association between the two companies had already been reflected in the choice of powerplants for the SR.177.

SR.177 was basically a simple aircraft. It was immensely strong, with most of its major structures machined from solid aluminium alloy. The 6 per cent thickness/chord ratio wing was constructed around four large spars, each pinned to a fuselage frame and prevented from moving

Disaster: the shattered wreck of SR.53 XD151 after the accident of 15 June, 1958. (*A&AEE*)

The full-size wooden mock-up of SR.177, Cowes, November 1957, showing the positions of the rocket and turbojet and the marked similarity of the fin/tailplane arrangement to that of SR.53. (*BHC*)

upwards by a butting mechanism at the centre-line. Fuselage bulkheads were simply bolted together.

During 1957, more details emerged. HTP and kerosene tanks would be located at the top of the fuselage while jet fuel would come from wing tanks and from a tank in front of the turbojet. The nose area was rather different from that of SR.53, housing the AI-23 in the long pointed cone, while a double-shock variable chin intake had been adopted, as well as a vee windscreen and a clamshell canopy.

Besides the inclusion of the new Red Top missile, various other armament configurations included cannon. The official service ceiling was 67,000 ft but the designers working on the HTP accessory systems used a maximum 1g ceiling of 94,000 ft. Figures show a capability of acceleration from 'top of climb' speed of Mach 1·4 to Mach 2 in 66 sec; this at 80,000 ft.

By mid-1957, there were various configurations of rocket and turbojet. The British aircraft maintained the use of Spectre 5A and Gyron Junior. However, by this time the Germans had become very interested in SR.177, and they wanted greater thrust, to be achieved by a Rolls-Royce Avon RA.24R instead of the Gyron Junior. The third option, designed for medium- and low-level missions, offered a single reheat Avon but no rocket, allowing much greater jet fuel tankage. Saro also attempted to

290

increase the usefulness of the SR.53, proposing a scheme whereby it would be launched from the back of an Avro Vulcan. For this parasite interception role, the SR.53 would have had only one Armstrong Siddeley PR.9 rocket and no turbojet, giving increased HTP tankage and a full-power range of 90 miles; but the plan was never adopted.

It is something of a surprise to observe how similar the SR.177 RAF and RN variants were. The RAF, who had followed the RN into the programme, had stipulated that on no account should its version be compromised by meeting also the RN needs. In fact the policy of commonisation was Saro's intention and SR.177 paid very little penalty for its dual capability.

During 1957 the SR.177 programme had grown both in size and momentum. Besides the expected large orders from the British Services (150 for the Navy and at least that number for the RAF), the West Germans had become involved. In July 1956, Saro representatives including Robert Perfect, the sales director, had met with German staff officers in Bonn. Talks were resumed in September at the SBAC Show. A speculative figure of 200 or more aircraft for Germany was mooted as a result of these conversations. By November, Saro had obtained permission for talks to proceed on the possible manufacture of SR.177 in Germany. In early 1957, the Kriegsmarine made its interest clear.

The SR.177 mock-up, Cowes, November 1957, showing the AI cone, chin intake and clamshell canopy. (*BHC*)

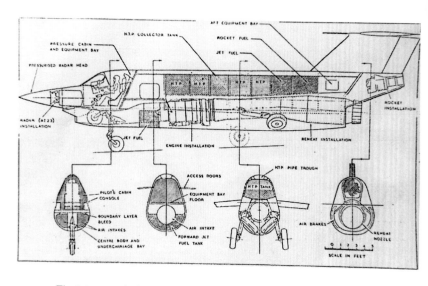

The 'phase two' aircraft; SR.177, showing the internal fuselage layout.

It seemed after this that the SR.177 programme could provide a catalyst for a large-scale collaborative manufacturing process across half of Western Europe. As Germany was so interested it seemed reasonable at Cowes to look for other foreign orders.

By early 1957 the first SR.177 mock-up had been completed on paper and component jigs were well advanced. At that time, it was proposed that Armstrong Whitworth provide a second source of production having taken over the work originally delegated to Marshalls.

During April 1957, a little before the first flight of SR.53 XD145, a Defence White Paper appeared, compiled by Defence Minister Duncan Sandys. The paper cancelled at a stroke almost all fighter development in Britain, with the one exception of the English Electric P.1. This included the SR.177 RAF version but surprisingly the SR.177 RN version remained (initially) outside the scope of the paper. Eventually, this too was cancelled, during August. By the time Sandys' White Paper had caused the cancellation of the entire Cowes programme, a full-size wooden mock-up of SR.177 was complete, the whole design was finalised and appropriate jigs and tools were ready for the large pre-production order. Six SR.177s were in various stages of construction.

The SR.177 had grown to be a real multi-role combat aircraft. The powerful Gyron Junior could permit operations on the turbojet alone, in the low-level strike, reconnaissance and attack roles, at high subsonic speeds. In this capacity, two overload (kerosene) tanks could be wingtip-mounted while offensive stores could be relocated on underwing hardpoints. Provision was to have been made for in-flight refuelling and for operation from short airstrips. Whereas the Viper of SR.53 was intended

292

Close-up of the Spectre installation of the SR.177 mock-up. *(BHC)*

merely to return the aircraft to base after each flight, inclusion of the Gyron Junior in SR.177 made for far greater versatility, as Maurice Brennan had planned.

While the SR.177 was designed to loiter and cruise on the turbojet alone, with the Spectre lit maximum speed became Mach 2·35. Spectre endurance

Model of SR.177 in Federal German markings, showing the refuelling probe and missile armament. (*BHC*)

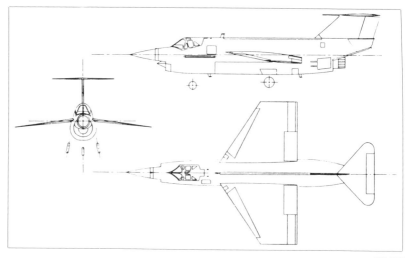

SR.177

294

was seven minutes at full power, but rocket power was adjustable in both SR.53 and SR.177 from 10 per cent to 100 per cent. In short, at the time of its development the SR.177 was the most versatile aircraft in its weight category.

The SR.177 programme appeared to be at an end by August 1957, but resistance came from the MoS, which agreed to the completion of the first five SR.177s to F.138D in September. These were XL905—XL907 and XL920—XL921. At the same time, it was hoped that Germany would continue to show enthusiasm for the project, but German interest never recovered.

The revised cockpit of SR.53 XD145, as it was in September 1958. (*A&AEE*)

In the meantime, Rolls-Royce had suggested that Saro redesign the SR.177 around its RB.133, for the benefit of the German market. This was done in outline form. Germany had by that time altered its requirements from high- to medium- and low-level duties. During November 1957, representatives from the German aviation industry including Heinkel AG visited Cowes to discuss the possible production of the SR.177 in Germany alone. In December, however, Germany officially abandoned its interest in SR.177.

By December 1957, however, a flicker of life still remained, when interest was expressed by Japan, who asked to buy SR.53 XD145 and two SR.177s; but this too came to nothing. Saunders-Roe was not consulted and Japanese interest terminated. On Christmas Eve 1957 Saunders-Roe received a letter from the MoS cancelling the remaining contract for the five SR.177s. A Saro proposal of January 1958 to build just three SR.177s for research purposes only was firmly rejected by the MoS.

The SR.53 XD145 which had not flown since October 1957, when a flash-back had severely damaged the Spectre, was used during 1958 for ground tests of improved Spectres, before moving to the Rocket Propulsion Establishment, Westcott, in the following year. Subsequently passing through the hands of the RAF Museum store at Henlow, in November 1978 XD145 arrived at RAF Brize Norton for restoration and eventual display at Cosford.

SR.53

One 8,000 lb st (full throttle) de Havilland Spectre rocket and one 1,640 lb st Armstrong Siddeley ASV.8 Viper turbojet.

Span (including tip shoes) 25 ft 1¼ in; span (missiles installed) 28 ft 1 in; length 45 ft; height 10 ft 10 in; gross wing area 274 sq ft.

Equipped weight without fuel 7,400 lb; including rocket fuel 10,500 lb; turbojet fuel 500 lb; maximum weight 18,400 lb; developed maximum weight 19,000 lb.

Maximum level speed Mach 2 above 35,000 ft; brake-release to 50,000 ft—2 min 12 sec; acceleration at 50,000 ft from Mach 0·9 to Mach 1·4—31 sec; radius of turn at Mach 1·4 at 50,000 ft—7,700 ft; radius of turn at Mach 1·6 at 50,000 ft—9,100 ft.

Armament: planned—two de Havilland Blue Jay IR missiles, actual—two de Havilland Firestreak IR missiles.

Three examples ordered. XD145, XD151, XD153. XD153 cancelled.

SR.177

One 10,000 lb st (full throttle) de Havilland Spectre 5A rocket and one 14,000 lb st de Havilland PS.50 Gyron Junior DGJ.10-1 turbojet (with afterburner).

Span (including tip shoes) 27 ft 1 in; span (missiles installed) 30 ft 3¼ in; length 50 ft 6 in; height 14 ft 3½ in; gross wing area 327 sq ft.

Equipped weight without fuel 14,533 lb; gross weight (normal warning sortie) 25,786 lb; gross weight (extended warning sortie) 28,174 lb.

Maximum level speed Mach 2·35; brake release to 20,000 ft—1 min 27 secs, to 40,000 ft—2 min 3 sec, to 60,000 ft—3 min 6 sec, to 70,000 ft—3 min 51 sec; service ceiling 67,000 ft, level acceleration at 80,000 ft from top of climb at Mach 1·4 to Mach 2—1 min 6 sec; radius of turn at Mach 1·6 at 60,000 ft—24,000 ft; endurance at full power 7 min.

Armament: two de Havilland Red Top IR missiles and two 1,000 lb category stores on underwing pylons.

All performance data estimated.

Pre-production batch of nine aircraft, XL905—907 non-service proto-types; XL920—922 SR.177RAF; XL923—925 SR.177RN. None completed.

APPENDIX ONE

S. E. Saunders: First World War sub-contracted production

1. Avro 504A and J

2890—2939 (50): A
A412—A461 (50): A
A3355—A3404 (50): A
A9763—A9812 (50): A and J

2. Short Seaplanes

8001—8030 (30) S.184
N1140—N1149 (10) S.320
N1600—N1624 (25) S.184
N1760—N1774 (15) S.184

3. Norman Thompson NT.2B

N.2500—N2523 (24)

4. Porte/Felixstowe F.2A

N4280—N4309 (30)
N4080—N4099 (20)
N4430—N4479 (50)

5. Porte/Felixstowe F.2A/F.5

N4580—N4629 (50)

6. Sundry

116 flying-boat hulls
389 seaplane floats
8 gondolas for large airships
416 seaplane punts

Postwar: reconditioning contract for de Havilland D.H.9A, J8190—J8207 (18).

APPENDIX TWO

Second World War sub-contracted production of Walrus and Sea Otter

Walrus Production

Saro produced 461 examples of the Supermarine Walrus. Of these, 191 were Mk IIs with Beaumaris-designed wooden hulls. These were used mainly for training.

The prototype wooden hull for the Mk II was designed and built on Anglesey, the prototype wooden-hulled aircraft (X1045) being flown for the first time, by Leslie Ash, on 2 May, 1940, and later by George Pickering. One Saro modification to the standard Walrus was the substitution of a rubber-tyred tailwheel for the original all-metal wheel of the Supermarine-built examples.

All were built under contract B.43393/39.

R6582—6591 (10); W2670—2689, 2700—2729, 2731—2760, 2766—2798, 3005—3051, and 3062—3101 (200) Mk I except: W3010, 3047, 3051, 3076 and 3078 (5) Mk II; X1045 fitted with Saro wooden hull as prototype Mk II. Erected by Supermarine, flight structure also supplied by parent firm; X1046 no record, assumed not built. X9460—9484, 9498—9532, 9554—9593 (100) Mk I to X9558, X9559—9593 (35) Mk II. (X9499, 9518, 9525, 9554, 9557—9558, 9560 (7), cancelled); Z1755—1784, 1804—1823 (50) Mk II; HD804—837, 851—878, 899—936 (100) Mk II.

Sea Otter Production

In January 1942, 250 Supermarine Sea Otters were ordered from Saunders-Roe under sub-contract. Some Sea Otters were built at Weybridge, as were some Walrus, but the first Sea Otter produced by Saro as a production aircraft was flown from Cowes by Jeffrey Quill during January 1943.

JM738—773, 796—837, 861—885, 905—922, 943—989, JN104—142, 179—205, and 242—259 ordered under contract Air/1806 as ASR.1, built as ASR.II from JN249 (250); RD869—898, 913—935, and 948—994 (100) ordered under contract Air/1806/CB20(b). Only RD869—922 built as ASR.II (Naval), the rest being cancelled; VF354—374 and 407—435 (50) ordered under contract Air/5068 but cancelled.

APPENDIX THREE

Second World War disposition of Saro plant

Locations

East Cowes, Isle of Wight
The Airport, Southampton
West Cowes
Fryars, Beaumaris, Anglesey
Tarrants High Road, Byfleet, Surrey
New Barn, New Barn Road, East Cowes
Osborne Hall, Osborne, Isle of Wight
Osborne Shops, Osborne

Melchett Court, Sherfield English, Romsey
The Round Chapel, Hersham
The Chapel, Addlestone Road, Weybridge
Weybridge trading estate, Addlestone, Weybridge
Bembridge Hangar, Bembridge, Isle of Wight
Somerton Aerodrome, Cowes
Cornubia Works, East Cowes
Osborne Garage, East Cowes
Fountain Garage, Northwood, Cowes
No. 1 and 2 Hangars, Park Green, near Newport, Isle of Wight
Halls Garage, Totland, Isle of Wight
Pinks Garage, Totland
St Josephs, Totland
Vittlefields, No. 1 and 2 Hangars, near Newport, Isle of Wight
The Old Power House, Riverside, Newport
Crabbe Stores, East Street, Ryde, Isle of Wight
Reflex Photo Co, East Street, Ryde
Reads Garage, Simeon Street, Ryde
Redmans Garage, Station Approach, Winchester

APPENDIX FOUR

Helicogyres

Vittorio Isacco's work on the helicogyre is today largely forgotten. An Italian by birth, Isacco worked in Spain, France and Britain on the problem of rotary-wing vertical flight. He spent some time, from 1917 to 1925, working with the Argentinian Pescara on the latter's helicopter designs, but these were found to be inherently unstable. Isacco began his own studies and produced from 1926 to 1935 four different helicogyres.

The helicogyre is a form of autogyro, and Isacco hoped his would be capable of ascending and descending vertically, hovering, and transitioning from vertical to horizontal flight and back again. Seeking to avoid the complications and weight penalty of rotor transmissions, Isacco used individually articulated rotors turning about a vertical stub-axle and propelled by small tractor engines mounted on the rotors themselves, a concept he called the 'sustaining system'.

His 'propelling system' consisted of a nose-mounted engine. The fuselage also had fin, rudder and elevators. Cockpit controls included a rotor incidence regulator. Incidence was altered through ailerons forming part of each rotor trailing edge. This mechanism was designed to make the helicogyre adaptable to the various conditions of flight. Rotor articulation at the hub was included, designed to eliminate the possibility of overturning and to prevent damage to the rotors while transition took place.

In 1926 Isacco went to France, where Helicogyre No. 1 was built. No. 1

had four rotors of which two carried 50 hp Anzani engines, and was stabilised by four trailing-edge flaps. The 'propelling system' consisted of a 35 hp Anzani. No. 1 was experimental and built to try to show that the helicogyre concept was feasible. It left the ground several times at a weight of 1,875 lb, and officially before the Commission of the French Aeronautical Technical Department on 22 February, 1927. No. 1 exposed concept flaws. Stability was found highly questionable, and the machine was never tested in wind of any strength. Also, control wires to the articulated blades proved impossible to maintain at the correct length.

No. 2, the second prototype, was also built for the French and incorporated some refinements. The flaps of No. 1 were replaced by almost full-length ailerons. Only two rotors were provided, each with a 32 hp Bristol Cherub, while a 50 hp Anzani (removed from No. 1) was located in the nose. As with the first helicogyre, considerable problems were experienced with play in the rotor control system and it became impossible to obtain equality of incidence between the two blades. Thus, a supplementary control was fitted, designed to regulate the incidence of each rotor separately in flight. Stability of No. 2 was better than that of No. 1; rotor revolutions were increased from 45 rpm in the case of the first prototype to 60 rpm in the second. Whereas the engines of No. 1 were mounted half-way along the rotors, those of No. 2 were placed at the tips. With a total weight

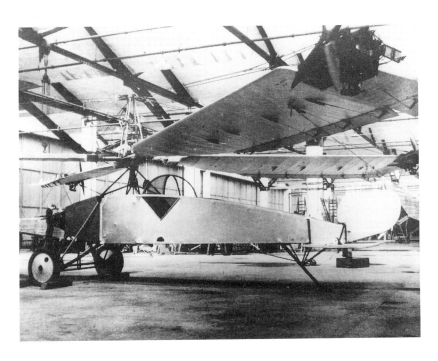

Helicogyre No. 3 in the Saunders-Roe shed, mid-1929. (*BHC*)

of 1,320 lb, this machine rose several times without use of the nose engine. Isacco put great store by the modifications included in his second helicogyre but evidently the French did not share his enthusiasm. Though trials of No. 2 continued in France, the third helicogyre was built in Britain by S. E. Saunders.

During 1928, the British Air Ministry ordered a third prototype helicogyre, No. 3. Construction of No. 3 took place during the first half of 1929 after negotiations for the contract were finalised. By this time of course, S. E. Saunders no longer existed, but the contract was sustained by the reconstituted company.

No. 3 was in some ways an improvement over earlier models. A Cherub engine was tip-mounted on each of the four blades. The forward engine was in this case a 100 hp Armstrong Siddeley Genet. As distinct from Isacco's original idea, it was considered necessary to provide definite lateral control. This was accomplished by a supplementary control rotor carrying four flaps. These were rigidly attached to an extended hub, but incidence was controlled from the cockpit. Articulated rotors were included and seating for two was provided.

The number of engine and flight controls required for the operation of No. 3 was one design disadvantage. Also, the Cherubs were found quite unsuitable. The horizontally-opposed twin-cylinder Cherubs invariably became choked with oil in their outermost cylinders as a result of the high centrifugal force present upon rotation. Oil starvation occurred in the innermost cylinders. Chronic carburation problems emerged, also arising from the centrifugal force. These troubles were eventually partially overcome by Saro engineers, and running of the Cherubs was made possible for short periods. The most important modifications involved the addition of a centrifugally-controlled orifice to meter fuel and close attention given to piston clearance.

However, No. 3 and the helicogyre principle in general did not meet with overwhelming enthusiasm when Isacco addressed the Royal Aeronautical Society in March 1929. Of course, No. 3 was still under construction at that time, so Isacco could not provide hard evidence that his idea would work. Principal criticism was that the airscrews might not be effective because of varying translational velocity. Apart from the theoretical and aerodynamic aspects, which it seemed would be very difficult to put into practice with any assurance of reliability, Frederick Handley Page made the point that if an engine failure were to occur, a disaster might ensue. Remembering especially the location of the Cherubs, this possibility seemed not unlikely. It was also suggested that if by chance a Cherub were to shed a plug or other component, such a part would be flung from the disc at considerable velocity; if the machine was on the ground at the time, consequences could be disastrous if anybody was standing in the vicinity.

No. 3, as K1171, was sent by road to RAE Farnborough for tests inside the balloon shed. The tests were not completed and development ended.

One 100 hp Armstrong Siddeley Genet and four rotor-mounted 32 hp Bristol Cherub. Rotor diameter 48 ft 2 in; length 28 ft 4 in. Maximum weight 2,920 lb.

One example, K1171.

APPENDIX FIVE

Projects

LARGE FLYING-BOATS

Saro R.3/38

To Specification R.3/38, received by the company 21 September, 1938. A four-engined Bristol Taurus powered monoplane flying-boat with twin fins and rudders. All-up weight about 46,000 lb. Dorsal and tail turrets. Crew of eight. Overload range 3,800 miles. Top speed estimated at 235 mph at 4,800 ft. Designed to carry a proportion of the fuel in the hull, in contravention of R.3/38 demands. Floats designed to split vertically and hinged at their base. Rejected by the Air Staff along with projects from Blackburn, Shorts and Supermarine, on the grounds that their defensive armaments were poor. R.3/38 cancelled.

Saro S.38 to Specification R.5/39

To R.5/39, received by the company 31 March, 1939. R.5/39 replaced R.3/38 and asked for a large Boulton Paul designed power-operated dorsal turret mounting four 20 mm cannon to be included, as well as one 20 mm cannon in the tail. Otherwise broadly similar to R.3/38. Design stabilised spring 1939 with Bristol Hercules, Rolls-Royce Griffon as alternative. Heavier than the specified weight of 45,000 lb, due to the heavy load of armour and armament. Proportion of the fuel carried in the hull, in contravention of R.5/39. S.38 placed second to Supermarine submission but R.5/39 not implemented. Saro built a flying scale model test-bed of the S.38 to assess hydro- and aerodynamic properties. This was the A.37

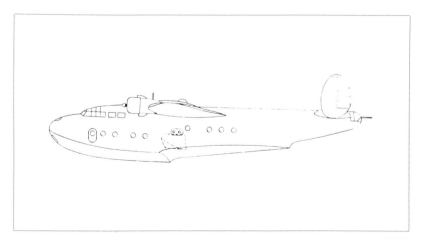

S.38

'Shrimp'. R.5/39 cancelled September 1939 but Saro continued work on a private venture basis, in the hope that it might be reinstated or a similar requirement emerge.

Four Bristol Hercules HE.1SM or Rolls-Royce Griffon.
Span 110 ft; length 97 ft; height 27 ft 9 in.
Normal all-up weight 54,935 lb; maximum all-up weight 68,885 lb (Hercules).
Hercules: maximum speed 284 mph at 15,000 ft, 273 mph at 5,000 ft; cruising speed 258 mph at 15,000 ft, 248 mph at 5,000 ft; climb to 5,000 ft—3 min 12 sec; maximum range about 4,000 miles.
Griffon: maximum speed 291 mph at 15,000 ft; cruising speed 268 mph at 15,000 ft.

Specification R.5/39 was reconsidered in February 1940 due to pressure from Coastal Command, it was revised and suggested along with many other schemes. All-up weight increased this time to a permissible maximum of 50–60,000 lb.

Saro S.38A
To revised R.5/39. Stabilised April 1940. All-up weight 62,000 lb, maximum overload weight 96,000 lb, maximum speed 285 mph at 15,000 ft. Range at overload weight 3,500 miles. Four-gun dorsal turret, single-gun tail turret (as S.38). 4,000 lb bomb load.

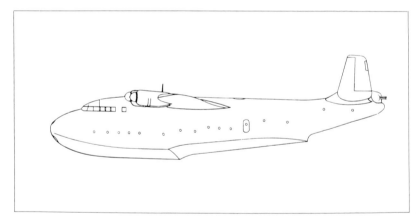

S.39

Saro S.39
Four engines. Design stabilised April 1940. An option to S.38A. Span 137 ft; length 105 ft; height 33 ft; wing area 2,200 sq ft. Empty weight 44,300 lb; normal 80,000 lb; maximum overloaded weight 96,000 lb. Maximum speed (normal all-up weight) 300 mph at 15,000 ft; range 5,000 miles.

Specification R.14/40
Issued July 1940 to Saro and Shorts; for large experimental DTD/Air

Ministry backed flying-boat with overload of 94,000 lb and c4,000 miles range.

Saro S.39 (Revised)
To R.14/40. Four-cannon dorsal turret, reverse-flow engine cooling.

Span 137 ft 6 in; length 101 ft 6 in; height 34 ft; wing area 2,200 sq ft.

Saro S.39A
Outlined summer 1940. Four Hercules, four-cannon dorsal turret, retractable planning surface. Not submitted for official appraisal.

Saro S.40
Civil flying-boat, proposed October 1940. Civil version of S.39. Conceptual arrangement evaluated by A.37 'Shrimp'.

Span 140 ft; length 102 ft; height 33 ft; wing area 2,360 sq ft.
Empty weight 47,500 lb.

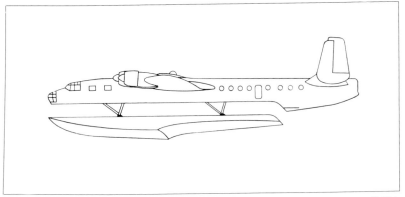

S.39A

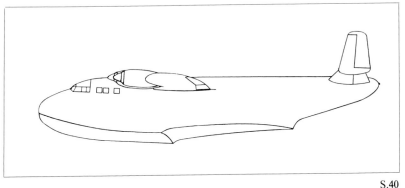

S.40

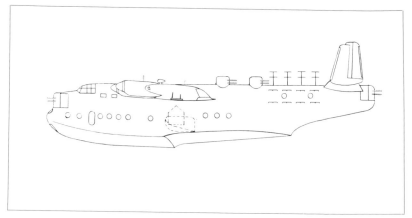

S.41

Saro S.41

Outlined January 1941. Intended to meet updated requirements of R.14/40. Extremely heavy defensive armament; four machine-guns in nose turret, four machine-guns in forward dorsal turret, four machine-guns in aft dorsal turret, four cannon in tail turret. Twin fins and rudders for maximum field of fire.

Four engines, reverse-flow cooling. All-up weight c110,000 lb, range c3,870 miles.

Short submission to R.14/40 preferred, Saro co-operated in manufacture of the eventual Shetland.

Saro S.42 and S.42A

Submitted to Air Ministry July 1942. Employed wing and engines of the Avro Lancaster bomber married to a hull similar to that of Project S.40.

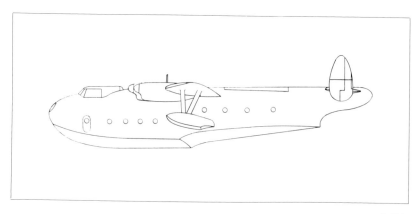

S.42A

S.42

Overload weight 70,000 lb, maximum speed 250 mph at 9,000 ft, range at overload weight 3,750 miles.

Armament: one cannon in nose, two machine-guns in dorsal turret, four machine-guns in tail turret.

S.42A

A freight version. Armament deleted. 35,800 lb cargo at overload weight.

Maximum speed 240 mph at 12,000 ft with Rolls-Royce Merlin XX; 260 mph at 16,000 ft with Bristol Hercules VI.

Not ordered because of the increasing use of landplanes in the transport role.

CIVIL FLYING-BOATS

Types of flying-boat suggested:
1. Extreme-stage examples.
Provision made for normal effective range of c3,450 miles (London—New York), after allowing for take-off, climb, deviation from course and headwinds. This range was thought sufficient for the longest stage of any probable British service. For shorter stages, fuel could be reduced and payload correspondingly increased. Two alternatives were suggested, Schemes V and VI (these being the serial numbers allocated in the course of the firm's investigations). Both were large six-engined flying-boats. Scheme V was essentially a heavy load carrier, while in Scheme VI payload was sacrificed to increase cruising speed.
2. Long-stage examples.
Provision made for range of 2,300 miles with full allowances. Two alternatives put forward, Schemes VIII and X. Scheme VIII was a large six-engined flying-boat with high load capacity, while Scheme X was a four-engined type of more moderate size.
3. Medium-stage examples.
Provision made for range of 1,400 miles with full allowances. Again, payload capacity designed to increase on shorter stages. The suggested type, Scheme XII, was a four-engined flying-boat generally similar to, but smaller than, Scheme X.
In each Scheme, full allowances made to pressurise entire passenger cabin and crew quarters to 5 psi.
These schemes, generated during the early 1940s, remained at a study stage only.
The Saro project office continued to reflect the attitude of the company that the flying-boat had an important future. During September 1944 the project office produced a proposal for a flying-boat with eight buried Rolls-Royce Merlin XX in coupled pairs, an all-up weight of 55,000 lb, a maximum speed of 275 mph at 20,500 ft and a range of 3,000 miles; in other words an unadopted replacement for the Sunderland.

Characteristics of flying-boats suggested for development					
	Scheme V	Scheme VI	Scheme VIII	Scheme X	Scheme XII
Effective range allowing for take-off, climb, 50 mph headwind, 5 per cent deviation, miles.	3,450	As V	2,300	As VIII	1,400
All-up weight, lb.	200,000	165,000	As VI	110,000	70,000
Engines	6	6	6	4	4
Operating height, ft	20,000	As V	As V	As V	As V
Mean cruising speed, mph	230	260	240	230	226
Crew (crew with mail)	12	11	12	12 (11)	12 (11)
Net payload, lb	15,000	9,600	11,000	7,700	7,150
Net payload with mail, lb	n/a	n/a	12,250	8,675	8,400
Passengers (with mail)	40	24	40	28	26
	n/a	n/a	(30)	(17)	(16)
Passenger and baggage load at 275 lb per passenger, lb.	11,000	6,600	11,000	7,700	7,150
Passenger and baggage load at 275 lb per passenger, with mail, lb.	n/a	n/a	8,250	4,675	4,400
Mail load, lb.	4,000	3,000	4,000 (or none)	As VIII (or none)	As VIII (or none)
Cubic space as freighter, cu ft	14,450	6,100	10,700	6,100	3,660

Also emerging in September 1944 were ideas for a six-engined long-range transport flying-boat intended for London—New York direct services, with an all-up weight of 187,000 lb, a maximum speed of 317 mph at 14,000 ft and a range of 3,600 miles. Payload was to be 13,150 lb. Another project considered was for an eight-engined 'boat for the civil market, employing buried and coupled Bristol Centaurus. All-up weight of this latter scheme was 250,000 lb, maximum speed was 331 mph at 14,000 ft, with a range of 3,600 miles and a payload of 21,700 lb.

Thus the process by which the Princess was arrived at can be traced back to Specification R.5/39, and through the Saro wartime projects.

Despite the general decline in interest for the flying-boat in the early postwar years, a school of thought arose which advocated the use of a small, modern flying-boat force for the military. The interest proved a transient one but a specification did emerge. This was R.2/48, to OR.231, the last specification issued for a British military flying-boat. R.2/48 was issued to the aircraft industry on 6 October, 1948.

R.2/48: main requirements

Weight—90,000–100,000 lb
Operable in sea temperatures of 29 deg F and in seas of 5 ft trough to crest.
Powered by four Napier Nomad compound engines.
Minimum speed of 233 mph when proceeding to the patrol area.
Highly variable offensive loads.
Crew of seven or eight.
ASP 20 ASV Radar.
A four-hour patrol to follow a 1,000 mile transit with 4,000 lb weapon load.
Two dorsal and two nose-mounted 20 mm cannon.

The Saro Project P.162 was the first choice of contenders for R.2/48 made by the Air Staff and Coastal Command. It had twin fins and rudders for a good field of defensive fire and a high length/beam ratio with high dead rise to provide a good rough sea performance. P.162 was designed to be powered by either Napier Nomad compounds, Rolls-Royce Griffon compounds or Turbo Griffons.

P.162 model under test in the Cowes alighting tank, 1952. (*Saro*)

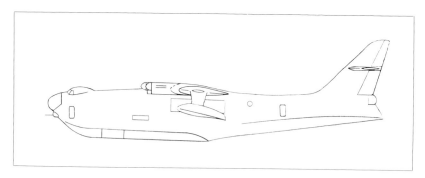

P.162

Saro P.162

Maximum cruising speed 285 mph at 15,600 ft (Griffon compounds), 233 mph at 15,000 ft (Turbo Griffons).
With Turbo Griffons and 99,000 lb all-up weight—8 hr 25 min cruising speed on patrol plus 2,330 mile round trip to and from area of patrol.

Napier Nomads were also considered because of the benefits of their economy, as well as due to the instructions of R.2/48.

Project P.162 to Specification R.2/48. (*Saro*)

P.162 was developed and refined until late 1952. Tests were made as late as 1955, with a hydroski attachment to the hull. Development ceased as the military interest in flying-boats ended.

The final development of the P.162 design had a single fin and rudder, and was referred to as the P.162B.

Saro P.162B

Four 3,000 hp Napier Nomad compound engines.
Span 155 ft; length 122 ft 6 in.
Normal weight 115,000 lb; maximum weight 135,000 lb.
Speed 327 mph at 20,000 ft.
Armament: two 20 mm cannon in nose turret, two 20 mm cannon in tail turret.

Saro P.192

Initiation of the P.192 programme began, in the mid-1950s, after a visit from J. Dundas Heenan, a consultant engineer to the P and O Shipping Line. Heenan suggested to Saunders-Roe that P and O was interested in exploring the possibility of a very large 1,000-passenger flying-boat with accommodation of a similar standard to that of the inter-war Imperial Airways 'boats. Provision for freight and mail-carriage was also required. The suggested route for this aircraft was Britain-Australia, intended stage lengths were nearly 2,000 miles, and the round trip was to last one week.

The Saro response was for a 'boat of 670 tons all-up weight powered by twenty-four Rolls-Royce Conways each of 18,500 lb thrust. Cruising speed was to be 454 mph at 30–40,000 ft and range 1,880 miles.

Six-passenger compartments were envisaged, for both day and night use. Bars and dining rooms were included, as were lounges and even dressing-rooms. Plans were made for a flight crew of seven, with their sleeping accommodation in the lowest of the five decks, and there was a special office for the purser. There was to be a crew lounge and 40 cabin staff were to be carried.

The installation of no less than twenty-four engines might have posed some huge problems, but an attempt was made to thwart potential trouble. The titanium engine bays were so huge that it would have been possible to work on the engines during flight, although, with up to six engines shut down, cruise power of 86 per cent rpm could be maintained. The engines were to be situated well outboard of the hull to avoid spray, and fed with air drawn through intakes on the upper surface of the wing when on the water. The main air intakes, conventionally situated, were to be deployed only in flight. Hydroflaps were installed in the rear area of the hull to aid manoeuvrability on the water.

All the control surfaces were to be fully powered. The system for this was derived from that of the Princess. Interconnected spoilers and ailerons were to be installed for adequate roll control. Split flaps would have been below the engine exhausts.

A main base was to be Southampton, while the staging points envisaged were Alexandria, Karachi, Calcutta, Singapore, Darwin, and Sydney. From Southampton to Sydney was expected to take 45 hr, and the return journey something in the order of 48 hr.

P.192 remained a paper outline as there were no funds made available for its construction.

Twenty-four 18,500 lb st Rolls-Royce Conway.
Span 313 ft; length 318 ft; height 88 ft.
Loaded weight 670 tons.
Typical cruising speed 454 mph at 30–40,000 ft; initial rate of climb (24 engines) 3,430 ft/min; initial rate of climb (16 engines) 2,058 ft/min; take-off run 4,695–7,890 ft; range 1,880 miles.

Saro SR.45 Princess landplane

To convert a flying-boat to a landplane would be unusual; nonetheless, this was contemplated briefly during 1957 for the Princess. An airframe unsurpassed in its own right, the Princess in flying-boat form had failed to find any buyers. In September 1957 Saunders-Roe issued a brochure outlining the conversion. Each aircraft would be powered by six Rolls-Royce Tynes rather than the earlier Bristol Proteus arrangement (single or coupled), while hydrodynamic aspects of the hull would be dispensed with. Main options provided were for a landplane troop-carrier/freighter.

In fact it would have been a fairly simple conversion, involving merely the removal of the hull bottom along the construction joint between the lower 'bubble' and the planing underside, and then the necessary fuselage re-tailoring for the landplane role. The aft hull area would have entailed a little more work in that the company decided to provide a large loading ramp in the rear underside.

The undercarriage would have had two four-wheel units retracting into bulbous fairings on each side of the fuselage. A power-operated twin nose-wheel unit was also included. Floats would have been discarded for simple wingtip endplates.

Carrying capacity would have been up to 96 troops or freight in the upper deck and a further 100 troops in the lower deck. Both decks would

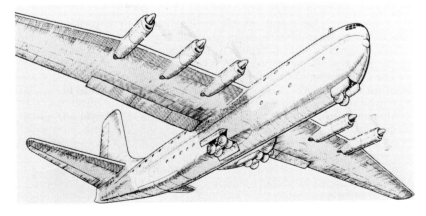

Princess landplane project with revised underbody, Hercules/Cargo-master-type undercarriage and six Rolls-Royce Tyne propeller-turbines.

have been pressurised and both would have featured the standard 20 in military grid for optional seat or freight attachment.

The brochure stated that all this conversion work could be done at Cowes. Since there was no suitable airfield available on the Isle of Wight, it was proposed that the first converted Princesss might be floated across to the mainland, accomplished by sealing the loading ramp and undercarriage doors, removing the new wingtips and attaching temporary floats. Tugs would then manoeuvre it to a suitable site on the mainland, such as Thorney Island, using the original beaching gear.

Six 5,525 ehp Rolls-Royce Tyne R.Ty.11.
Span 220 ft; length 148 ft; height 53 ft 6 in; wing area 5,140 sq ft.
Empty weight 140,000 lb; loaded weight 330,000 lb.

1953 Brochure on SR.45 Princess powered by six Bristol BE.25s

Six 5,045 ehp part-buried Bristol BE.25 propellor-turbines. Total fuel capacity 14,500 gal. Take-off weight 345,000 lb.
With payload 40,385 lb; 130 passengers, freight and mail (low-density version), range 6,125 miles; with payload 52,437 lb; 200 passengers, baggage, (high-density version), range 5,402 miles.
At 345,000 lb take-off weight and cruising at 32,000 ft the estimated cruising speed on a United Kingdom—New York nonstop flight was 358 mph; initial rate of climb 1,000 ft/min.

Saro Duchess

Henry Knowler's Duchess project was a logical extension to Saro's development of large waterborne aircraft: a transition to the turbojet-powered variety. No prototype Duchess was ever constructed for by 1950, when the design emerged, the future of flying-boats was uncertain; subsequent commercial failure with the Princess ensured that the Duchess remained a paper study.

The Duchess was designed as a medium-stage civil flying-boat, powered by the simple, cheap and reliable de Havilland Ghost turbojet. All-up weight was to be 130,000 lb and economical cruising speed 468 mph. Work on the design was done in parallel with development of the Princess and, in the spring of 1950, more details of the new type were issued from Cowes.

The Duchess was to be powered by six Ghosts, three in each wing root between the spars, with removable panels over the installations to facilitate maintenance. Up to three fuel tanks were to be provided: 6,000 gal contained in two main tanks in the outer wing sections and an optional 1,250 gal tank in the centre-section. The wings were to be high-mounted on a distinctive 'hump', to prevent water entering the engines. At the roots, thickness/chord ratio expanded from 12·5 per cent to 14 per cent to accommodate the buried engine installation. The outer wing panels were of 12 per cent thickness/chord ratio. To achieve the high critical Mach number required, the thicker root sections were more swept back than the outer panels. Slotted flaps were to be installed and these were designed to droop with the ailerons. The ailerons would have had leading-edge slots to maintain lateral control right up to the stall. Tip floats were adopted and

Saro Duchess project. After the commercial failure of the Princess, the Duchess was abandoned. (*Saro*)

were made retractable in the same way as those of the Princess. These floats were of adjustable pitch to aid on-water manoeuvrability.

Hull form was unusual in that length-to-beam ratio was designed to be rather higher than was the practice at that time, yet the forebody surface loading was kept low. The main step was elliptical and faired into the long afterbody, which terminated in a knife-edge water rudder coincident with the rudder trailing-edge. This hull form was designed to minimise the possibility of porpoising and was developed after exhaustive tank-tests.

The tailplane was of swept configuration, though of a lower thickness/chord ratio than the wings to ensure a slightly greater critical Mach number, and high-mounted to avoid jet efflux. As the engines were set close to the hull, with consequently limited manoeuvring aid on the water, a split water-rudder/drogue was included as well as the adjustable floats.

Four flight crew positions were in the extreme nose of the Duchess, with a mooring facility slightly aft and to starboard. A 3,500 lb freight hold was included. Baggage room provided 600 cu ft or 66 lb for each passenger. Passenger accommodation was for 74, in two compartments connected by a gangway passing the freight hold. Each compartment was to be provided with its own toilet.

Wingtip float retraction and pitch, flaps and water rudder were to be operated using compressed-air rams, with air supplied by Heywood-type

314

A painting showing the beautiful lines of the projected Duchess. (*Saro*)

315

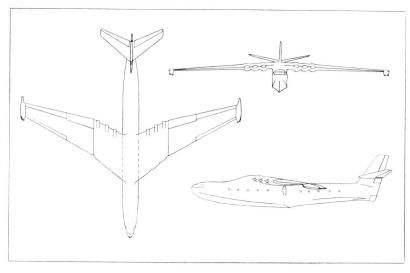

Duchess

compressors driven by the Ghosts. Pressurisation was to be provided by simply tapping the compressors of the engines and passing the air obtained through suitable humidifying and temperature controls to the cabins and cockpit. De-icing of the wing leading-edge was to be by hot gas taken from the engines, and of the tail unit by a separate heater located in the aft hull. All flight controls except for the flaps were to be power-operated by the system derived from Saro's experimental Sunderland and the Princess, incorporating the same type of irreversible surfaces.

Six 5,000 lb st de Havilland Ghost turbojets.
Span 129 ft; length 124 ft 6 in; wing area 2,364 sq ft.
Loaded weight 130,000 lb; maximum payload 20,908 lb, baggage 4,884 lb; freight 3,500 lb.
Maximum speed 550 mph at 12,000 ft; maximum cruising speed 500 mph at 30,000 ft; economic cruising speed 468 mph; initial rate of climb 2,900 ft/min at 130,000 lb; time to 30,000 ft—15 min at 130,000 lb; designed stage length 1,300–1,500 miles; equivalent still-air range with maximum payload 2,600 miles; maximum equivalent still-air range 3,100 miles; take-off run against 10 mph wind at sea level 3,600 ft.

HYDROSKIS

Efforts to create water-based military aircraft, especially fighters, of performance comparable with land-based equivalents, date back to the Sopwith Tabloid floatplane of 1914. Central problems were those of weight and drag, imposed by the necessary deep hull of the airscrew-driven flying-boat, or the float and strut assemblies of similar seaplanes. The development of the turbojet negated this problem to some extent; the SR.A/1, for example, had a relatively shallow hull.

316

The advent of the turbojet eased to some extent the difficulties of the water-based aircraft thrust-line, but the technological advances in step with this development created fresh problems. By the early 1950s, the density of a jet fighter capable of subsonic and supersonic speeds had become so great that insufficient natural buoyancy was available for the flying-boat variety. The provision of additional buoyancy (and thus weight) through the use of a larger hull would have seriously offset the advantages afforded by the turbojet, especially in terms of drag.

By the early 1950s, paper studies and tank work using models was being directed by manufacturers toward finding some means of lifting an aircraft from the water without the use of the deep hull. Low reserve buoyancy had necessarily to be accepted from then on. This led to consideration of the hydroski, both in the United States and in Britain. Saunders-Roe was included in this new field of work.

The Cowes firm's thinking lay not only in the circumvention of the water-based fighter problem. Reluctant to depart completely from their maritime tradition, but with postwar flying-boat designs unsold by 1950, Saro felt the hydroski could revitalise interest in operating aircraft from water. It was hoped that the hydroski, by encouraging the return of marine aircraft, could alleviate problems of building long, expensive and sometimes socially unacceptable concrete runways, as well as the vulnerability of such runways in time of war. Of course, this argument was not altogether sound, for many runways had already been built and paid for as a consequence of the Second World War. Perhaps more pertinent was the notion that problems associated with take-off and landing of very heavy land-based aircraft—higher pressure tyres, brakes capable of absorbing huge amounts of kinetic energy, hosts of aerodynamic aids to maximise thrust, and because of these factors, soaring development and servicing costs—might be alleviated if the hydroski was developed and large waterborne aircraft became popular again. The problem of drag associated with the deep hull or floats would of course disappear; the hydroski could be designed to retract into a much reduced hull when not in use. Substantial reductions in hull structure weight would also be a benefit, as it would be necessary to consider structural strength only in relation to static buoyancy conditions. A hydroski might be fitted to an existing flying-boat design, allowing the aircraft to operate from very rough seas, with the ski able to absorb the high impact and pounding loads more readily than the hull itself. This would have produced a true-ocean-going flying-boat capable of very high take-off speeds. This notion, it was felt, could lead to the development of large flying-boats capable of very high speed but subsonic at low altitude. All this was observed at Cowes and prompted serious studies.

Henry Knowler offered this explanation of the principle of the hydroski in the summer of 1953:

'Lift from a planing surface is the vertical component of the water pressure on the area in contact with the water, which varies with the square of the speed, the surface area and its attitude; hence, to obtain lift at low speeds, with a given area, a high attitude is necessary. Since it is the vertical component which provides the lift, there must be a corresponding horizontal component in the form of resistance to

317

motion and with hydroskis it is found that the ratio of resistance to weight is not as favourable as that obtained with a conventional flying-boat. However, this is of little moment since, because of the high flight performance requirements which have to be met with aircraft of the fighter type, more than ample reserve of power is available for take-off'.

Thus the applications of the hydroski initially considered at Cowes were in the areas of the pure hydroski high-performance type, and the hydroski-assisted larger, slower type, incorporating a conventional hull.

Serious work began at Cowes in September 1949, based on high-speed fighter designs. The first attempts were made with skis of high fineness ratio (long and narrow) but this form was found to suffer with high water resistance and was abandoned. Improvement was made when the skis were shorter and wider (low fineness ratio); both stability and resistance were found much improved. A system of three low aspect ratio planing plates, positioned fore-and-aft and of semi-circular cross-section, was also developed theoretically. This system held the advantage of being easily retracted flush with the hull. The forward plate provided a powerful lift force at speed and prevented the nose from diving, the central ski gave the main lift force between the hump and take-off while the aft ski provided lift normally associated with a planing afterbody. Tests with this system were promising, though hump resistance was found to be high. To reduce resistance, the next step examined was the low fineness ratio ski able to tilt, so that it projected downward like a normal ski heel for water operation. With this system, resistance was found much reduced.

In addition, two further ski types were tested: the Butterfly and Flipper arrangements. These took the form of pairs of longitudinal hull sections designed to roll through 90 deg so that they took up attitudes of reversed dead rise underneath the aircraft. The Flipper seemed far the more promising, combining the virtue of single curvature with the reversed dead rise. The Butterfly was found to suffer from poor trim characteristics and was not developed further. Also considered alongside these developments were effects of lateral and longitudinal curvature, convex and concave skis, aspect ratio, beam loadings and allowable ski positions relative to the centre of gravity.

Early research culminated in the Saro P.121, which became public in the Saro house magazine *Saro Progress* in the summer of 1953, though work had started during early 1950. The P.121 was designed from the outset as a fast waterborne fighter with built-in buoyancy and the ability to operate in open sea conditions. Before the design was settled, comprehensive tests took place. The stabilised P.121 took the form of a single-seat, single-engined, swept-wing subsonic fighter. The turbojet was mounted over the top of the hull to clear spray and the tailplane was also high-mounted. A single central ski of low fineness ratio was adopted for this project, along with a single nose-plate to increase lift at high speeds. The ski system was designed to retract fully through an arrangement of double hinges, and when retracted formed an integral part of the hull. Estimates showed that the ski assembly would weigh less than half the weight of a conventional landplane undercarriage which might support a similar class of land aircraft. When at rest afloat, the P.121 was designed to sit with its wing trailing-edges on a level with the water, the bulges on the wingtips (which

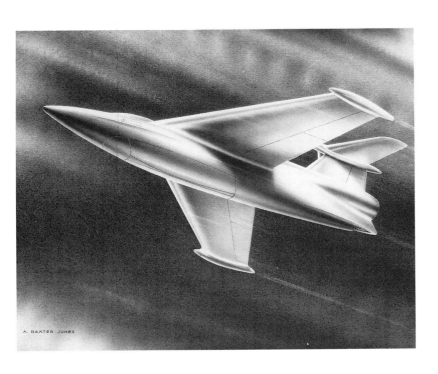

P.121, the waterborne hydroski fighter project, with skis retracted.

carried small auxiliary skis) providing lateral stability. It was hoped that if the P.121 was actually built, it could operate from coastline hangars with the addition of small wheels or rollers fitted to the ski heels. On such wheels, the company felt that take-off runs from a slipway into the water would be quite possible; tests revealed that only a short distance was necessary to reach planing speed, which was thought to be about one-third of take-off speed. Unfortunately there was no official interest in P.121 and the company never had a chance to put theory into practice with this design.

Another ski aircraft examined by Saro was a variant of the P.162 ocean reconnaissance flying-boat stemming from Specification R.2/48. By early 1955, P.162 models were undergoing exhaustive tank tests, with skis. A four-engined design, P.162 had a faired-step flying-boat hull, to which was added a single retractable ski working in conjunction with the existing wingtips floats. In this case, the ski was incorporated to combine with the V-section and pointed stem in reducing impact loads and improving alighting characteristics in rough seas; in fact, seas that might well have damaged even the strongest of conventionally-hulled flying-boats. By providing a lightweight ski to absorb harsh loads, the company could speak truthfully of the P.162 as an ocean-going flying-boat, and also pointed out

319

The P.121 with skis lowered.

that such skis could easily be incorporated in landplanes as provision for ditching.

Official interest in these ideas was minimal, but in late 1954 the company did have some very limited commercial success. Working for the Ministry of Supply, Saro tested ski-assisted models of the Jindivik target aircraft. Again, the arrangement adopted was a central ski in conjunction with tip stabilisers. Trials were successful but nothing came of them.

The most important conclusions on skis reached by the company was that they could be fitted to any type of aircraft for some duty or another connected with a great variety of surfaces. It became clear during tests that in conjunction with a wheeled undercarriage, aircraft could be made to operate from grass, concrete or water, and even from snow, ice and sand. The ability to operate from such a variety of surfaces created a new term: the 'panto-based' aircraft.

Before 1954, all Saro hydroski studies were confined to theory and model work. Though the MoS continued to be uninterested, the company funded a full-size experiment in the field of the refined hydroski aircraft: the panto-based Auster J-5G Autocar.

The Auster project was of fundamental importance because it proved that Saro could very successfully put its hydroski theory into practice. Not that Saunders-Roe was the first; in the United States, the All American Engineering Co had experimented with a panto-based Cessna 180 and a Harvard. Saro did not feel that the Auster was an ideal aircraft for ski or

Two views of the panto-based Auster Autocar G-AMZV under test. On early trials, buoyancy 'floats' were carried under the wings.

panto-based tests, because of its relatively low wing- and power-loading. However, it was considered adequate to evaluate the skis then under development and at the time the type was readily available. Again, comprehensive model tests came first but exposed no real problems.

J-5G G-AMZV (c/n 3065) arrived at Eastleigh during the early spring of 1954. One of ninety-four Cirrus Major 3 powered examples, it was kept as standard apart from the inclusion of a fine-pitch airscrew to increase thrust at sea level, and the application of an aluminium coating to the welded steel tubular structure. The skis adopted for the Auster were attached to the standard undercarriage in such a way that the wheels functioned normally on hard ground, allowing the panto-based operations. Each ski consisted of a light alloy structure with a wheel aperture and retractable side-plates, or 'flips', operated by a single hydraulic jack. The 'flips' were included in order to be able to examine the effects on performance caused by changing the ski aspect-ratio. Though the skis were allowed to pivot freely, they could also be locked in a number of different positions. A hydraulic fore-and-aft trim facility was also included.

The first taxi-ing trials and flights of G-AMZV took place from Eastleigh, where the skis had been manufactured. Subsequently test-flown from Bembridge, the Ryde Sands, and Columbine slipway, the first planing runs were accompanied by poor acceleration and difficulty was experienced in keeping the tail down. This was due to the forward centre of gravity position associated with the minimum weight at which the aircraft was being tested. After various ballast weights had been fitted to the aft picketing posts, the normal all-up weight CG position was restored. To provide the best indication of performance during take-off tests the aircraft was operated at constant engine speeds with various elevator angles.

Various planing tests were undertaken. On water, the performance at any given rpm, skis locked, was found to be some 12 mph faster than with skis free. This proved conclusively that the ability to control ski attitude was of great importance, because the drag of the ski/wheel combination at low angles (adopted when free to trim) was much greater than when the skis were locked. Take-off tests revealed that, with skis locked, elevator control was very responsive and acceleration to take-off speed was rapid. With skis free these qualities were reduced, water drag increased and the take-off run became much longer. Alighting trials suggested that with skis free drag remained greater than if they were locked, causing comparatively rapid deceleration. On-water manoeuvrability was much improved when the skis were locked. Unfortunately, prolonged trials in rough water were not possible, but in waves of one foot no difficulty was experienced. It was found that only four to five aircraft lengths were necessary to achieve planing speed from a brakes-release on land. Naturally (for the skis had no buoyancy of their own), take-off runs could not begin from the water, nor alighting runs end without reaching dry land.

G-AMZV's ski equipment was of course experimental. The firm envisaged the day when the protruding wheels would retract flush with the bottom of the skis when planing, which would have reduced low trim drag significantly. The 'flips' would have been discarded on later planing projects, except for those requiring very high take-off speeds or long runs. The later skis would have been made retractable, not only for the benefit of the pure hydroski aircraft, but to provide maximum clearance when panto-based types operated from land.

The planing concept was thus proved fully viable in Britain as well as in the United States. Experiments, model tests and full-size trials provided Saunders-Roe with a background of experience and success that would have allowed the design of hydroskis for almost any aircraft. However, even after the successful trials with the Auster ended in the late summer of 1954, official interest remained low and nothing of a commercial nature resulted.

SARO P.154 TO F.124T

The forerunner of the SR.177, the P.154 was the original 1952 Saro submission to Specification F.124T, the pure rocket-powered interceptor considered before the notion of an additional (turbojet) engine arose. This

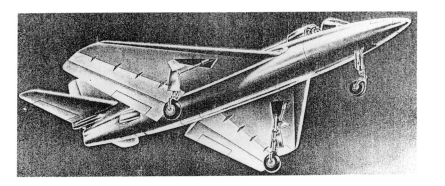

Poor but very rare illustration of P.154, design ancestor of SR.53.

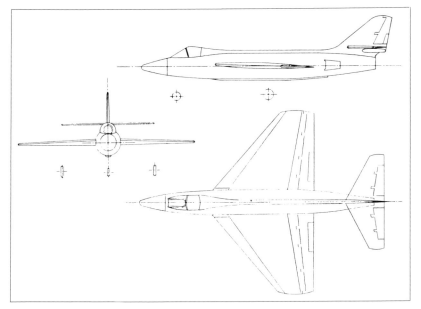

P.154

early work by Maurice Brennan, including aerodynamic features, performance, stability and control, was done in co-operation with the Projects and Flight Test groups at the Aerodynamics Department, RAE.

The P.154 project was a single-seat mid-wing monoplane with a two-chamber Saro-designed rocket motor mounted in the rear fuselage, with the combustion chambers at the tail. The wing had full-span slotted flaps with independently-moving aft portions serving as ailerons, together with

323

full-span droop leading edges. This was intended to allow low landing speeds (since P.154 was designed to land without fuel remaining), together with favourable high-speed characteristics. The wings, as well as the tailplane and fin, had a low (6 per cent) thickness /chord ratio to give satisfactory control during transonic and supersonic flight. Adequate stiffness of the wings was ensured by multi-web construction together with the two main spars. An adjustable incidence tailplane with orthodox elevators was low-mounted just above the fuselage, on a conventional fin.

Undercarriage arrangements provided for an optional, jettisonable main undercarriage take-off trolley in addition to a conventional tricycle layout for landing. Also, two Mayfly cordite rockets could be installed to provide a boosted, very short take off. The nosewheel was included in all options. An underbody landing skid was provided, and there was a detachable M.L. Aviation pressurised cabin section.

The rocket ran on kerosene and HTP, and comprised two identical units each of 4,000 lb st at sea level. Both were to be used for takeoff, climb and acceleration at supersonic speeds, but for cruising at the speed of Mach 0·95 demanded by Specification F.124T, only one chamber was to be used. HTP tanks were situated in the central area of the fuselage, kerosene in integral inner wing tanks.

Nearly all fixed services employed hydraulic power, which allowed electrical energy to be provided by two 40 ampere-hour aerobatic accumulators, with a consequent saving in weight. All the control surfaces

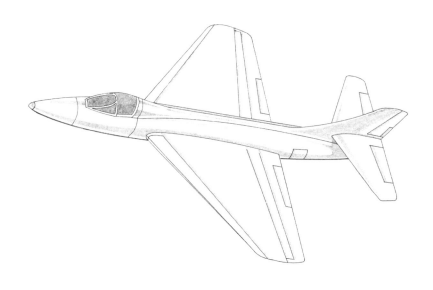

Ancestor to the SR.177—Saro Project P.154 rocket-powered interceptor.

were fully mass-balanced; the elevators and ailerons had hydraulic boost at high speed. The major exception to this extensive use of hydraulics was the means of detaching the cabin section, which was achieved by firing a cordite cartridge to unlock the locating spigots and push the cabin forward.

Armament of the P.154 comprised a battery of air-to-air missiles in a retractable underbody pod, and, at a later stage, two Blue Jay missiles, one beneath each wing.

P.154 was never built; instead it was extensively developed by Brennan into the SR.53, which itself led to the SR.177. The P.154 design is important, however, because it represents the threshold of Saro rocket-powered interceptor ideas, from which Brennan created his later designs.

One Saro bi-fuel rocket motor comprising two chambers, each of 4,000 lb st at sea level, rising to 4,535 lb at 60,000 ft. Thrust variation from 600 lb at sea level to 9,070 lb at 60,000 ft.

Span 26 ft; length 37 ft 1 in; height 11 ft 9 in; wing area 272 sq ft.

Empty weight 4,825 lb; basic operationally equipped weight 5,500 lb; all-up boosted take-off weight 12,780 lb; all-up (free take off excluding jettisonable undercarriage) weight 13,260 lb.

Maximum speed (limited by fuel available) Mach 2·44 at 60,000 ft; maximum speed at 30,000 ft Mach 1·17; maximum rate of climb at sea level 13,600 ft/min; maximum rate of climb at 50,000 ft—52,000 ft/min; take off to 60,000 ft (boosted take off) 2 min 11 sec; take off to 60,000 ft (free take off) 2 min 23 sec; take off run (boosted take off) 40 ft; take off run (free take off) 1,340 ft.

Endurance profile: take off, climb to 60,000 ft, 10 min cruise at 60,000 ft, 2 min combat at 60,000 ft, about 20 min gliding descent.

Armament: battery of air-to-air missiles, later two Blue Jay.

SELF-PROPELLED MODELS

Self-propelled water-based model aircraft of projects originating at Cowes were neither catapulted nor towed but operated under their own power. They could be made more complex than those used in the towing and free launching tanks, and allowed the study of some aspects of hydrodynamic behaviour that could not be accurately assessed in any other way. Self-propelled models provided far more realism than any other variety, for their performance was not hampered by any artificial launching or towing mechanism. For example, a model might be required to test a long take-off run over large (scale) waves. Acceleration would not be constant as the impact of each wave would tend to slow the model down, according to the amount of thrust available, its method of application and the inertia of the model itself. It was found at Cowes that a true representation of how a model would perform under specific conditions was almost impossible to achieve unless the model was able to function under its own power.

For models of flying-boats or, in some cases, hydroski aircraft, the motive power was provided by either a small rocket motor or a compression ignition engine driving an airscrew. The rocket motor was found to be much more reliable. The fuel used in this variety was HTP, and the motors gave a thrust of up to about 10 lb, as required. Pressures of up to 1,500 psi were developed in the fuel chamber, from which the HTP was driven by compressed nitrogen, which tended to create an atmosphere of circumspection on the occasions the motors failed to start.

The rocket motors were, however, very robust. The models tested were not always restricted to operations within tanks but were sometimes launched from the Medina, which must have been rather demanding for them. Some impromptu testing of the motors' water-resisting qualities was sometimes made during less successful experiments. In the instances when it was possible to recover the models (from the test-tanks; it is difficult to recover anything from the waters off Cowes), subsequent examinations of the motors frequently revealed that they were still in good working order.

A certain amount of radio control equipment was carried by some of the models, but this was naturally dependent on the weight limitations involved. Similarly, few recording instruments could be carried to provide data on the behaviour of the self-propelled models. The company relied mostly on photography to obtain this data, producing extremely thorough cine-film records. One of the biggest problems in using the Medina for model work was the weather, and this necessitated some very unsociable overtime hours. Nonetheless, self-propelled models played an important part during the early 1950s in assessing the characteristics of Saunders-Roe's water-based aircraft projects.

SARO ROTORCOACH

The Rotorcoach project was conceived by the Helicopter Division during 1952, under the supervision of Maurice Brennan. Designed with British European Airways in mind, a brochure on the Rotorcoach had been produced by September 1953.

Saro Rotorcoach project for a tandem-engined feeder transport. (*Saro*)

326

The Rotorcoach was a large civil rotary-wing craft with an all-up weight of 34,000 lb. Tandem, mechanically-driven rotors were employed, with two Napier turbine engines. Low-set stub wings were used to unload the rotors in forward flight, when the power was transferred to a ducted fan at the extreme rear end. The Rotorcoach was designed to carry 50 passengers over distances of about 200 miles.

Of particular note in the design was the large rear loading ramp and the freight area within, which could accommodate a family car. Undercarriage arrangements were novel and consisted of a single nosewheel, twin rear wheels and small single wheels under the stub wings for lateral stability on the ground. Full side-by-side dual control was provided, in an extensively-glazed cockpit with side teardrops for good downward vision. The two Napier engines were fed air from two ram orifices, one in the upper nose area, the other in the fin fillet. A tailplane with twin endplate fins and rudders was set high on the central fin.

APPENDIX SIX

Saro-Hiller 1033 XROE-1 Rotorcycle

The Hiller-designed XROE-1 Rotorcycle first flew during January 1957. An unusual machine, it was a one-man collapsible helicopter, and was developed with the United States Marine Corps in mind. Weighing only

Saro-Hiller Rotorcycle G-46-3, Eastleigh, 1960.

300 lb, power was supplied by a Nelson two-stroke motor which drove a two-blade 18 ft diameter rotor. The pilot was totally exposed and sat on what was virtually a bicycle saddle. Rather than having a conventional undercarriage, the XROE-1 had three tapered spring tubes ending in small pads. It was found that assembly or collapse of the machine could be carried out by one man in under five minutes. Suggested uses were liaison, observation and, when folded into a container, drops to downed pilots for their recovery.

Though the Rotorcycle was developed in answer to a USMC requirement, the design was also evaluated by the Germany Federal Republic and Switzerland, the Hiller licensee in Europe being Helicop-Air of Paris. It was Helicop-Air which in November 1958 sub-contracted to Saunders-Roe production of a small batch of ten XROE-1s, with the notion that it would be less expensive to finance a limited initial production run in Europe than in the United States.

Though many major components for the Saro-built Rotorcycles were supplied by Hiller, the Eastleigh works manufactured the gearing, transmission and what there was of the 'airframe', using Hiller drawings. The first flight of a Saro-built XROE-1 took place on 19 October, 1959, the pilot being Phillip Johnston, head of Hiller's Flight Department. All ten examples were completed by the spring of 1960. The XROE-1 did not find favour with potential users, though it was evaluated by the USMC. The activities and fates of the Saro-built examples remain obscure. Only one appeared on the British Civil Register, the others being allotted Class B marks.

One 45 hp Nelson two-stroke four-cylinder opposed air-cooled petrol engine manufactured by Barmotive Products Inc.

Main rotor diameter 18 ft; height 6 ft 11 in; tail rotor diameter 3 ft.

Empty weight 300 lb; loaded weight 556 lb.

Maximum speed 66 mph; typical cruising speed 49 mph; initial vertical rate of climb 330 ft/min; maximum rate of climb (inclined) 920 ft/min; hover ceiling (free air) 2,600 ft; service ceiling 12,000 ft.

APPENDIX SEVEN

Pre-Saro Simmonds/Spartan Aircraft

Simmonds Spartan

The Simmonds Spartan, designed by O. E. (later Sir Oliver) Simmonds was a light two-seat biplane of wooden construction. All four wings were, remarkably, identical and interchangeable. Similarly, the fin was identical to the outer third of the tailplane, undercarriage legs were interchangeable and the rudder could take the place of the half elevator. This principle was designed to keep the cost of maintenance and spares as low as possible and thus appeal to a wider section of the market.

Prototype Simmonds Spartan G-EBYU, powered by a Cirrus III, with its 1928 King's Cup Air Race number. (*A.J. Jackson collection via R.T. Jackson*)

The prototype Spartan was built at Woolston, Southampton. Registered G-EBYU and powered by a 90 hp Cirrus III four-cylinder air-cooled inline engine, it participated in the July 1928 King's Cup Air Race. It was later loaned to the Isle of Purbeck Flying Club and during October 1928 was flown by Flg Off H.W.R. Banting to Berlin and back, carrying on its return journey Lieut-Col L.A. Strange as passenger.

So impressed with the aircraft was Strange that he approached Oliver Simmonds, who declared his interest in producing the type commercially. Accordingly, the two formed Simmonds Aircraft Ltd and acquired production premises at Weston, Southampton, during November 1928.

Subsequently, forty-nine Spartans were manufactured at Weston, using Hamble aerodrome for erection and pre-delivery testing. Twelve examples, G-AAMA—G-AAML, were ordered by National Flying Services Ltd for instructional use, principally out of Hanworth. A total of twenty-four Spartans were British-registered, others going mostly to the Dominions.

Modifications were made to various examples. G-AAMH was fitted with wings of 4 ft greater span, and this was found to improve the take-off and climb. Several Spartans were converted to carry two passengers in tandem ahead of the pilot; these were G-AAGV, G-AAJB, VQ-FAA, ZK-

329

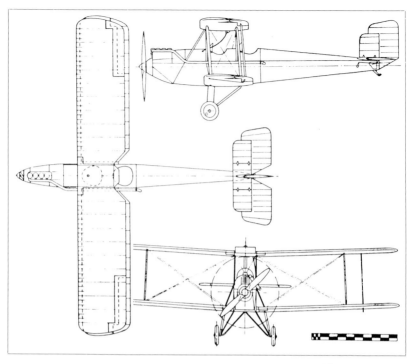

Simmonds Spartan

ABK, ZK-ABN and ZK-AAY. Additionally, VQ-FAA was fitted with floats, as was G-AAMG. Altogether, five different types of engine were used.

One 85 hp Redrup Fury Mk II (one example, possibly c/n 2), 100 hp ADC Hermes I, 100 hp de Havilland Gipsy I (c/n 25 only), 105 hp ADC Hermes II (c/ns 17, 23, 38), 120 hp de Havilland Gipsy II (c/n 29 for King's Cup).

Span 28 ft 7 in; length 23 ft 11 in; height 9 ft 3 in; wing area 240 sq ft.

Empty weight 940 lb (two-seater), 1,050 lb (three-seater); loaded weight 1,680 lb (two-seater), 1,750 lb (three-seater).

Two-seater; maximum speed 100 mph; cruising speed 85 mph; initial rate of climb 600 ft/min; range 320 miles. Three-seater; maximum speed 107 mph; cruising speed 95 mph; initial rate of climb 500 ft/min; ceiling 16,000 ft; range 300 miles.

Known examples:

C/n 1 G-EBYU O.E. Simmonds 18.7.28, Simmonds Aircraft 11.28, damaged beyond repair Bury St Edmunds 10.3.29; c/n 3 G-AUIT/ VH-UIT; c/n 4 G-AULI/ZK-AAY 10.29 for Hawkes Bay Aero Club, to New Zealand Airways, rebuilt as three-seater; c/n 5 G-AUKQ/VH-UKQ crashed in New Guinea 1942; c/n 6 CF-ABC Dominion Aircraft 1929; c/n 7 CF-ABD Dominion Aircraft 1929; c/n 8 ZX-AAP *All Black* 19.4.29, built for H.F. Mace England-New Zealand flight. Crashed in France; c/n 9 for evaluation by South African Air Force; c/n 10 G-AAWM Brooklands School of Flying 8.4.29, damaged beyond repair 12.30; c/n 11 G-AAFP Simmonds Aircraft 17.4.29, dbr 3.30; c/n 12 G-AAFR Simmonds 27.4.29, Hampshire Aeroplane Club 5.29, dbr 27.3.30; c/n 14 G-AAGN Simmonds 27.4.29 dbr 1930; c/n 15 G-AAGY Simmonds 7.5.29, B.S. Thynne 9.29, F/O J.F.X. McKenna 5.31, Phillips & Powis 1.33, Eastern Flying Club 8.38, scrapped 1947; c/n 17 G-AAMA NFS 15.7.29, withdrawn 12.32; c/n 19 G-AAJB three-seater, Simmonds 25.6.29, sold abroad 11.29; c/n 20 G-AAMC NFS 28.6.29, crashed Hanworth 28.7.29; c/n 21 G-AAMB NFS 31.7.29, Alexander Duckham & Co 11.30, Wiltshire School of Flying 2.33, F.S. Davies and S.A. Kew 5.38, ditched off Southend 26.2.39; c/n 22 G-AAMH NFS 19.8.29, F/O T.P. Gleave 11.32, crashed in Turkey 19.10.33; c/n 23 G-AAHA C. Coombes 27.6.29, F.G. Gibbons 6.31, Spartan 8.31, sold abroad 3.32 probably as ZS-ADC; c/n 24 G-AAMD NFS 19.7.29 not delivered, became G-ABHH Lieut Finch White 16.12.30, sold abroad 3.32 probably as ZS-ADI; c/n 25 G-ABNU built by Col. of Aeronautical Engineering Brooklands. Scrapped 1948; c/n 26 G-AAME NFS 3.8.29, withdrawn 12.31; c/n 27 G-AAGV three-seater Pleasure Flying Services 17.5.29, Cramlington Aircraft 11.29, damaged and rebuilt 1934 as G-ABXO. To H.G. Hubbard, cancelled 1.12.46; c/n 28 VH-UMP; c/n 29 G-AAGO Simmonds, 26.6.30, Spartan 5.31, withdrawn 12.33; c/n 31 VT-AAT *Frontier of Dawn* used by F.N. Kabali on Paris-Karachi attempt; c/n 33 G-AAMF NFS 19.7.29, not delivered; c/n 34 G-AAMG NFS 19.7.29, not delivered. Tested at Felixstowe as floatplane, reverted to landplane,

Simmonds Spartan G-AAHV *Silver Wings II*, showing the conversion to allow the carriage of two passengers. (*A.J. Jackson collection via R.T. Jackson*)

crashed at Ratcliffe 6.9.30; c/n 35 G-AAMI NFS 2.8.29, not delivered. To Norway 4.30 as N-43, later LN-ABG; c/n 36 G-AAMJ NFS 2.8.29, not delivered, cancelled 12.30; G-AAMK NFS 2.8.29, not delivered, cancelled 12.30; c/n 38 G-AAML NFS 11.4.30, to Lieut C.R.V. Pugh 3.31, crashed at Croydon 3.10.31; c/n 39 ZK-ABL used by Wellington Aero Club; c/n 42 ZK-ABN New Zealand Airways, rebuilt as three-seater, repainted as *Southern Cross Kitten* 1.33; c/n 43 ZK-ABZ Air Travel, to Marlborough Aero Club, to New Zealand Airways. Restored for Marlborough Aero Club 40th anniversary April 1968; c/n 44 G-AAHV three-seater Simmonds 15.8.29, Pleasure Flying Services 8.29, Rev C.D.C. Boulton 1937, stored during war, scrapped 1953; c/n 45 VH-UMQ Western Air Service, to Wings Ltd; c/n 46 ZK-ABK three-seater, to New Zealand Airways, 1929 for Dunedin-Timaru route; c/n 47 VQ-FAA three-seater on floats. To Fiji for G. Fenton 18.4.30. Used by Fiji Airways; c/n 48 ZK-ABC Hawkes Bay Aero Club; c/n 49 ZK-ABU Air Travel.

Dates are those for registration.

Gipsy II powered Spartan Arrow G-ACHF, which survived until 1940.
(*A. J. Jackson collection via R. T. Jackson*)

Spartan Arrow

During spring 1930, Simmonds Aircraft Ltd was reconstituted and became known as Spartan Aircraft Ltd. This concern produced two new designs which appeared during the summer of 1930, one, the Arrow, being the two-seat replacement for the Simmonds Spartan.

Much of the interchangeability of the Simmonds Spartan was retained in the new design, though the wing was non-symmetrical; however, wingtips and ailerons were detachable, permitting a wing to be easily fitted on either side. Construction consisted of a spruce and plywood fuselage and wooden, fabric-covered folding wings. An increased wingspan together with Clark Y, high-lift aerofoil section was adopted and found to improve the climb performance of the new design compared with the Simmonds Spartan.

The prototype Arrow, registered G-AAWY, flew during May 1930 with a 105 hp Hermes II four-cylinder in line air-cooled engine. The second (G-AAWZ) and third (G-ABBE) examples, Gipsy II-powered, were entered in the 1930 King's Cup Air Race, G-ABBE being flown by Capt H.H. Balfour of Whitehall Securities.

Beginning in December 1930, twelve production examples were sold and a thirteenth, G-ABST, was used as a flying testbed for extensive trials of the Napier E.97 six-cylinder air-cooled engine which became known as the Javelin. G-ABBE and G-ABMK (Hermes II) both had floats, the latter in response to an order (later cancelled) from the Hon A.E. Guinness. The last six examples to be registered had ailerons on the lower mainplanes only.

Production of the Arrow ended during 1933 with the delivery of G-ACHE, G-ACHF and G-ACHG.

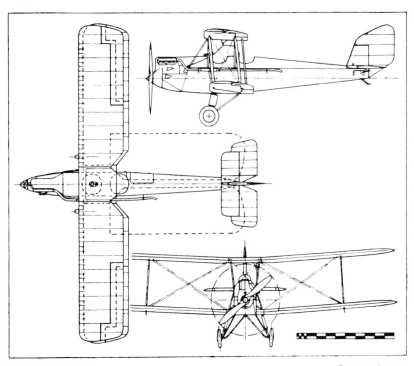

Spartan Arrow

333

One 95 hp ADC Cirrus III, 100 hp de Havilland Gipsy I, 105 hp Cirrus Hermes II, 120 hp de Havilland Gipsy II, 160 hp Napier Javelin III.

Span 30 ft 7 in; length 25 ft; height 9 ft 6 in; wing area 251 sq ft.

Empty weight 965 lb; loaded weight 1,750 lb. With Napier Javelin empty weight 1,207 lb; loaded weight 1,730 lb.

Maximum speed 106 mph; cruising speed 92 mph; initial rate of climb 830 ft/min; range 432 miles.

Fifteen examples:
C/n 51 G-AAWY Sandown and Shanklin Flying Services 26.6.30, Isle of Wight Flying Club 8.34, dismantled 1940; c/n 52 G-AAWZ Spartan 27.6.30, W.C. Mycroft 2.39, Yapton Aero Club 8.39, scrapped; c/n 75 G-ABBE H.H. Balfour 27.6.30, tested as floatplane at the MAEE, Spartan 2.31, to ZK-ACQ 5.31, destroyed in gale 2.2.36; c/n 76 G-ABKL Bristol and Wessex Aeroplane Club 4.4.31, Capt W.H. Amory 10.32, E.D. Ward 12.36. Destroyed in hangar fire at Hooton 8.7.40; c/n 77 G-ABGW B.S. Thynne 10.12.30, crashed 10.34; c/n 78 G-ABWP Henlys Ltd 23.7.32, R.O. Shuttleworth 12.36, stored, Spartan Group 1953, R.E. Blain 8.64; c/n 79 G-ABWR R.V. L'Estrange Malone 24.9.32, Flying Hire Ltd 8.35, W.J. Gunther 7.36 to Denmark 8.38 as OY-DOO; c/n 80 G-ABHD single-seater G.P. Fairbairn 19.1.31 for UK-Australia flight, freighted from France to Australia, became VH-UQD. Crashed at Melbourne 11.6.35; c/n 81 G-ABHR Household Brigade Flying Club 7.1.31, A.W.A. Whitehead 7.33, withdrawn 3.39; c/n 82 G-ABMK O.S. Baker for A.E. Guinness 26.6.31. Originally 5–1, to G. Duller 2.33, to LN-BAS 7.35; c/n 83 G-ABOB Spartan 28.7.31, 13th in *Morning Post* race 21.5.32 and Heston-Cramlington race 16.8.33, to A.L. Maffery 11.36, Exeter Aero Club 5.38, Thanet Aero Club 4.39. Crashed 1939; c/n 84 G-ACHE Spartan 16.6.33, F.H.C. Cornell 12.34. Crashed at Horsham 28.4.35; c/n 85 G-ACHF Lady D. Clayton 7.7.33, Marquess of Kildare 8.35, T.A.S. Webb 7.36, Romford Flying Club 3.39. Destroyed in hangar fire at Maylands 6.2.40; c/n 86 G-ACHG Spartan 19.6.33, to Denmark 10.35 as OY-DUK, to C. Peyron 4.37 as SE-AFR, to Östersunds Flygklubb 1951; c/n 87 G-ABST D. Napier 21.4.32, dism. 1936.

Dates are those for registration.

Spartan Three Seater I and II

Noting the advantage of those Simmonds Spartans arranged to carry three people, Spartan Aircraft contemplated a replacement and in 1930 produced the Three Seater biplane. This design shared the structural arrangements of the plywood fuselage and wood/fabric wings of the Arrow but the rudder was based on the same principle as that of the Simmonds aircraft.

Beginning with G-ABAZ, a total of nineteen Three Seaters were built at Cowes between 1930 and 1932, powered by either the de Havilland Gipsy II or the Cirrus Hermes II. The type was used mostly by pleasure flight operators and some examples enjoyed a remarkable longevity.

By 1932, the enhanced design, the Three Seater Mk II, had appeared. This offered improved entry and visibility for the passengers by putting the two-seat cockpit at the rear and use of the Hermes IIB inverted engine

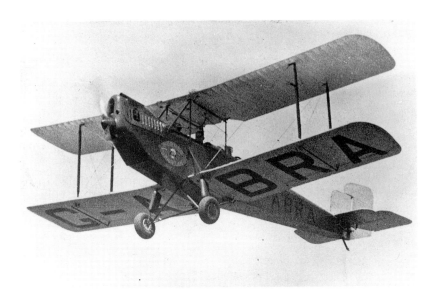

Spartan Three Seater G-ABRA, powered by a Hermes II, became EI-AAT during June 1934. *(A.J. Jackson collection via R.T. Jackson)*

which lowered the nose profile. One prototype (G-ABTR) and six production examples were built. The nineteen earlier examples consequently became classified as the Three Seater Mk I.

The Mk I aeroplane G-ABWX and the Mk II G-ABTR were fitted with passenger cabins, G-ABTR being given a deeper rear fuselage.

Three Seater Mk I—one 120 hp de Havilland Gipsy II, 115 hp Cirrus Hermes II; Three Seater Mk II—115 hp Cirrus Hermes II B (G-ABTR), 120 hp Cirrus Hermes IV.
Span 28 ft 10 in; length 26 ft 3 in; height 9 ft 8 in; wing area 240 sq ft.
Empty weight 1,030 lb Mk I, 1,150 lb Mk II, loaded weight 1,680 lb Mk I, 1,850 lb Mk II.
Maximum speed 103 mph Mk I, 107 mph Mk II; cruising speed 90 mph Mk I, 95 mph Mk II; initial rate of climb 600 ft/min Mk I, 750 ft/min Mk II; ceiling 15,000 ft Mk I, 14,500 ft Mk II; range 300 miles Mk I, 260 miles Mk II.

Nineteen Mk Is and seven Mk IIs:

Mk I

C/n 53 G-ABAZ C. Coombes 26.6.30, Sandown and Shanklin Flying Services *Island Queen* 4·31. Used until 1939 then stored. Cancelled 12.46; c/n 54 G-ABET Capt L. Wigham Hall 7.11.30, Nottingham Airport Ltd 5.36, Kennings Ltd 5.39, cancelled 12.46; c/n 55 G-ABKJ Spartan 24.4.31, W. L. Gordon 1.32, Kennings Ltd 5.39, cancelled 12.46; c/n 56 G-ABJS Spartan 31.3.31, C. D. Barnard 1931, Air Trips 3.32, to VH-UUU 12.35,

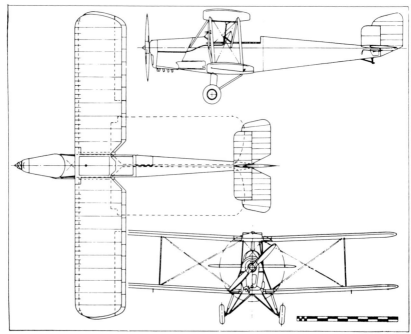

Spartan Three Seater

cancelled 7.36; c/n 57 G-ABKT L. S. Tindall 10.4.31, Lincolnshire Aero Club 1.33, Peterborough Flying Club 3.39, T. H. Ward 3.41, stored, cancelled 12.46; c/n 58 G-ABKK Spartan 1.5.31, Dorothy Spicer *Helen of Troy* 1932, British Hospitals Air Pageants 1933, Hunstanton Jubilee Air Displays 1934–35. Crashed at Coventry 10.5.36; c/n 59 G-ABLJ PSIOWA 22.7.31, Yapton Aero Club 9.38, A. C. Thomas 2.39, C. J. Rice 1943. Given to ATC 1944; c/n 60 G-ABPZ Skywork 7.10.31, re-registered ZS-ADP 11.32. Crashed 12.12.33; c/n 61 G-ABRA Oscar Garden 6.10.31, to J. Stark 10.32, E.A. Rance 3.33, to EI-AAT 6.34; c/n 62 G-ABRB Oscar Garden 9.10.31, to VR-TAJ 11.32. Crashed at Ladysmith 26.5.34; c/n 63 VH-URB James Taxiplanes, to Airlines (WA). Crashed at Mundaring Reservoir, WA, 16.10.38; c/n 64 G-ABTT Spartan 20.2.32, crashed at Stanton during *Morning Post* race 21.5.32; c/n 65 G-ABTU British Air Transport 13.5.32, scrapped 1936; c/n 66 G-ABWO Spartan 26.5.32, W. Westoby 5.36, Romford Flying Club 3.39. Destroyed in hangar fire at Maylands 6.2.40; c/n 67 G-ABWU Spartan 3.6.32, Southend Flying Services 1.33, H. V. Armstrong 9.35. Destroyed in hangar fire at Hooton 8.7.40; c/n 68 G-ABWV Spartan 15.6.32. Rollason Aviation 6.32. Crashed at Grantham 28.9.33; c/n 69 G-ABWX Spartan 25.6.32, J. Miskelly 8.32. Crashed at Dumfries 12.9.32; c/n 70 G-ABYG Scarborough Aero Club 27.7.32, Joan Hughes and N. M. Browning 5.35. Cancelled 12.46; c/n 71

G-ABYH Henlys Ltd 19.11.32, F. G. Barnard 7.33. Crashed at Hayling Island 20.7.35.

Mk II

C/n 101 G-ABTR Spartan 2.6.32, British Airways 5.36, F. G. Barnard 9.37. Burned at Gatwick 1947; c/n 102 G-ABYN Spartan 14.9.32, E. G. Croskin 7.35, to EI-ABU. Stored at Cloughjordan in 1971; c/n 103 G-ABZH Spartan 4.10.32, Henleys Ltd, Aerofilms 7.33, withdrawn 10.33; c/n 104 G-ABZI Spartan 31.12.32, Iraq Airwork 1.33 as YI-AAB. To No. 601 Squadron Flying Club 7.35. Crashed at Farnborough 7.8.36; c/n 105 G-ACAD Lady D. Clayton 10.2.33, R. O. Shuttleworth 6.36, D. B. Prentice 6.38, cancelled 12.46; c/n 106 G-ACAF Hill and Phillips 31.3.33, Air Publicity 9.36, L.C.G.M. Le Champion 6.38, cancelled 1.39; c/n 107 G-ACEF H. Pritchett 27.10.36, Malling Aviation 3.37, scrapped.

Dates are those for registration.

Spartan Clipper
A departure from previous Spartan aircraft, the Clipper was designed by H.E. Broadsmith and was a light, single-engined low-wing cantilever

Last Spartan Three Seater built, G-ACEF at Ramsgate during 1937. (*A.J. Jackson collection via R.T. Jackson*)

Sole example of the Spartan Clipper. Seen with Pobjoy R. (*A.J. Jackson collection via R.T. Jackson*)

monoplane. Construction consisted of a wooden fuselage carrying stub wings, to which were attached outer wings identical to those of the Monospar ST.4. This arrangement saved considerable amounts of detail design and tooling expenses. The enclosed cabin contained two side-by-side seats and dual controls were fitted. The engine was a 75 hp Pobjoy R seven-cylinder air-cooled radial. The first (and in the event only) example of the Clipper, c/n 201, first flew on 14 December, 1932, piloted by L. A. Strange and carrying the B-class markings S-5.

After cowling, cabin glazing and undercarriage modifications, including the addition of spats, the aircraft was registered G-ACEG. The C of A was awarded on 29 June, 1933. G-ACEG was entered in the 1933 King's Cup Air Race but came last in Heat One of Round Two.

During 1938, G-ACEG was fitted with a 90 hp Pobjoy Niagara III and was used by Saro for general communication duties. It was finally destroyed in the Cowes air-raid of 4 May, 1942.

Span 34 ft; length 28 ft 2 in; height 6 ft 7 in; wing area 150 sq ft.
Empty weight 770 lb; fuel and oil 140 lb; loaded weight 1,300 lb.
Maximum speed 110 mph; initial rate of climb 800 ft/min.

338

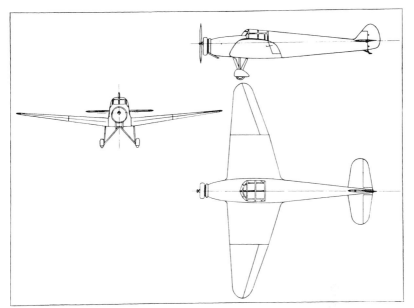

Spartan Clipper

The reworked Clipper with Pobjoy Niagara III, dorsal spine, modified cockpit glazing. Spats have yet to be added. (*A.J. Jackson collection via R.T. Jackson*)

APPENDIX EIGHT

B-Class Markings

L	23.12.29—31.12.47	Saunders-Roe	
G-12	1.1.48—14.6.59	Saunders-Roe	
G-12	15.6.59—23.10.60	Saunders-Roe Fixed Wing Division	
G-12	24.10.60—4.66	Westland Aircraft, Saunders-Roe Division	
G-46	15.6.59—23.10.60	Saunders-Roe Helicopter Division	
G-46	24.10.60—3.5.62	Westland Aircraft, Saunders-Roe Helicopter Division	

L1	4.30	Cutty Sark	Later VH-UNV
L2	30	A.10	Later K1949
L3	30	Cutty Sark	Later 3
L4	7.30	Cloud	Later G-ABCJ, CF-ARB, G-ABCJ
L5	31	Cutty Sark	Later G-ABVF
G-12-1	7.49	SR.A/1	Ex-TG263
G-12-1	—	Skeeter 51	Possibly became SC-501
G-12-2	3.58	Skeeter 50	Later PC-117 and PF-156
G-12-3		no known allocation	
G-12-4	1.6.59	SR-N1	Experimental Hovercraft
G-12-5	61	SR-N2	Experimental development Hovercraft
G-46-1	—	Saro-Hiller XROE-1	
G-46-1	25.10.59	Saro-Hiller XROE-1	
G-46-2	—	Saro-Hiller XROE-1	
G-46-3	—	Saro-Hiller XROE-1	
G-46-4	—	Saro-Hiller XROE-1	
G-46-5	—	Saro-Hiller XROE-1	

Ten Saro-Hiller Rotorcycles built by Saro but only six appear to have received B-class markings.

INDEX

General Index

Aircraft Index

Page references in Italic refer to main entries.

Engine Index

349

Missile and Rocket Motor Index